ANNUAL REPORT

OF THE

BOARD OF REGENTS

OF THE

SMITHSONIAN INSTITUTION,

SHOWING

THE OPERATIONS, EXPENDITURES, AND CONDITION OF THE INSTITUTION FOR THE YEAR 1875.

WASHINGTON:
GOVERNMENT PRINTING OFFICE.
1876.

The following resolution was agreed to in the Senate, April 20, 1876, and concurred in by the House of Representatives May 24, 1876:

Resolved by the Senate (the House of Representatives concurring,) That ten thousand five hundred copies of the Report of the Smithsonian Institution for the year 1875 be printed, one thousand copies of which shall be for the use of the Senate, two thousand copies of which shall be for the use of the House of Representatives, and seven thousand five hundred copies for the use of the Smithsonian Institution: *Provided,* That the aggregate number of pages shall not exceed four hundred and fifty, and that there shall be no illustrations, except those furnished by the Smithsonian Institution.

2

LETTER

FROM THE

SECRETARY OF THE SMITHSONIAN INSTITUTION,

TRANSMITTING

The annual report of the Smithsonian Institution for the year 1875.

———————

SMITHSONIAN INSTITUTION,
Washington, April 7, 1876.

SIR: In behalf of the Board of Regents, I have the honor to submit to the Congress of the United States the annual report of the operations, expenditures, and condition of the Smithsonian Institution for the year 1875.

I have the honor to be, very respectfully, your obedient servant,

JOSEPH HENRY,
Secretary Smithsonian Institution.

Hon. T. W. FERRY,
President of the Senate.

Hon. M. C. KERR,
Speaker of the House of Representatives.

6545

ANNUAL REPORT OF THE SMITHSONIAN INSTITUTION FOR 1875.

This document contains:

1. The annual report of the Secretary, giving an account of the operations and condition of the establishment for the year 1875, with the statistics of collections, exchanges, &c.

2. The report of the executive committee, exhibiting the financial affairs of the Institution, including a statement of the Smithson fund, the receipts and expenditures for the year 1875, and the estimates for 1876.

3. The proceedings of the Board of Regents for the session of January, 1876.

4. A general appendix, consisting principally of translations from foreign journals or works not generally accessible, but of interest to the collaborators and correspondents of the Institution, teachers, and others interested in the promotion of knowledge.

THE SMITHSONIAN INSTITUTION.

ULYSSES S. GRANT, President of the United States, *ex officio* Presiding Officer.
MORRISON R. WAITE, Chief Justice of the United States, Chancellor of the Institution, (President of the Board of Regents.)
JOSEPH HENRY, Secretary, (or Director of the Institution.)

REGENTS OF THE INSTITUTION.

MORRISON R. WAITE, Chief Justice of the United States, *President of the Board.*
T. W. FERRY, acting Vice-President of the United States.
H. HAMLIN, member of the Senate of the United States.
J. W. STEVENSON, member of the Senate of the United States.
A. A. SARGENT, member of the Senate of the United States.
HIESTER CLYMER, member of the House of Representatives.
BENJAMIN H. HILL, member of the House of Representatives.
GEO. W. McCRARY, member of the House of Representatives.
JOHN MACLEAN, citizen of New Jersey.
PETER PARKER, citizen of Washington.
ASA GRAY, citizen of Massachusetts.
J. D. DANA, citizen of Connecticut.
HENRY COPPEE, citizen of Pennsylvania.
GEORGE BANCROFT, citizen of Washington.

EXECUTIVE COMMITTEE OF THE BOARD OF REGENTS.

PETER PARKER.   JOHN MACLEAN.   GEORGE BANCROFT.

MEMBERS EX OFFICIO OF THE INSTITUTION.

U. S. GRANT, President of the United States.
T. W. FERRY, Vice-President of the United States.
M. R. WAITE, Chief Justice of the United States.
H. FISH, Secretary of State.
B. H. BRISTOW, Secretary of the Treasury.
ALPHONSO TAFT, Secretary of War.
G. M. ROBESON, Secretary of the Navy.
MARSHALL JEWELL, Postmaster-General.
Z. CHANDLER, Secretary of the Interior.
E. PIERREPONT, Attorney-General.
R. H. DUELL, Commissioner of Patents.

OFFICERS AND ASSISTANTS OF THE SMITHSONIAN INSTITUTION AND NATIONAL MUSEUM.

JOSEPH HENRY, *Secretary, Director of the Institution.*

SPENCER F. BAIRD, *Assistant Secretary and Curator of the National Museum.*

WILLIAM J. RHEES, *Chief Clerk.*

CLARENCE B. YOUNG, *Clerk in charge of Accounts.*

DANIEL LEECH, *Clerk in charge of Correspondence.*

HERMANN DIEBITSCH, *Clerk in charge of Exchanges.*

J. A. TURNER, *Clerk in charge of Library.*

M. E. GRIFFIN, *Clerk in charge of Distribution of Publications.*

S. G. BROWN, *Clerk in charge of Freight.*

Prof. G. B. GOODE, *Assistant Curator of the National Museum.*

Prof. F. M. ENDLICH, *in charge of Mineralogical Division.*

Prof. ROBERT RIDGWAY, *in charge of Ornithological Division.*

Prof. W. H. DALL, *in charge of Conchological Division.*

Prof. EDW. FOREMAN, *in charge of Ethnological Division.*

T. W. SMILLIE, *Photographer.*

JOSEPH PALMER, *Taxidermist.*

Prof. THEODORE GILL, *Resident Collaborator in General Zoology.*

Prof. F. B. MEEK, *Resident Collaborator in Palæontology.*

Prof. E. COUES, *Resident Collaborator in Mammalogy and Ornithology.*

Prof. CHAS. RAU, *Resident Collaborator in Ethnology.*

Prof. O. T. MASON, *Resident Collaborator in Ethnology.*

JOSEPH HERRON, *Janitor.*

REPORT OF PROFESSOR HENRY, SECRETARY OF THE SMITH-SONIAN INSTITUTION, FOR 1876.

To the Board of Regents of the Smithsonian Institution :

GENTLEMEN : I have the honor herewith to present to your honorable board the report of the condition and operations of the Smithsonian Institution during the year 1875. In presenting this report, I am happy to be able to inform you that nothing has occurred since the close of your last session which in the least degree has interfered with the prosperity of this establishment. On the contrary, it will be manifest from the report that the Institution has continued with unabated energy to carry out the intention of its founder, as expressed in the terms of his will, by increasing and diffusing knowledge among men.

The several annual reports of the Secretary are intended to form a continuous history of the Institution, and, therefore, it is necessary to state, what is already known to the Regents, that since the date of the last report several changes have taken place in the board. Among the first of these we have to mention is that occasioned by the death of the late Vice-President of the United States, Hon. Henry Wilson. He was *ex officio* a member of the board, and took part in the deliberations of its last session. In his death science and education have lost a warm friend, who always exerted his influence for their advancement. He ever advocated all propositions submitted to Congress for explorations and researches which might extend the bounds of knowledge. In two previous instances of vacancy in the office of Vice-President, the place in the Board of Regents was supplied first by the Hon. L. F. S. Foster, of Connecticut, and, second, by the Hon. B. F. Wade, presiding officers at the time of the Senate. In conformity with this usage, the place of Mr. Wilson will be filled by the Hon. T. W. Ferry.

The Speaker of the House of Representatives, in accordance with the law of organization of the Institution, has filled the vacancies occasioned by the expiration of the term of service of Messrs. Cox, Hoar, and Hazelton, by the appointment as Regents from the House of Representatives of the Hon. Hiester Clymer, of Pennsylvania, Hon. B. H. Hill, of Georgia, and the Hon. G. W. McCrary, of Iowa.

The operations of the Institution at present consist principally of two classes : first, of those relating to the immediate objects of the bequest, viz, the increase and diffusion of knowledge among men, through researches, publications, and exchanges; and, second, those which pertain to the care and management of the Government collections in nat-

7

ural history and ethnology, constituting the *National Museum,* of which the Institution is the custodian. In regard to the latter, the operations and responsibilities of the directors have been greater than ever before. Congress, at its last session, not only made the usual appropriation of $20,000 for the care of the museum, $10,000 for cases, and $2,500 for an extension of the heating-apparatus, but also, in addition to these sums, granted $67,000 for the display of the collections of the National Museum at the Centennial Exhibition in Philadelphia. A part of this latter sum, however, was reserved for the payment of a portion of the cost of a temporary building for the exhibition of the articles belonging to the Government, leaving about $50,000 for the display by the Institution. This latter appropriation was made in connection with a series of appropriations to enable the several Departments of the Government, as well as the Smithsonian Institution, to participate in the Exhibition. Each of these parties was directed to appoint a representative, the whole forming an executive board, to which was to be given the power to control the disbursements of the appropriations; the bills to be paid by a disbursing-officer, upon vouchers certified by the respective representatives, and countersigned by the chairman of the board. Although the appropriation in question was made by Congress to enable the Institution to discharge certain duties, it was by the arrangement above mentioned relieved from all responsibility as to the expenditure of the money.

To Prof. Spencer F. Baird, Assistant Secretary of the Institution, I assigned the duty of representing it in the Government board of exhibitors. He has with much energy devoted his time and thoughts to the work, and has prepared a report, a copy of which is herewith presented, of what has been done on the part of the Institution to carry out the intention of Congress.

The results of the operations of the Institution in connection with the Centennial Exhibition will probably have a much greater effect on the future of the establishment than is at first sight apparent. The large number of specimens which have been collected by the several Departments of Government and by the Institution itself in view of this Exhibition will greatly increase the contents of the National Museum, and if we add to these the specimens which will be presented by foreign powers, of which we have already had intimations, the number will be swelled to an extent far beyond the capacity of the present building to contain them, and an additional edifice will be required for their accommodation.

In the consideration of this matter, the questions will arise whether the building required shall consist of an extension of the present Smithsonian edifice, or an entirely separate building; and these questions will involve another, viz, whether it is advisable to continue, at least without some modification, the connection which now exists between the Smithsonian Institution and the National Museum.

In regard to the first question, I may be allowed to say that as the Smithsonian Institution was compelled by an act of Congress to erect the present building, which has cost in all nearly $500,000, principally for the accommodation of the National Museum, it would now be manifestly unjust to the former establishment to transfer the specimens, as has been proposed, from the present edifice to the new building contemplated for the accommodation of the National Library. The plan, therefore, which, in my opinion, should be adopted is for the Government to take entire possession of the present edifice, making such additions to it from time to time as would be required for the care and exhibition of the increasing collections, and to repay the Smithsonian Institution for at least a portion of the cost of the building, the latter to erect a separate edifice in the vicinity, better suited to its wants, with a portion of the money thus repaid, the remainder being added to the principal of the Smithson fund.

In regard to the second question, whether the connection which now exists between the National Museum and the Smithsonian Institution should continue as it is without modification, I would say that it is desirable that a more definite distinction between the two establishments, if not an entire separation, should be made.

According to the existing arrangement, it is necessary that the Institution should apply to Congress every year for an appropriation for the support of the museum, and it is therefore presented to the world as a suppliant for perpetual aid, whereas, for carrying out the legitimate objects of the bequest, no annual appropriation is necessary from the public Treasury; for although more than one-half of the whole income of the Smithson bequest has been devoted to a museum and other local objects, it has succeeded (through its researches, its publications, and its exchanges) in establishing a reputation as extensive as the civilized world; and I doubt not, from the disposition which Congress has previously shown to faithfully discharge the duty which it has devolved upon itself in accepting the guardianship of a trust for the benefit of mankind, it will not refuse, when the public finances are in a better condition, to repay to the Smithson fund at least a portion of the amount which, through a misapprehension of the will of the founder, has been devoted to the National Museum, and also to make such separate provision for the maintenance of the latter establishment as will obviate the necessity of a constant appeal to Congress, on the part of the Institution, for aid not necessary for its own operations.

Furthermore, the museum is destined to an extension far beyond its present magnitude. It is an object of much interest to all who visit the National Capital, and is of great value as exhibiting the natural resources of the country, as well as a means of public education; and as Smithson intended the Institution founded by his bequest as a monument to himself, since he gave it his own name, it is not proper that it should be merged in any establishment of the Government, nor, on the

other hand, is the Government called upon to make annual appropriations for the advance of science to be credited to an establishment founded
by an individual to perpetuate his own memory. The Smithson fund
should be exclusively devoted to the increase and diffusion of knowledge
among men in the manner best calculated to produce the desired effect,
and its operations should be as little complicated as possible with those
of Government establishments.

FINANCES.

The following is a statement of the condition of the funds at the
beginning of the year 1876 :

The amount originally received as the bequest of James Smithson, of England, deposited in the Treasury of the United States in accordance with the act of Congress of August 10, 1846.....	$515, 169 00
The residuary legacy of Smithson, received in 1865, deposited in the Treasury of the United States, in accordance with the act of Congress of February 8, 1867..........	26, 210 63
Total bequest of Smithson........................	541, 379 63
Amount deposited in the Treasury of the United States, as authorized by act of Congress of February 8, 1867, derived from savings of income and increase in value of investments...................................	108, 620 37
Amount received as the bequest of James Hamilton, of Carlisle, Pa., February 24, 1874.......................	1, 000 00
Total permanent Smithson fund in the Treasury of the United States, bearing interest at 6 per cent., payable semi-annually in gold....................	651, 000 00
In addition to the above, there remains of the extra fund from savings, &c., in Virginia bonds and certificates, viz: consolidated bonds, $58,700; deferred certificates, $29,375.07; fractional certificate, $50.13; total $88,125.20, now valued at............................	42, 000 00
Cash balance in United States Treasury at the beginning of the year 1876 for current expenses..................	20, 555 82
Amount due from First National Bank, Washington, $2,056.23, (present value unknown.)	
Total Smithson funds January 20, 1876......	713, 555 82

The receipts during the year were $51,388.20, and the expenditures
$46,809.98, leaving a balance of $4,578.22 to be added to the balance
on hand at the beginning of the year 1875.

The interest on the Hamilton bequest has been received from February 24, 1874, to December 31, 1875, amounting to $118.49, which will be expended in accordance with the will of the donor.

The interest on the Virginia bonds collected during the year amounted to $4,750.11.

It was stated in the last report that at the time of the suspension of the First National Bank of Washington, (19th September, 1873,) in which the current funds had been deposited by direction of the board, there were $8,224.87 to the credit of the Institution. The following dividends have been received on this deposit: November 11, 1873, 30 per cent.; on the 7th April, 1874, 20 per cent.; on the 5th May, 1875, 10 per cent.; and on the 27th December, 1875, 15 per cent., or a total of 75 per cent., or $6,168.64, leaving a balance still due of $2,056.23.

PUBLICATIONS.

The publications of the Institution are of three classes, viz: the CONTRIBUTIONS TO KNOWLEDGE, the MISCELLANEOUS COLLECTIONS, and the ANNUAL REPORTS. The first consist of memoirs containing positive additions to science resting on original research, and which are generally the result of investigations to which the Institution has, in some way, rendered assistance. The Miscellaneous Collections are composed of works intended to facilitate the study of branches of natural history, meteorology, &c., and are designed especially to induce individuals to engage in these studies as specialties. The Annual Reports, besides an account of the operations, expenditures, and condition of the Institution, contain translations from works not generally accessible to American students, reports of lectures, extracts from correspondence, &c.

The following are the rules which have been adopted for the distribution of the several publications of the Institution:

1st. They are presented to learned societies of the first class which in return give complete series of their publications to the Institution.

2d. To libraries of the first class which give in exchange their catalogues and other publications, or an equivalent from their duplicate volumes.

3d. To colleges of the first class which furnish catalogues of their libraries and of their students, and all other publications relative to their organization and history.

4th. To States and Territories, provided they give in return copies of all documents published under their authority.

5th. To public libraries in this country, containing 15,000 volumes, especially if no other copies are given in the same place; and to smaller libraries where a large district would be otherwise unsupplied.

6th. To institutions devoted exclusively to the promotion of particular branches of knowledge are given such Smithsonian publications as relate to their respective objects.

7th. The Annual Reports are presented to the meteorological observers, to contributors of valuable material to the library or collections, and to persons engaged in special scientific research.

The distribution of the publications of the Institution is a matter which requires much care and judicious selection, the great object being to make known to the world the truths which may result from the expenditure of the Smithson fund. For this purpose, the principal class of publications, namely, the Contributions, must be so distributed as to be accessible to the greatest number of readers, and this will evidently be to large central libraries.

The volumes of Contributions are presented to institutions on the express condition that, while they are carefully preserved, they shall be accessible at all times to students and others who may desire to consult them, and be returned to the Institution in case the establishments to which they are presented at any time cease to exist. These works, it must be recollected, are not of a popular character, but require profound study to fully understand them; they are, however, of importance to the professional teacher and the popular expounder of science. They contain materials from which general treatises on special subjects may be elaborated.

The publications of the Institution during the past year have been less in number than in preceding years, but this has not been on account of want of materials, but because most of the resources of the Institution have been devoted to the completion of two volumes of the quarto series, which are nearly ready for the binder, one of which will be credited to 1875 and the other to 1876.

The twentieth volume of the Smithsonian Contributions to Knowledge will consist entirely of the discussion of a series of tabular results relative to the "*Winds of the Globe*," prepared at the expense of the Institution by the late Prof. James H. Coffin, of Lafayette College, Pennsylvania, and completed by his son, Prof. Selden J. Coffin, with the assistance of Dr. Alex. J. Wœikof, of the Imperial Geographical Society of Russia.

The twenty-first volume of the Smithsonian Contributions to Knowledge will be made up of the following papers, viz:

Statement and Exposition of Certain Harmonies of the Solar System. By Prof. Stephen Alexander, of the College of New Jersey. 4to. 104 pp.

On the General Integrals of Planetary Motion. By Simon Newcomb, professor of mathematics, United States Navy. 4to. 40 pp.

The Haidah Indians of Queen Charlotte's Island, British Columbia, with a brief description of their carvings, tattoo designs, &c. By James G. Swan, Port Townsend, Wash. Ter. 4to. 22 pp. 7 plates.

Tables, Distribution, and Variations of the Atmospheric Temperature in the United States and some adjacent parts of America. Collected by the Smithsonian Institution and discussed under the direction of Joseph Henry, Secretary. By Charles A. Schott, assistant United States Coast Survey. 4to. pp. 360. 9 diagrams, 2 plates, 3 charts.

These papers have all been described in previous reports, and, with the exception of the last, that on Temperatures, have been distributed separately to individuals and institutions especially interested in the subjects to which they relate.

The publication of the Antiquities of Tennessee, mentioned in previous reports, has been deferred in order to give the author an opportunity of revising the work and abridging it by omitting a large amount of bibliographical matter which could scarcely be published under the title of contributions to knowledge, since it is already in print. The illustrations, however, for the work have been engraved, and it will be put to press as soon as the revision is completed.

The engravings for the work on Lucernaria, by the late Prof. H. J. Clark, have been completed, with the exception of one plate, which was so badly executed that it was thought necessary to reject it. As soon as this is satisfactorily engraved, the work will be put to press and will form a part of the Contributions to Knowledge of the next year.

In the report for 1872 is given an account of a series of investigations then in progress in regard to the Tides. Beside the labor expended in this work in the line of higher mathematics, it involved arithmetical computations of a very laborious character, the expense of which was to be defrayed by the Institution. This work has been found of so much practical importance that it has been adopted as a part of the investigations of the Coast Survey. In this case, as in many others, the Institution has inaugurated valuable investigations, which have subsequently been carried on by other means. This is in accordance with the established usages of the Institution, to do nothing with its funds which can be equally well done through other agencies.

Of the octavo series or "Miscellaneous Collections," the Monograph of American Wasps, prepared by Professor de Saussure, of Geneva, Switzerland, has been completed and is nearly ready for distribution. A full account of it has been given in previous reports. It forms an octavo of 408 pages, and will doubtless be considered a valuable addition to the sources of knowledge of the natural history of this country.

Another number of the series of Miscellaneous Collections, published during the past year, is a Catalogue of the Fishes of the East Coast of North America. By Dr. Theodore Gill. It was prepared and published at first as an appendix to the report of the United States Commissioner of Fish and Fisheries for 1871–'72; but, on account of the many calls for it, and the fact that the work was prepared at the Institution, and the copies of the Government edition having been exhausted, it was thought advisable to strike off a new edition from the stereotype plates and incorporate it in the series of Miscellaneous Collections. It forms an octavo pamphlet of 54 pages.

The Botanical Index, a work mentioned in previous reports, is still in the course of preparation. It will be of much importance in enabling the botanist to find, amid the various reports of surveys made under the direction of the United States Government and other sources of information, an account of the various plants existing in this country. The work will be prosecuted as rapidly as the time which can be devoted to it by Prof. Sereno Watson, who has it in charge, will permit; 184 pages having already been stereotyped. The cost of its preparation has been defrayed by contributions from the principal botanists of the United States, a fact which sufficiently indicates its value.

Another publication made during 1875 belongs to the Miscellaneous Collections, and is the fourth of the Toner Lecture Series. It is on "A Study of the Nature and Mechanism of Fever," by Horatio C. Wood, M. D., of Philadelphia, and contains a series of original experiments and observations on the subject.

The phenomena of fever, according to the author, will be found to be capable of being grouped in three sets: first, acceleration of the beats of the heart and disturbance of the circulation; second, nervous disturbance; third, elevation of bodily temperature. It is the opinion of the author that the first two are merely secondary and depend upon the third; i. e., the essential phenomenon of fever is elevation of temperature. It forms a pamphlet of 48 pages, and has been extensively called for by the medical profession.

In order to assist in defraying the expense of the publication of the Toner Lectures, a charge is made of 25 cents for each number. As an answer to many inquiries, it may be stated in this place that the second lecture of the series has not yet been published, the Institution having failed to receive the manuscript from the author.

The preparation of the tables of the "Constants of Nature" has been in part interrupted, by the appointment of the principal author, F. W. Clarke, to the professorship of chemistry in the Cincinnati University, all his time having been absorbed in the preparation of his course of instruction. He has, however, resumed his labors on the constants, and will probably furnish us during 1876 with another installment of materials for the extension of the tables. There has been a large and increasing demand for this work, which is of much importance to the analytical chemist in facilitating his investigations.

During the past year another series of publications, which will form a part of the Miscellaneous Collections, has been commenced. It is entitled " Bulletin of the National Museum," and is intended to illustrate the collections of natural history and ethnology belonging to the United States, and constituting the National Museum, of which the Smithsonian Institution is the custodian. Of this series two numbers have been issued in octavo form, printed at the Government Printing-Office, by authority of the honorable Secretary of the Interior.

The first number is a check-list of North American Batrachia and Reptilia, with a systematic list of the higher groups, and an essay on geographical distribution, based on the specimens contained in the United States National Museum, by Prof. Edw. D. Cope. It is a contribution to

North American Herpetology, undertaken some years ago, at the request of the Institution. The materials which have been accumulating in the National Museum offer great advantages for the investigation of the anatomical structure, variation of specific characters, and geographical distribution of animals. These subjects are especially elucidated by the study of batrachians and reptiles, since these animals are especially susceptible to effects from physical influences, and are unable, like birds and mammals, to escape these by extended migrations. Their habitats, therefore, express the simplest relations of life to the special conditions under which it exists. The great number of specimens in the National Museum enables the investigator to discover the range of variations of a given species, and to reduce to the rank of varieties many which have been supposed to be distinct species—the definition of species being simply a number of individuals having physical peculiarities belonging to them alone, and at the same time found in all. Nothing is more difficult than to divide the flora or fauna of the world into distinct species, having the above characteristics, since, passing from one locality to another of varying physical conditions, the variations in form and character are so gradual that it is almost impossible to say where the line of demarkation shall be placed.

In the investigation of cold-blooded North American vertebrata, Professor Cope has found that many which have been regarded as separate species are merely geographical varieties. Bulletin No. 1 is divided into three parts.

Part I consists of an arrangement of the families and higher divisions of the batrachia and reptilia provisionally adopted by the Institution.

Part II is a check-list of the species of batrachia and reptilia of the nearctic or North American realm.

Part III relates to the geographical distribution of the vertebrata of the nearctic realm with especial reference to the batrachia and reptilia, and is divided into eleven sections.

Life in different regions of the earth presents marked peculiarities, depending in a great measure upon the geographical and topographical relations of the continents. The districts thus marked out are the Australian, the neotropical, the nearctic, or North American, the Ethiopian, the Palæological, and the Palæartic, and to these the name of "realms" has been given. The total number of species of vertebrata found in the North American realm is 2,249, which is below the truth, since many of the fishes, both of the ocean and of the fresh waters, remain undescribed. It is more difficult to give the number of species of the inferior divisions of the animal kingdom. It is stated that 8,000 species of coleopterous insects have been discovered in the same region, and that this is probably about two-thirds of the whole. Probably 50,000 is below the mark as an estimate of the number of species of insects. In relation to other realms, several species of vertebrata are common to our northern regions and Europe and Asia. Thus the wolf, fox, ermine, and perhaps the beaver extend throughout the northern hemisphere. But few species are common to the nearctic and the southern neotropical realms—but one mammal and no reptiles, batrachians nor fresh-water fishes extend into Brazil, but a number of birds are permanent residents throughout both realms. Considerable variation exists in the fauna of the several parts of our region, exhibiting as many as six principal subdivisions. The warmer regions are much richer in birds, reptiles, and insects than the cooler, as we advance northward many species disappear, while a few others are added. The natural division of the eastern part of the continent is in a measure dependent on the isothermal lines which traverse it. In accordance with this fact, the following districts of the eastern region have been proposed, viz: The Carolinian; the Alleghanian; the Canadian, and the Hudsonian. The central region is characterized by the general absence of forests. It presents two divisions, each peculiar in its vegetation; the division of the plains which extends from the eastern border to the Rocky Mountains to the 100th meridian, and the Rocky Mountain region itself, which extends to the Sierra Nevada. The former is covered with grass and is almost totally treeless; the latter is covered with sage-brush.

In regard to the batrachia and reptilia, from their small amount of animal heat, it follows that temperature has the greatest influence on their life and distribution. This is exhibited not only in multiplication of forms, but in the brilliancy of color. Another important influence in regard to these animals is the amount of terrestrial and atmospheric moisture. A peculiarity of cold-blooded vertebrata of arid regions is that by means of which they readily assume the color of the body on which they rest. That a prevalent color of such bodies should lead to a habit of preference for that color is necessary, and as such habits become automatic, the permanence of the color is naturally established.

Appended to the paper is a bibliography of works and memoirs which embrace discussions of systematic or distributional relations of the reptiles of North America. Those embracing descriptions of species only, will be added in a future publication. This number forms a pamphlet of 108 octavo pages, and has been distributed to the principal museums and naturalists of the world.

The second number of the Bulletin of the National Museum is an account of the birds of Kerguelen Island, by Dr. J. H. Kidder, Surgeon United States Navy, and edited by Dr. Elliott Coues. These specimens were collected by Dr. Kidder, surgeon and naturalist of one of the parties organized for observing the transit of Venus in the southern hemisphere. The party to which Dr. Kidder was attached landed from the United States ship Swatara at the upper end of Royal Sound, a deep indentation in the southern part of Kerguelen Island, otherwise known as Desolation Island, one of the most extreme islands of the southern hemisphere. It is a region of almost constant precipitation, only twenty-seven days out of four months being recorded as without snow or rain, and a still smaller number of nights. The range of the thermometer was not far from the freezing-point, being a little below in September and October and a little above in November and December. The violent gales, which almost constantly prevailed, and which often arise with great suddenness, rendered it dangerous to make collections in small boats. The climatic conditions greatly affect the flora and fauna of the island, there being no trees or shrubs, no plant, indeed, larger than a kind of cabbage. As a consequence of this condition, there are no land-birds or mammals strictly indigenous, and but a single shore-bird. The island is of considerable size, about ninety miles long by fifty miles wide, and is composed of volcanic rocks. No flying insects were observed except minute gnats, nor were the remains of any found in the stomachs of birds. But two species of vegetable-feeding birds were observed, all the others living exclusively on fish or marine invertebrata. An English party (also to observe the transit) established itself about fourteen miles southwest of the American station, and at about the same distance to the northwest was a German party, associated with each of which was a naturalist.

The ornithological collections made by Dr. Kidder are believed to fully indicate the character of the avi-fauna of the locality, very few species having been overlooked. The specimens possess a high interest from the fact that they are among the rarities of American museums, while most of the eggs are new to collections, if not hitherto unknown to naturalists. "The contribution to science which the specimens represent," says Dr. Coues, "is very ably complemented by Dr. Kidder's field-notes, carefully recorded upon the spot when the impressions of the observer were fresh. They possess a vigor and vividness not invariably accompanying descriptions of nature, while their entire trustworthiness is assured both by the character of the observer and by the favorable circumstances of observation." The extended biographical sketches of the Kerguelen birds will be welcomed by ornithologists as an important and interesting contribution to the life-history of these imperfectly-known species. This paper forms an octavo pamphlet of 60 pages, and has been distributed to naturalists and museums.

The first volume of the exploration of the Colorado River of the West and its tributaries, by Prof. J. W. Powell, under the direction of the Secretary of the Smithsonian Institution, has been published during the last year by the Department of the Interior. It forms a quarto volume of 303 pages with 80 illustrations and a map. It gives a history of the explorations during the years 1869, 1870, 1871, and 1872. The work to which this volume relates was originally commenced as an exploration, but was afterward developed into a survey embracing the geography, geology, ethnography, and natural history of the country. It is expected that the results of the several investigations relative to these subjects, which have been intrusted to several specialists for elaboration, will in due time be published by the General Government in a style in accordance with that of the present volume. The whole work will do honor to the appreciation by the Government of scientific information of this kind, as well as of the ability and perseverance of Professor Powell and his assistants.

As an evidence of the estimation in which the labors of Professor Powell are held, it should be mentioned that he has been placed in charge of the second division of the geological survey of the Territories, under direction of the Department of the Interior, (the first division being in charge of Professor Hayden,) and that the subsequent volumes of the series of his reports will be published by that Department. It may be further mentioned that Congress has not yet ordered any extra copies of the first volume of Powell's report; those that have been printed have been published by the Interior Department. It is hoped, however, that Congress at its present session will order a new edition, granting a sufficient number of extra copies to the Smithsonian Institution to supply the principal public educational and scientific establishments of the world.

Report.—The annual report of the operations of the Institution for the year 1874, was presented to Congress as usual, and an edition of 10,500 copies printed; 2,000 of which were for the use of members of the House of Representatives, 1,000 for the use of the Senate, and 7,500 for distribution by the Institution.

The appendix to the report contains translations of eulogies on La Place by Arago, Quetelet by Mailly, De la Rive by Dumas; a lecture on tides and tidal action in harbors, by Professor Hilgard, of the Coast Survey; a translation of observations upon the electricity of the atmosphere and the aurora borealis, by Professors Lemström and De la Rive; a translation of an article on a dominant language for science, by Professor de Candolle, with notes by Dr. Gray of the British Museum; on underground temperature, by Chas. A. Schott of the Coast Survey, with the results of Professor Everett's researches on the same subject for the British Association for the Advancement of Science; on the earthquakes in North Carolina in 1874, by Professor du Pre, with notes by Professor Henry; a translation of Professor de la Rive's report on the transactions of the Geneva Society of Physics and Natural History for 1872 and 1873; the translation of the conclusion of an extensive and important paper, by General Morin of France, on warming and ventilation, with numerous illustrations; and a large number of original communications on ethnology, describing the antiquities of different parts of the United States.

This report, as usual, has been distributed to various educational establishments, to the Meteorological observers, and other contributors to the objects of the Institution, and to such persons as have made special application for them in writing.

Indian vocabularies.—During the year a number of Indian vocabularies have been received from different persons engaged in explorations in the Territories. These have all been referred to J. H. Trumbull, LL. D., of Hartford, Conn., for critical examination and arrangement for the press.

A full list of all the manuscript Indian vocabularies in possession of the Institution will be given in a subsequent report. We hope during the next year to commence the publication of the extensive collection of materials of this character, so important to the labors of the ethnologist.

RESEARCHES.

Meteorology.—In the beginning of 1874 the meteorological system of records by voluntary observers, which had been in operation by the Institution for twenty-five years, was transferred to the Signal-Office of the War Department, under General A. J. Myer. This transfer was made in accordance with the general policy of the Institution, viz, that of abandoning any field of enterprise as soon as the work could be done as well through other agencies. This transfer has received the approbation of the observers generally, who, while they are now co-operating with the Signal-Service, still keep up a correspondence with the Institution on subjects of general scientific interest. The meteorological system of the United States under General Myer is in an admirable condition. The total number of daily reports filed at the Office of the Chief Signal-Officer are now as follows: Number of daily-service simultaneous telegraphic reports, 109; number of international daily simultaneous reports, 268; number of reports of voluntary observers, 393; number of reports of medical corps of the Army, 102; number of reports of medical corps of the Navy, 5; making a grand total of 877 daily reports received regularly for discussion. Such an extensive series of observations, if continued for twenty years, will furnish the data for determining the peculiar climatology of North America with a precision hitherto unknown in the history of meteorology. The labors of the Smithsonian Institution in the line of meteorology are now principally confined to working up the materials in this branch of science, which it has collected during the last quarter of a century. These materials include not only the observations of the Institution itself, but all that could be obtained from other sources relative to North America, from the first settlement of the country down to the present time. The first work of this class which has been published is that of the rain-fall. It included all the materials which had been collected down to 1866. During the last two years preparations have been made to publish a new edition of this work, including the additions from new materials, and with new maps on a larger scale. In the preparation of this new edition we have received important assistance, through the politeness of General Myer, from the system of the Signal-Service.

The work published by the Institution on the rain-fall of the United States is of great importance in relation to our agricultural resources, to the various engineering enterprises which are proposed from time to time, as well as to the manufacturing interests of the country. It is also intimately connected with the subject of forest-culture, which at present is occupying a large share of public attention. It must be the basis of all the improvements which are attempted in regard to irrigation, and is of especial value in this respect to the western portion of the United States.

There are two great systems of rain-bearing winds in North America; that from the west on our Pacific coast, which blows across the several chains of mountains, constituting the western system, precipitating its moisture principally on the western slopes of the mountains, so that on the eastern sides of these mountains, as well as on the slopes and plains east of the Rocky Mountains, there are arid portions of scanty vegetation, on account of deficient moisture. How far these may be rendered fertile by irrigation depends upon the amount of rain-fall and the conformation of the surface by which the water may be utilized. The other system of rain-winds is from the Gulf of Mexico and the Atlantic. These winds blow principally in the direction of the axis of the Appalachian system of mountains, and consequently precipitate their moisture along the valleys and on both sides of the mountain slopes, covering the whole region with fertility. In connection with this subject we would commend to public attention the plan adopted by the State of Maine in making a hydraulic survey of the whole State, to ascertain the amount of water-power available for manufacturing purposes.

In view of the limited, though in this country comparatively great, quantity of coal-power, it is our duty to use, in preference in all cases where it is possible, water-power, which is constantly renewed and must be continued as long as the sun's energy elevates water from the surface of the ocean and precipitates it on the higher portions of the land. We have in the falls of Niagara a source of active energy, which we doubt not in the course of years will be utilized to an extent which shall affect the well-being of man in every part of the civilized world. The time of the utilization of this power will depend upon the varying price of coal. When this, from the constantly-increasing demand, assumes a certain price, water-power will more generally be resorted to and the large amount of energy which is now dissipated, as in the case of the falls of the Potomac and other rivers, will be carefully husbanded.

The next work of the same class is that of the *Winds of the Globe*, comprising the results of the discussions of not only observations made under the direction of the Institution in the United States, but of those of every other part of the world of which the records were attainable. This work has been prepared by the joint agency of the late Prof. Jas. H. Coffin, of Lafayette College, Pennsylvania, and the Smithsonian Institution, the former furnishing the general plan and oversight of the work, the latter contributing the greater part of the material and defraying the cost of making the reductions and numerical computations.* This work may be considered an extension of the Winds of the Northern Hemisphere, prepared by Professor Coffin, and published by the Institution in 1853. It is designed to show principally—

First. The mean direction in which the lower currents of the atmosphere move over all parts of the surface of the earth.

Second. The ratio that the progressive motion bears to the total distance traveled.

Third. The modification that the currents undergo in different seasons of the year.

Fourth. The direction in which the forces act that produce these modifications.

Fifth. The amount of intensity of these forces as reckoned on the same scale as that which determines their mean annual direction.

The data used for elucidating these points consist of series of observations of winds made at 3,223 different stations on land and during numerous voyages at sea, extending from the parallel of 82° 16′ north to beyond the parallel of 75° south latitude, altogether embracing an aggregate period of over eighteen thousand five hundred years. The whole material is arranged in the form of tabular series, and for convenience in discussion the entire surface of the earth is divided into thirty-six zones by parallels of latitude drawn five degrees asunder, commencing at the North Pole and proceeding southwardly. The method of reduction is not that which has usually been adopted of obtaining the prevailing direction or the point from which the wind blows most frequently, but the traverse of the whole is made out in the same manner as that of a ship at sea. Suppose a particle of air to start at a given point and to move with uniform velocity for nine days, viz, from the northeast for a period of three days, southeast four days, south two days, at the end of this time the particle will be found at a certain point; the distance from the starting-point and the direction of the line joining the ending-points will be formed by a traverse. In this way the resultant direction of the wind is determined for a given place. If no deflecting force was exerted, the mean direction and relative progress of the wind would be the same for each month of the year; but as this is not the case, by comparing different resultants, an idea of the deflecting force is obtained, or, in other words, of the *monsoon* influence which tends in different seasons of the year to vary the resultant direction.

At the time of the death of Professor Coffin in 1873, the principal series of tables was mainly completed, yet there were blanks left to be filled. The supply of these deficiencies and the preparation of the illustrative plates was undertaken without pecuniary compensation by his son and successor in Lafayette College, Prof. Selden J. Coffin, who executed the work with a feeling of pious regard for the memory of a venerated parent, interest in science, and a devotion which merits special commendation.

---

*Altogether 80 persons were engaged in these reductions, the principal assistant of Professor Coffin being Mr. Henry Mansfield, a skilful computer.

The Institution also availed itself of the meteorological knowledge and skill in investigation of Dr. Alex. Woeikof, of the Imperial Geographical Society of Russia, during his late visit to this country, for a series of deductions from the tables and charts which the untimely death of Professor Coffin prevented him from undertaking.

Perhaps one of the most important additions to the meteorology of the present day is the establishment of the dependence of the force and direction of the wind upon the pressure of the atmosphere at different points. This subject was especially studied by Professor Espy and Professor Coffin, in this country, and by Professor Buys Ballot, in Holland, and later by Professor Buchan, in Edinburgh. This relation may be expressed as follows : *At the surface of the earth the wind blows from a region of high pressure to a region of low pressure, and is deflected to the right owing to the rotation of the earth ; while in the region above a reverse wind, deflected to the left, is taking place.* Professor Buchan has rendered great service to meteorology by extending this law to the general phenomena of the winds of the globe. For example, during the winter months the land becomes cold by radiation below the temperature of the sea, and, consequently, the air is more condensed over the former than over the latter, the barometer stands higher, and currents of air in accordance with the law in question tend to pass at the surface of the earth from the land to the ocean, and in an opposite direction above, while the reverse phenomena take place in summer.

It is fully established that there are on the surface of the earth five systems of winds, which roughly correspond with the zones of climate and temperature, and that the boundaries of these systems vary in latitude with the change in declination of the sun. In the torrid zone the resultant of the wind is from an easterly direction toward a variable middle line, giving rise to what are called the trade-winds. In the temperate zones the average direction of the wind is from the west; and again, in the arctic and antarctic regions, the resultant is from an easterly direction; and, furthermore, the limits of these systems of winds are connected with regions of high or low barometer. Thus, in the equatorial regions, the barometer above the middle line is below the average height of 30 inches, while along the northern and southern limit of this region there is a belt of high barometer, and again on the northern and southern limit of the winds of the temperate zone there is a belt of low barometer. The direction of the wind in these several regions and the belt of high and low barometer are referred to the unequal action of the heat of the sun in rarefying the air at the equator, causing an indrawing current at the surface of the earth, which takes a westerly direction on account of the revolution of the earth on its axis, and a current toward each pole, which, from the same reason, has a direction from the west. The equatorial current, cooling above, descends by its superior weight at the northern limit of the trade-winds, producing the belt of high barometer, from which, in opposite directions, two currents move, one returning toward the equator, forming the trade-wind, and the other, proceeding northward, having a westerly component by the revolution of the earth, tends to move in a direction from the west. It is probable, however, that a portion of the upper wind from the equator flows entirely to the pole, and there, by cooling, descends, consequently having a north-easterly direction. The point of union of these two currents produces an upward motion, again giving rise to the northern belt of lower barometer.

This sketch of the direction of the wind at the surface of the earth is shown by Professor Coffin to exist by deductions from actual observations, while it is also proved by Professor Ferrel, of the Coast Survey, as a mathematical deduction from the theory of a fluid subjected to difference of temperatures at different parts on the surface of a rotating globe.

The material which Dr. Woeikof has supplied to this work consists in an elaborate comparison of the actual winds, as tabulated from the reductions of Professor Coffin, with the varying pressure of the atmosphere at different seasons of the year due to the relative variation of the heat of the land and of the sea, on the principle adopted by Buchan. The result of his labor gives a satisfactory account in all cases where the pressure has been determined of the perturbations in the direction and intensity of the wind in different seasons of the year; and is a valuable first approximation to a full analysis of the causes of the complex phenomena of the local and periodical changes in the atmosphere.

The results given in the tables of the whole world are represented and illustrated by twenty-six plates drawn by Prof. S. J. Coffin, and engraved by Henry Chandler, of Buffalo, N. Y. These plates present, at a single view, the relation of the different parts of the same system of winds to each other and to the different systems of the globe. For the illustration of the deductions of Dr. Woeikof, two plates are reproduced from the paper of Professor Buchan in the Transactions of the Royal Society of Edinburgh. We trust this work will be accepted by the scientific world as a monument to the memory of Professor Coffin, and as an illustration of the judicious policy of the Smithsonian Institution.

The extended series of tables relative to the *Temperature* of the United States which has been in progress of preparation for a number of years, is now nearly through the press, and will be ready for distribution in the course of 1876.

This memoir contains the results of all observations to the end of the year 1870, from the following sources:

1st. The registers of the Smithsonian Institution, embracing upward of 300 folio volumes.

2d. The joint publications of the Institution, the Patent-Office, and the Department of Agriculture.

3d. All the publications and unpublished records of the meteorological system of the United States Army.

4th. The records of the United States Lake Survey under the Engineer Department of the United States Army.

5th. The records of the United States Coast Survey under the Treasury Department.

6th. The volumes compiled by Dr. F. B. Hough from observations made under the direction of the Regents of the University of the State of New York.

7th. The records made in Pennsylvania under the direction of the Franklin Institute of Philadelphia.

8th. The transactions of various societies and periodical publications.

All the material collected was first classified, and a series of tables of temperature in detail constructed, and from these were deduced the consolidated tables of average temperature. The first of these series, owing to its great bulk, must at present remain in manuscripts; it can, however, at any time be consulted at the Institution. The series of tables which is now about to be published consists of average temperatures, and is sufficient for the study of the climate of the United States generally, or for any particular part of it, as far as it depends upon temperature. The whole work was done under the superintendence of Mr. Charles A. Schott, of the United States Coast Survey, who has also given special attention to the revision of the accuracy of the computations. The character of Mr. Schott for scientific knowledge, sagacity, and skill, as exhibited in the previous publications on meteorology by the Institution, gives assurance that the present work on the temperature is a valuable contribution to knowledge.

Perhaps the best idea of the character and extent of the work can be given in a brief space by the following extract from the table of contents:

Section I.—General remarks and explanations of tabular results.

Special table of corrections for daily variation of temperature in each month and the year, for every hour and for various combinations of hours.

Tables of mean temperature for each month, season, and the year, at various stations, principally in North America.

Graphical representation and explanation of the isothermal charts.

Deductions from the charts of the distribution of the mean annual temperature, and of the distribution of the temperature during the winter and the summer seasons.

Section II.—Discussion of the daily fluctuation of the atmospheric temperature.

Times of sunrise and sunset in different latitudes and for every tenth day in each month.

Tables of bi-hourly, hourly, and semi-hourly mean temperatures for each month and the year at various places in North America.

Tables of differences from the mean of the day, of bi-hourly, hourly, and semi-hourly mean temperatures for each month and the year.

Systematic representation of the daily fluctuation of the temperature, by means of a periodic function.

Analysis of the daily fluctuation.

Variability of the temperature at any hour of the day from the normal value of that hour.

Section III.—The annual fluctuation of the temperature expressed in terms of a periodic function.

Table of computed annual fluctuation of the temperature at forty-six stations.

Discussion of the results for dates of mean annual values and for maxima and minima; and annual range in connection with the geographical distribution of the stations.

Examination into alleged interruption in the regularity of the annual fluctuation at certain epochs, with tables of temperature of each day of the year, deduced from a series of years.

Investigation of the variability of the temperature of any one day in a series of years.

Inequality in the epoch of the minima and maxima of the annual fluctuation.

Tables of observed extremes of temperatures, arranged by months, for a selected number of stations.

Analysis of tabular results for greatest heat and greatest cold with regard to geographical distribution.

Extreme annual range of temperature and monthly absolute variability; exhibition of the law of annual distribution.

Tables of the mean annual temperature, principally in the United States, for a succession of years from the earliest records to the close of the year 1870.

Investigation of the secular variation of the annual mean temperature, and of the permanency of the climate.

Comparison of the secular variation of the temperature with the variations in the frequency of the solar spots.

Comparison of the secular variation in the temperature and rain-fall in the United States.

Comparison of the secular variation in the temperature with the average annual direction of the wind.

Range of variability in the secular variation of the annual temperature.

Secular variation in the annual minima and maxima, compared with the variation in the annual means.

The tables in the first section contain the number and name of each station, its latitude and longitude, its elevation above the sea, its mean temperature for each month and for each season, and for the whole year, the extent of the series, the observing hours, and the name of the observer. In cases where observations were made at hours of the day differing from those of the general series, they were reduced to uniformity by corrections derived from tables of observations made at each hour of the twenty-four, continuously for a number of years. Such tables were furnished by the observations at Toronto, Mohawk, New Haven, and Philadelphia. The tables of this section will be of much importance to those interested in meteorology, as furnishing data for the special climatology of the various portions of the United States. The institution has been frequently applied to by State authorities, agricultural and medical societies and others, for information as to the temperature of peculiar localities, which can now be more readily supplied than before the tables were printed.

The tables of the second section relate to the daily fluctuation of the temperature during the year. The regular variations of the temperature due to changes in the sun's altitude and the length of the day are affected by perturbations from day to day on account of aqueous vapor suspended in the atmosphere, by the serenity or cloudiness of the sky, and by the direction of the wind. As a general rule the maximum heat occurs some time after the sun has reached his greatest altitude, and the greatest cold somewhere between midnight and sunrise. Even in mid-winter in high latitudes, during the continued absence of the sun, these periodic fluctuations are still perceptible; which may be accounted for by supposing waves of heat transported from more southern regions where the sun still rises above the horizon.

The tables of the third section relate to the annual fluctuations of the temperature and the perturbations from the curve derived from observations made during a series of years. These are of importance in determining questions as to the secular changes in climate.

The work is illustrated by three charts of isothermal spaces, one for summer, another for winter, and the third for the year; also two plates and a number of wood-cuts.

The next series of meteorological observations which remains to be discussed and analyzed is that which relates to the pressure of the atmosphere, which, it is evident from what has been said in regard to the winds, is an important element in determining the peculiar climatology of the North American Continent and its relation to that of the other parts of the world. This work will be commenced during the latter part of the present year.

Another work will be continued—that on the collation and discussion of the observations on thunder-storms and other casual phenomena. The observations in regard to these phenomena have been copied from the original records and arranged in tables previous to their discussion.

The miscellaneous work done by our computers in regard to meteorology during the year 1875 is as follows:

Manuscript temperature tables were prepared for the first seven months of 1871 and for March, 1872, these records not having been accessible before. Many additions were made to the general tables from new material sent by observers and others. The collection and tabulation of the observations for rain-fall at the Smithsonian stations for 1874 has been completed, and also for those at the Signal-Service stations by permission of General Myer, Chief Signal-Officer, from 1872 to 1874 inclusive, also for Army stations for the last six months of 1874, and for Canadian stations from 1872 to 1874 complete.

For the exhibition of the results of the meteorological labors of the Institution at the Centennial Exhibition, an outline map 16 by 12 feet has been prepared. This map will be of use to the lecturer and to the different departments of the Government in exhibiting on a large scale the results of various statistical inquiries. Already a number of different parties have applied for copies, for which such a charge will be made as to considerably diminish the cost to the Institution of the original production of the map.

INTERNATIONAL LITERARY AND SCIENTIFIC EXCHANGES.

This system has been prosecuted during the past year with unabated energy, and the results have been commensurate with the labor expended. As an evidence of the high estimation in which this branch of the operations of the Institution is regarded, as well as to give proper credit to the parties who have transmitted free of cost the packages of the Institution, we reprint, as usual, the following list of their names :

Cunard Steamship Company.
Anchor Steamship Company.
Pacific Mail Steamship Company.
Panama Railroad Company.
Pacific Steam Navigation Company.
New York and Mexico Steamship Company.
New York and Brazil Steamship Company.

North German Lloyd Steamship Company.
Hamburg American Packet Company.
French Transatlantic Company.
North Baltic Lloyd Steamship Company.
Inman Steamship Company.

The special thanks of the Institution are again tendered to the above-mentioned companies for their enlightened liberality.

It should also be mentioned that Messrs. Prin, Trow and & Co., of New York, agents of the Atlas Steamship Company, have made a very liberal concession to the Institution in the reduction of charges for transmission of parcels to the West Indies; one dollar in gold being charged for any package not exceeding three cubic feet in measurement, instead of the usual charge, three times this sum.

The following are the foreign centers of reception and distribution of the Smithsonian exchanges :

London—William Wesley, 28 Essex street, Strand.
Paris—G. Bossange, 16 rue du 4 Septembre.
Leipsic—Dr. Felix Flügel, 49 Sidonien Strasse.
St. Petersburg—L. Watkins & Co., 10 Admiralty Place.
Amsterdam—F. Müller. Heerengracht kk, No. 130.

Milan—U. Hoepli, 591 Galeria Cristoforia.
Harlem—Prof. Baumhauer.
Christiania—Royal University of Norway.
Stockholm—Royal Swedish Academy of Sciences.
Copenhagen—Royal Danish Society.
Lisbon—Royal Academy of Sciences.
Madrid—Royal Academy of Sciences.
Havana—Dr. Felipe Poey.
Santiago—University of Chili.
Mexico—Mexican Society of Geography and Statistics
Montreal—Geological Survey of Canada.

The packages of the Institution for the West Indies have been kindly forwarded by Mr. Thomas Bland, of New York, and those for Turkey and some other points by the American Board of Commissioners for Foreign Missions, Boston.

The following table exhibits the number of foreign establishments with which the Institution is at present in correspondence, or, in other words, to which it sends publications and from which it receives others in return:

Foreign Institutions in correspondence with the Smithsonian Institution.

Australia	29	India	31
Argentine Republic	13	Java	5
Algeria	6	Japan	4
Belgium	110	Liberia	1
British America	27	Mexico	14
Bolivia	1	Mauritius	4
Brazil	8	New Zealand	14
British Guiana	3	Norway	24
Central America	1	Polynesia	2
Chili	9	Portugal	21
Colombia	3	Philippine Islands	2
Cape Colony	5	Peru	3
China	1	Russia	161
Denmark	28	Spain	14
Dutch Guiana	1	Sweden	21
Ecuador	2	Switzerland	68
Egypt	8	St. Helena	2
France	290	Syria	1
Germany	642	Turkey	11
Greece	8	Venezuela	2
Great Britain and Ireland	350	West Indies	7
Holland	65	General	6
Iceland	2		
Italy	177	Total	2,207

Statistics of exchanges sent during the last seven years.

	1869.	1870.	1871.	1872.	1873.	1874.	1875.
No. of boxes..............	112	121	108	179	196	131	208
Bulk in cubic feet.......	1,033	1,189	772	954	1,476	933	1,503
Weight...................	23,376	31,383	28,950	26,850	44,236	27,990	45,300

We may also mention as an evidence of the high appreciation of the character of the Smithsonian exchanges, that the packages bearing the marks of the Institution are admitted free of duty and without examination into all foreign ports.

The value of this system, as a means of advancing civilization, can scarcely be too highly estimated. Accounts of all the results of scientific investigations in the old and new world are through it interchanged, and men in both hemispheres are rendered efficient co-operators in the great work of enlarging the bounds of knowledge, and thus one great impediment to human advancement, that of isolation, is, in a measure, overcome.

The system has now become so extended that it requires the constant attention of several assistants and a large amount of correspondence. It has, however, been reduced to such general regulations as usually to prevent loss or the missending of packages. It has happened in a few cases that loss has occurred on account of shipwreck, and among these we have to mention that of the four large cases shipped from Germany in December last, on the Deutschland, three of which contained recent publications of German learned societies, and the fourth specimens of ornithology for the National Museum. The latter alone was insured. In connection with this loss we have received the following expression of regret from Dr. Felix Flügel, the warm friend and for more than twenty years efficient agent of the Institution:

"It is now a disagreeable thought that I hurried the transmission of the last case as much as possible, in order to insure its being forwarded by the unfortunate vessel. I feel quite sorry that I cannot any longer boast that not a single leaf intrusted to my care for your Institution had been lost."

During the past year 4,661 packages, each containing several articles, have been received from abroad for distribution to institutions and individuals in this country.

Two hundred and eight boxes, averaging 7 cubic feet each, with a total weight of 45,300 pounds, were sent abroad by the Institution during the year. The total number of separate parcels contained in these boxes was about 12,000.

To facilitate the business of the exchanges, the following rules have been adopted:

1. Every package, without exception, must be enveloped in strong

paper, and secured so as to bear separate transportation by express or otherwise.

2. The address of the institution or individual, for whom the package is intended, must be written legibly on the cover, and the name of the sender on one corner of the same.

3. No single package must exceed the half of a cubic foot in bulk.

4. A detailed list of addresses of all the parcels sent, with their contents, must accompany them.

5. No letter or other communication can be allowed in the parcel, excepting such as relates exclusively to the contents of the package.

6. All packages must be delivered in Washington free of freight and other expenses.

7. Every parcel should contain a blank acknowledgment, to be signed and returned, either through the agent of the Institution, or, what is still better, through the mail, to the sender.

Should returns be desired for what is sent, the fact should be explicitly stated on the list of the contents of the package. Much disappointment is frequently expressed at the absence of any return in kind for transmissions; but unless these are specifically asked for, they will fail in many instances to be made. It will facilitate the labors of the Institution very greatly if the number corresponding to the several addresses in the Smithsonian printed catalogue be marked on the face of each parcel; and for this purpose a copy of the catalogue will be forwarded to all who apply for it.

Specimens of natural history will not be received for transmission unless with a previous understanding as to their character and bulk.

8. Unless all these conditions are complied with, the parcels will not be forwarded from the Institution; and, on the failure to comply with the first and second conditions, will be returned to the sender for correction.

In regard to exchanges we have to state, at the request of the Societé Americaine de France, 20 Rue Madame, Paris, that it will gladly exchange its publications with societies especially devoted to the archæology of the New World. We are also requested to announce that the Royal Society of New South Wales desires to enter into correspondence with similar scientific societies and institutions in other countries, for the purpose of making a friendly interchange of information and publications. The annual transactions published by this society consist of original scientific articles, which usually relate to the geography, geology, mineralogy, natural history, meteorology, and general resources of the colony of New South Wales.

The materials of exchanges are in some cases furnished by special acts of Congress. As an example of this, we may state that at the last session it was ordered that one thousand copies of the Report of the Geological Survey of the Territories, by Dr. Hayden, for the year 1873, be furnished to the Smithsonian Institution. These will be distributed to foreign societies during the coming year.

EXCHANGE OF GOVERNMENT DOCUMENTS.

In 1867 a proposition was made to the Institution, by the Librarian of Congress, relative to establishing a system of exchange of official documents between the Government of the United States and those of foreign nations.

The object in this was to secure regularly and systematically all reports and other documents relative to the legislation, jurisprudence, statistics, internal economy, technology, &c., of all nations, so as to place the material at the command of the committees and members of Congress, heads of bureaus, &c.

In accordance with this, a circular* was addressed to the different governments having relations with the United States, for the purpose of ascertaining their views as to such an exchange.

The following governments responded favorably: France, Belgium, Great Britain, Switzerland, Spain, Costa Rica, Netherlands, Chili, Denmark, Argentine Confederation, United States of Colombia, Würtemburg, Finland, Hamburg, Baden, Sweden, Victoria. The latter government forwarded a collection of books at once, which was placed in the Library of Congress.

At the Thirty-ninth session of Congress, the following resolution was adopted:

[No. 55.] A RESOLUTION to provide for the exchange of certain public documents.

Resolved by the Senate and House of Representatives of the United States of America, in Congress assembled, That fifty copies of all documents hereafter printed by order of either house of Congress, and fifty copies additional of all documents printed in excess of the usual number, together with fifty copies of each publication issued by any Department or Bureau of the Government, be placed at the disposal of the Joint Committee on the Library, who shall exchange the same, through the agency of the Smithsonian Institution, for such works published in foreign countries, and especially by foreign governments, as may be deemed by said committee an equivalent; said works to be deposited in the Library of Congress.

Approved March 2, 1867.

In consequence of an oversight in not ordering the Public Printer to furnish the necessary extra copies of public documents for this purpose, the Library Committee could not carry out the foregoing resolution, and at the ensuing session, Fortieth Congress, the following additional resolution was adopted:

[No. 72.] A RESOLUTION to carry into effect the resolution approved March two, eighteen hundred and sixty-seven, providing for the exchange of certain public documents.

Resolved by the Senate and House of Representatives of the United States of America, in Congress assembled, That the Congressional Printer, whenever he shall be so directed by the Joint Committee on the Library, be, and he hereby is, directed to print fifty copies, in addition to the regular number, of all documents hereafter printed by order of either house of Congress, or by order of any Department or Bureau of the Government, and whenever he shall be so directed by the Joint Committee on the Library,

---

* Report of the Smithsonian Institution for 1867, page 71.

one hundred copies additional of all documents ordered to be printed in excess of the usual number; said fifty or one hundred copies to be delivered to the Librarian of Congress, to be exchanged, under direction of the Joint Committee on the Library, as provided by joint resolution approved March two, eighteen hundred and sixty-seven·

SEC. 2. *And be it further resolved,* That fifty copies of each publication printed under direction of any Department or Bureau of the Government, whether at the Congressional Printing-Office or elsewhere, shall be placed at the disposal of the Joint Committee on the Library, to carry out the provisions of said resolution.

Approved July 25, 1868.

The following is the provision in relation to the subject in the Revised Statutes:

SEC. 3796. The Congressional Printer shall, when so directed by the Joint Committee on the Library, print, in addition to the usual number, either fifty or one hundred copies, as he may be directed, of all documents printed by order of either house of Congress, or of any Department or Bureau of the Government. [Revised Statutes.]

The exchange proposed by this action of Congress, from unforeseen difficulties, has never been fully carried into effect, although several attempts have been made to do so.

In October, 1874, by special direction of Mr. Spofford, Librarian of Congress, four cases of documents were sent to the government of Ontario, Toronto; and in November, 1874, five cases to the Parliamentary Library, Ottawa, five cases to the government of Japan, and four cases to the Bibliothek des Deutschen Reichstag, Berlin.

A number of boxes were also shipped to the agents of the Institution in Europe, to be held by them for further instructions.

A large quantity of these public documents having accumulated at the Institution, it became necessary to provide for their distribution without further delay, and accordingly the Institution issued, in October last, the following circular:

The Congress of the United States has authorized the exchange, under direction of the Joint Library Committee of Congress, through the Smithsonian Institution, of a certain number of all United States official documents for the corresponding publications of other governments throughout the world; the returns to be placed in the National Library at Washington. The works to be distributed consist of reports and proceedings of Congress, messages of the President, annual reports and occasional publications of Departments and Bureaus, &c., the whole relating to the legislation, jurisprudence, foreign relations, commerce, statistics, arts, manufactures, agriculture, geography, hydrography, &c., of the United States, and including everything, of whatever nature, published, either by direct order of Congress or by any of the Departments of the Government. The series embraces a large number of volumes each year, the most of which are bound.

The exchange expected from each government is a complete series of its publications, to include the documents of special bureaus or departments as well as the general publications, of whatever nature, printed at the public expense, and also embracing all such works as are published by booksellers with the aid of grants or subscriptions from governments.

The Smithsonian Institution, in behalf of the Joint Library Committee of Congress, is prepared to deliver the publications of the United States, free of charge for freight, to any person in the city of Washington or in New York who may be designated by the governments which enter into the arrangement.

The books intended for the United States are to be delivered to either of the Smithsonian agents, viz:

London, William Wesley, 28 Essex street, Strand; Paris, G. Bossange, 16 rue du 4 Septembre; Leipsic, Dr. Felix Flügel, 12 Sidonien Strasse; St. Petersburg, L. Watkins & Co., 10 Admiralty Place; Amsterdam, F. Müller; Milan, U. Hoepli, 591 Galeria Cristoforia; Haarlem, Bureau Scientifique Central Neerlandais à Harlem; Christiania, Kongelige Norske Frederiks Universitetet; Stockholm, Kongliga Svenska Vetenskaps Akademien; Copenhagen, Kongelige Danske Videnskabernes Selskab.

For all other countries, packages may be delivered to the United States ministers. An invoice of each transmission should be sent by mail to the Institution.

JOSEPH HENRY,
Secretary Smithsonian Institution.

This circular was sent with the following letter to the foreign ministers in Washington representing the following countries: Argentine Republic, Austria-Hungary, Belgium, Brazil, Chili, Denmark, France, German Empire, Great Britain, Guatemala, Hawaii, Hayti, Italy, Japan, Mexico, Netherlands, Peru, Portugal, Russia, Salvador, Spain, Sweden and Norway, Turkey, United States of Colombia, Venezuela.

SMITHSONIAN INSTITUTION,
Washington, D. C., October 30, 1875.

SIR: I have the honor, accompanying this, to transmit a circular relative to the exchange of the documents published by the United States with those of other nations, and to request you to state to whom the boxes now ready for transmission, intended for your government, shall be delivered.

Very respectfully, your obedient servant,

JOSEPH HENRY,
Secretary Smithsonian Institution.

In accordance with the instructions received by the Institution in response to the foregoing letter, the following distribution of documents was made:

6 cases for Turkey, sent to legation, H street, Washington, D. C.

6 cases for France, sent to consul-general of France, New York.

6 cases for Portugal, sent to consul-general of Portugal, 148 Pearl street, New York.

6 cases for Sweden, sent to consulate, 18 Exchange Place, New York.

6 cases for Brazil, sent to vice-consul, 52 South Gay street, Baltimore.

6 cases for Argentine Republic, sent to G. Videla Dorna, Albermarle Hotel, New York.

4 cases for Belgium, sent to Peter Wright & Sons, Philadelphia.

1 case for Chili, sent to Muñoz & Espriella, 52 Pine street, New York.

6 cases for Mexico, sent to Juan N. Navarro, 50 Exchange Place, N. Y.

When these boxes had been distributed we were requested by the Librarian of Congress to stop further proceedings until instructions could be procured from the Library Committee. As soon as the difficulties which have impeded this work are removed, the Institution will go on to complete the arrangement.

LIBRARY.

The library of the Institution, as has been stated in previous reports, is deposited in the Capitol of the United States, with the Librarian of

Congress, under whose direction it is arranged and catalogued as a part of the Library of the Government.

The following is a statement of the books, maps, and charts received in 1875:

Volumes:

Octavo, or less	819	
Quarto, or larger	301	
		1,120

Parts of volumes:

Octavo, or less	2,139	
Quarto, or larger	1,877	
		4,016

Pamphlets:

Octavo, or less	1,524	
Quarto, or larger	273	
		1,797
Maps and charts		114
Total receipts		7,047

These articles are entered as they are received at the Institution in a large record-book, and afterward transferred to the Library of Congress. The number received in 1875 was considerably larger than that in the preceding year.

During the past year much use has been made of the books of the Institution which are in the Library of Congress as well as those of the latter library by the collaborators of the Institution. The value of the library will, however, be enhanced when the new edition of the catalogue of transactions of learned societies has been published, the old edition having been deficient in the names of the works received since the date at which it was issued.

The following are some of the more valuable works received in 1875:

From the Ministry of War, St. Petersburg: Artillery Journal, 1868–1874, 37 parts; Engineering Journal, 1868–1873, 27 parts; Ordnance Magazine, 1868–1874, 14 parts.

From His Highness the Maharajah of Travancose, Trevandrum: Observations of Magnetic Declination, made at the Trevandrum and Augustia Observatories in the years 1852 to 1869. Vol. I. London, 1874. 4to.

From the British government: Fac-similes of National Manuscripts of Ireland, selected and edited under the direction of the Right Hon. Edward Sullivan, Master of the Rolls in Ireland, by J. T. Gilbert, Secretary of the Public Record Office of Ireland, and photozincographed by command of Her Majesty Queen Victoria, by Major-General Sir Henry James. Part I. Dublin, 1874. Folio.

From the University of Chili, Santiago: Anales 1872, 1873. Government Documents, 12 volumes and six parts. Topographical and Geological Chart of Chili, in 13 parts.

From the Ambrosian Library, Milan: Codex Syro-Hexaplaris Ambrosianus photolithographice editus curante et adnotante sac. obl. Antonio Maria Ceriani. Milan, 1874. Folio.

From the publishers, Paris: Revue des Cours Littéraires, 1863–1874; Revue des Cours Scientifiques, 1863–1874, 28 vols. 4to.

From the Royal University of Norway, Christiania: The Cathedral of Throndheim. Christiania, 1859. Folio. Die Pflanzenwelt Norwegens. Christiania, 1873–1895. 4to. Magnetism der Erde von Christopher Hansteen. 4to, with folio atlas. Christiania, 1819. Norges Melodier, arrangerede for pianoforte med text. Kjöbenhavn. 8vo. Die Aegyptischen Denkmäler in St. Petersburg, Helsingfors, Upsala, und Copenhagen, von J. Lieblein, mit 35 autographirten Tafeln. Christiania, 1873. 8vo. Norges Mynter i Middelalderen af C. A. Holmbre. Christiania, 1865. 4to. Geologisk Kart over det söndenfjeldske Norge af Dr. Kjenelf. Meteorologisk Storm-Atlas af H. Mohn. Christiana, 1870. Folio. Denkmale der Holzbaukunst in Norwegen. Folio. Noske Nationaldragter af C. Tonsberg. Christiania. 4to. Portola Sögur, ved C. R. Unger. Christiania, 1874. 8vo. Remains from the Iron Age of Scandinavia, by O. Montelius. Stockholm, 1869. 4to.

From Mr. James L. Bowes, Liverpool: Keramic Art of Japan. By George Ashdown Auderley and James Lord Bowes. Parts I and II. Illustrated. London and Liverpool, 1875. Folio. Also descriptive catalogue of art works in Japanese lacquer, 1875. 4to.

From the Public Library of Buenos Ayres: Government documents, scientific, historical, biographical and poetical works, 68 volumes, 114 parts of volumes, and 35 pamphlets.

From the Royal Library, Stockholm: Government documents, 100 volumes.

From the Bureau of Statistics, Stockholm: Bidrag till Sveriges Officiela Statistik, 24 parts, 4to, and Notices sur la Suède. Stockholm, 1875. 8vo.

From the Finnish Scientific Society, Helsingfors: 9 volumes of their publications.

From the Universities of Dorpat, Helsingfors, Berlin, Bonn, Breslau, Erlangen, Freiburg, Göttingen, Halle, Heidelberg, Jena, Leipzig, Marburg, Rostock, Basel, and Zürich: Inaugural dissertations for 1874.

From the Library of Parliament, Ottawa, Canada: 15 volumes government documents.

From the Board of Admiralty, London: 26 charts published by the Hydrographic Office, from January, 1874, to January, 1875. The Admiralty Catalogue of Charts, Plans, &c., 1875; Catalogue of the Admiralty Library, 1875; and 10 lists of lights.

From the State Library of Illinois: 16 volumes State documents.

From the State Library of Vermont: 9 volumes State documents.

From Sir Charles Hartley, in behalf of the European Commission of the Danube: The second volume of lithographed plates of surveys, &c.,

of the commission, with descriptive texts. The first volume of this very valuable and important work was presented to the Institution some years ago by Baron d'Offenberg, the late Russian Minister at Washington.

Among the most interesting works presented is that of the first part of the series of fac-similes of the National Manuscripts of Ireland. The art of photozincography was invented by Maj. Gen. Sir Henry James, in 1860, and in 1866 he was ordered to produce five hundred fac-simile copies of Domesday Book, and afterward a series of national manuscripts to illustrate the changes in the English language and writing since the time of the Conquest. The publication of the first series in four volumes was finished in 1869. The government then concluded to have a series of documents of a similar character produced from the Scotch Records, with translation, which was finished in 1872. Her Majesty's government next authorized the publication of a series from the Irish Records, the first part of which, with all the other series, has been received by the Institution. The English series of fac-similes contains a great number of extremely valuable historical manuscripts of various kinds— legal, diplomatic, and epistolary. The Scotch series consists mainly of copies of a large number of royal and other charters and important state papers. The Irish series is remarkable not only for the great antiquity of many of the manuscripts comprised in it, but also for the splendid examples of pictorial art which it contains.

Among the articles presented to the library is a photograph of an Egyptian papyrus, about 40 feet in length, from Mr. John S. Edgar, United States consul at Beirut, Syria, discovered in December, 1874, in a previously unopened tomb at Thebes, Egypt.

It is proper to state, in connection with the library, that the following act of courtesy to the Regents of the Smithsonian Institution, residing in Washington, was passed by Congress March 3, 1875: "That the Joint Committee of both Houses of Congress on the Library be authorized to extend the use of books in the Library of Congress to Regents of the Smithsonian Institution resident in Washington on the same conditions and restrictions as members of Congress are allowed to use the Library."

TELEGRAPHIC ANNOUNCEMENT OF ASTRONOMICAL DISCOVERIES.

The important arrangement which was concluded between the Smithsonian Institution and the Atlantic cable companies in 1873, by which free telegraphic transmission of astronomical discoveries was granted between Europe and America, has been continued during the past year. The following is a list of the *asteroids* discovered in 1875:

No. 141, discovered by Paul Henry, at Paris, January 13.
No. 142,   "   by J. Palisa, at Pola, January 28.
No. 143,   "   by J. Palisa, at Pola, February 23.
No. 144,   "   by C. H. F. Peters, at Clinton, June 4.
No. 145,   "   by C. H. F. Peters, at Clinton, June 4.

No. 146, discovered by A. Borelly, at Marseilles, June 8.

No. 147,   "   by Schulhof, at Berlin, July 11.

No. 148,   "   by Prosper Henry, at Paris, August 7.

No. 149,   "   by Perrotin, at Toulouse, October 6.

No. 150,   "   by Watson, at Ann Arbor, October 18.

No. 151,   "   by Palisa, at Pola, November 1.

No. 152,   "   by Paul Henry, at Paris, November 2.

No. 153,   "   by Palisa, at Pola, November 2.

No. 154,   "   by Prosper Henry, at Paris, November 4.

No. 155,   "   by Palisa, at Pola, November 8.

No. 156,   "   by Palisa, at Pola, November 22.

No. 157,   "   by Borelly, at Marseilles, December 1.

CORRESPONDENCE.

The correspondence of the Institution continues to increase from year to year. Not only are there upward of 2,000 foreign institutions that require acknowledgments for works presented to libraries, or for specimens to the museum, but there are also an increasing number of individuals in different parts of the old and new worlds who, through the institution, make inquiries as to subjects connected with various branches of knowledge relative to America.

In this country the public generally consider the Institution as an establishment to which requests may be addressed asking information on all branches of knowledge, the solution of various scientific problems, the examination and indorsement both of scientific investigation and crude unscientific speculations. In the line of mathematics during the past year, we have had communications the object of which was the duplication of the cube, the quadrature of the circle, and the tri-section of an angle, in which the writers confidently anticipated that no flaw could be found in their reasoning; and indeed in some cases much labor was required to point out the fallacy. But the most troublesome correspondents are persons of extensive reading, and in some cases of considerable literary acquirements, who in earlier life were not imbued with scientific methods, but who, not without a certain degree of mental power, imagine that they have made great discoveries in the way of high generalizations. Their claims not being allowed, they rank themselves among the martyrs of science, against whom the scientific schools and the envy of the world have arrayed themselves. Indeed, to such intensity does this feeling arise in certain persons that on their special subjects they are really monomaniacs, although on others they may be not only entirely sane, but even evince abilities of a high order. This mental condition is not confined to our country. A notable example of it is found in the case of the celebrated German poet, Goethe, who, examining a dark patch on a white wall through a prism, saw the upper and lower edges of the dark figure bordered with the colors of the rainbow. On this observation he founded a theory of colors, which included the idea that blackness was a compound of all colors, and that the ordinary theory, which had been propounded by Newton, was an absurdity. So thoroughly did he become imbued with this conception that it was in vain to attempt to convince him of its fallacy, and he was irritated almost to madness when the name of Newton was mentioned with commendation.

In this connection we may mention as a somewhat singular coincidence, that at the beginning of this Institution the author of this report was called upon to examine a paper, presented for publication by a professor in one of the most prominent universities of this country, in which the author had adopted as an original suggestion the same hypothesis as that of Goethe, and whose indignation on account of its rejection was expressed in terms of little courtesy. Two persons of this class have recently made a special journey to Washington, from distant parts of the country, to demand justice from the Institution, in the way of recognition of their claims to discoveries in science of great importance to humanity, and each of them has made an appeal to his Representative in Congress to aid him in compelling the Institution to acknowledge the merits of his speculations.

Providence vindicates in such cases the equality of its justice in giving to such persons an undue share of self-esteem, and an exaltation of confidence in themselves, which in a great degree compensate for the want of what they conceive to be the just appreciation of the public. Unless, however, they are men of great benevolence of disposition, who can look with pity on what they deem the ignorance and prejudice of leaders of science, they are apt to indulge in a bitterness of denunciation which might be injurious to the reputation of the Institution were their effects not neutralized by the extravagance of the assertions themselves. The representatives of this class of persons are increasing with the increase of the diffusion of popular knowledge.. It must not be understood that this remark is made to disparage the diffusion of scientific knowledge, but simply to indicate that there are classes of minds of a peculiar idiosyncrasy which tend to expend their power in unconditioned and unfruitful speculation ; neither do we condemn scientific speculation, for the discovery of all great principles of science is the result of antecedent hypotheses or speculations, which are, however, founded on definite analogies of the known, and finally adopted or rejected by the test of the exact agreement of predictions based upon them with the actual phenomena of nature.

During the past year a number of communications have been received in regard to the discovery of new motive-powers as to which extravagant ideas have been entertained relative to superseding coal-power as an element for the propulsion of machinery. In regard to these, we may say that science has established the great fact, without the possibility of doubt, that what is called power, or that which produces changes in matter, cannot be created by man, but exists in nature in a state of activity or in a condition of neutralization; and furthermore, that all the original forces connected with our globe, as a general rule, have assumed a state of permanent equilibrium, and that the crust of the earth as a whole, with the exception of the comparatively exceedingly small proportion, consisting of organic matter, such as coal, wood, &c., is, as it were, a burnt slag, incapable of yielding power; that all the motions and changes on its surface are due to actions from celestial space, principally from the sun. These are comprised under the heads of wind-power, water-power, tide-power, and heat-power as developed in the combustion of coal. Beside these there are no indications of any other motive-powers. It is true, the heat of the interior of the earth may hereafter be utilized—that wind, water, and especially tide power may also be more generally employed than at present. Great improvements are possible also in the application of coal-power; the present steam-engine is exceedingly wasteful of useful effect, and the perfection of the air-engine is much to be desired.

The application of the direct heat of the sun to produce motive energy can scarcely ever compete with the indirect application of this power through growing plants and the subsequent combustion of the fuel which they furnish.

All attempts to substitute electricity or magnetism for coal-power must be unsuccessful, since these powers tend to an equilibrium from which they can only be disturbed by the application of another power, which is the equivalent of that which they can subsequently exhibit. They are, however, with chemical attraction, &c., of great importance as intermediate agents in the application of the power of heat as derived from combustion.

Science does not indicate in the slightest degree the possibility of the discovery of a new primary power comparable with that of combustion, as exhibited in the burning of coal. Whatever unknown powers may exist in nature capable of doing work, must be in a state of neutralization, otherwise they would manifest themselves spontaneously, and from this state of neutralization or equilibrium they can only be released by the action of an extraneous power of equivalent energy, and we therefore do not hesitate to say that all declarations of the discovery of a new power which is to supersede the use of coal as a motive-power, have their origin in ignorance or deception, and frequently in both. A man of some ingenuity in combining mechanical elements, and having some indefinite scientific knowledge, imagines it possible to obtain a certain result by a given combination of principles, and by long brooding over this subject, previous to experiment, at length convinces himself of the certainty of the anticipated result. Having thus deceived himself by his sophisms, he calls upon his neighbors to accept his conclusions as verified truths, and soon acquires the notoriety of having made a discovery which is to change the civilization of the world.   The shadowy reputation which he has thus acquired is too gratifying to his vanity to be at once relinquished by the announcement of his self-deception, and in preference he applies his ingenuity in devising means by which to continue the deception of his friends and supporters long after he himself has been convinced of the fallacy of his first assumptions.   In this way what was commenced in folly generally ends in fraud.

The records of the Patent-Office of this country exhibit a greater amount of thought and ingenuity employed in the way of invention than perhaps in any other country, but for want of more definite conceptions of scientific principles, an immense amount of labor is expended in futile attempts to produce results which are unattainable.

Another branch of the correspondence relates to questions in regard to the naming of objects of natural history, and especially to specimens of mineralogy.   The interest which is felt in regard to the mining-products of the country induce large numbers of specimens of ores to be submitted to the Institution for examination.   The rule adopted in regard to these, is to give the results of a qualitative analysis, that is, an enumeration of the substances contained in each specimen, without giving the percentage of each.   This information can be given without very much labor for a single specimen, whereas an exact quantitative analysis would require more time than the Institution can devote to an inquiry which may be of commercial value to an individual, but of no especial interest to the public at large.   When information as to the percentage of ingredients is required, the party is referred to some expert who will make the examination desired for a proper compensation. This distinction in the kind of information furnished is necessary to prevent the name of the Institution from being connected with transactions of a character which have been injurious to the reputation of those concerned in them.

In carrying on the correspondence, much assistance has been rendered by the collaborators of the Institution.

ETHNOLOGY.

From the commencement of the Institution to the present time, the archæology of the United States has been to it an object of special interest. In all cases in which information has been received of the locality of a field of probable interesting discovery, an appropriation has been made for its ethnological explorations.   The articles obtained from such sources have been deposited in the National Museum, with the intention of having descriptions and discussions of them published in the Smithsonian Contributions to Knowledge.   The archæology of the United States has not been the only part of ethnology to which attention has been given, but also special effort has been made from the first to obtain illustrations and descriptions of the now-existing native inhabitants of the North American continent.   This latter subject is very important in furnishing the materials for ascertaining the uses of the implements of the Stone Age found in the ancient mounds, since many of them with perhaps slight modification are in use at the present time among the more remote Indians of the western portion of this country. For example, pointed stone implements found in the mounds which have been thought to be arrow and javelin points, are now employed as knives, to which wooden handles are attached by means of a vegetable cement, and from the transmission of usages we may confidently assume that similar handles, long since decayed, were also originally attached to like implements of undoubted ancient origin.

The subject of ethnology has received a very great impetus through the appropriation of Congress for the display of illustrations at the Centennial, circulars having been distributed, requesting the correspondents of the Institution to aid in collecting specimens and to give information as to the existence of special collections, from which unique specimens could be borrowed for copying in plaster. The Institution has also engaged the services of Dr. Rau, of New York, the well-known ethnologist, to classify and arrange the whole collection in the National Museum, and to prepare a descriptive catalogue for publication. He has commenced with the classification of the specimens of the Stone Age, and has nearly completed this part of the general work. In this classification it has been thought proper to separate the objects belonging to times anterior to the occupation of the continent by Europeans, from those which have been used since that period. The first archæological series more particularly comprises objects found in mounds and other burial-places of early date, in caves, shell-heaps, &c., or, in other words, those which cannot with certainty be ascribed to tribes still in existence, or which have become extinct within historical times.

The second, or more strictly ethnological, series, consists of objects obtained from existing native tribes, and contains almost every article tending to illustrate the domestic life, hunting, fishing, games, warfare, navigation—in short, every phase of Indian existence that can be exhibited by tangible objects.

An account of what has been added to this department will be found in the report on the Museum by Prof. Baird, and also in the Appendix.

MISCELLANEOUS.

The Institution, as in former years, has been in harmonious co-operation with the Department of Agriculture, the Army Medical Museum, and the Corcoran Art Gallery. With the first it has deposited plants and other articles relating to agriculture; to the second it has transferred a large number of articles pertaining to comparative anatomy and materia medica, and has received in return ethnological specimens; in the third, the Corcoran Art Gallery, it has deposited a number of engravings.

The Secretary of the Institution being one of the trustees of the Art-

Gallery, the connection between the two establishments is not only cordial, but of an intimate character. The gallery during the year has been enriched by a large collection of rare plaster-casts, copies of the principal statues of the Vatican, and has been visited by a large number of citizens and strangers as a source of refined pleasure, and by a number of persons as means of practical improvement in art. We learn with pleasure that Mr. Corcoran, in addition to his munificent gifts to the city of Washington, is making provision for a series of art-studios, which cannot fail to add to the refined culture of the national capital.

Chemical laboratory.—During the past three years the laboratory of the Institution has been in charge of Dr. Oscar Loew, the chemist and mineralogist of the Wheeler survey; and during this time he has made various analyses for the Institution of minerals, mineral-waters, and other substances referred to the Institution for examination by the Government and other parties.

In behalf of the Wheeler expedition he has investigated and analyzed the waters of twenty different thermal springs, mineral springs, and alkaline lakes of Southern California; soils of arable lands and of the desert of Southern California; saline efflorescences from numerous localities in the Mohave desert, and ores and rocks from the same locality.

Photography.—The photographic laboratory, under the direction of Mr. T. W. Smillie, has been removed to the new building erected expressly for its accommodation and for the use of the taxidermists and naturalists engaged in preparing specimens for the Centennial Exhibition. A large number of photographs have been made of ethnological and natural history specimens for the use of the Institution, and a large amount of work done for others, especially for the United States Fish-Commission and Government surveys.

The Institution has been engaged for several years in collecting photographic likenesses of distinguished cultivators of science in all parts of the world, of the meteorological observers who for many years furnished valuable records of their observations, of the contributors to the ethnological department of the National Museum, of and other correspondents of the Institution. Of these photographs, four hundred have been received, which are neatly framed and form an interesting feature of the collections.

Light-house duty.—I have been a member of the Light-House Board since its first organization, and during all this time have discharged the duty of chairman of the committee on experiments. On the resignation of Admiral Shubrick in 1871, I was honored by an the election as chairman of the board. In the discharge of the duties connected with this service, I usually devote one day in the week and the greater proportion of my summer vacation. It may not be improper for me to remark that for the labors which I have thus bestowed upon the light-house service for upward of twenty years, I have received no other remuneration than that which results from the consciousness of having labored somewhat successfully in advancing the efficiency of a service which is one of the benevolent institutions of the present day tending to facilitate the harmonious intercourse of nations widely separated by intervening oceans.

During the last summer I devoted the entire vacation to the investigation of sound in its relation to fog-signals, the results of which have been published in the report of the Light-House Board for 1875. These investigations were a continuation of those of former years, and tend to establish the facts previously obtained, as well as to extend the knowledge of the phenomena of sound in its application to the uses of the mariner.

In these investigations the following conclusions have been arrived at:

1. That the rays of a beam of sound do not, like those of a beam of light, move parallel to each other from the surface of a concave reflector, but constantly diverge laterally on all sides, and although at first they are more intense in the axis of the reflector, they finally spread out so as to encompass the whole horizon, thus rendering the use of reflectors to enforce fog-signals of little value.

2. That the effect of wind in increasing or diminishing sound is not confined to currents of air at the surface of the earth, but that those of higher strata are also active in varying its transmission.

3. That although sound is generally heard farther with the wind than against it, yet in some instances the reverse is remarkably the case.

4. That sound may be heard in some cases at a greater distance, while it is inaudible at a less distance from its origin.

5. That a distant sound may be heard at the top of a tower in some cases when it is inaudible at the bottom.

6. That sound experiences a refraction deflecting it, in some cases, in a horizontal direction, and in others in a vertical plane, which explains most of the phenomena above mentioned.

The results obtained have excited considerable interest in this country and in Europe, and have given rise to criticism and discussions which will tend to enlarge and diffuse the knowledge of this important subject.

I have also, in behalf of the Light-House Board, made a series of experiments on petroleum as a light-house illuminant. These experiments were in continuation of those which I had previously made in regard to the introduction of lard-oil. Previous to the establishment of the Light-House Board, sperm-oil had been exclusively used in our system of light-houses, but the expense of this gradually increased from year to year until it became as high as $3 per gallon. After a laborious series of experiments, it was found that, under certain conditions, lard-oil might be substituted, and as this could be purchased at the time for from 50 to 60 cents per gallon, a saving of more than a hundred thousand dollars per annum was the result of the change. At the same time, a series of investigations, was made in regard to petroleum, but at that period the only refined petroleum submitted to the board after advertisement was that of a volatile character, and too dangerous to be adopted for light-house purposes. Since then, however, the price of lard-oil has constantly increased, while refined petroleum can now be obtained of such a character as to be safely employed by ordinary light-house keepers. Its introduction, therefore, in regard to economy, is a matter of much importance. But great care must be exercised in selecting oil of a proper quality, and hence the necessity of a thorough knowledge of its peculiarities in regard to safety.

In the investigations on this subject, it was ascertained that the fire-test usually employed to establish the character of a given oil in reference to safety was not in itself sufficient to settle this question. Many of the oils in general use, which, at the temperature of the atmosphere, increased by that from the burning of the lamp, give off a vapor which, if suffered to accumulate and mingle with the air in the space above the oil in the reservoir, produces a mixture which, if in definite proportion, explodes with the violence of gunpowder. It is true, on the doctrine of chances, an explosion may seldom take place, but still, the conditions necessary are frequently present, and only requires the application of a flame to produce a disastrous effect.

Although the discovery of the petroleum wells of Pennsylvania has been an immense boon to humanity, yet the advantage gained from it has been dearly bought by the accidents which have resulted from its incautious use. Its sale ought to be regulated by rigid enactments of legislatures, and none suffered to be sold which exhales a vapor capable of producing an explosion when mixed except at a temperature much above that at which the lamp is subjected in the warmest period of the year.

Fish Commission.—The investigation in regard to food-fishes and the methods of their propagation, for which an appropriation for several years has been annually made by Congress, has been continued under the direction of Professor Baird. This work was commenced in 1872, and has been prosecuted with satisfactory results to the present time. The species to which special attention has been given are shad, the fresh-water herring, the striped bass or rock-fish, the California salmon, the salmon of Maine, the land-locked salmon, the white-fish, and the carp, each of these having special relations to certain portions of the country, and promising in their anticipated aggregate an extremely important addition to the food-resources of the United States.

The States which have, up to this time, been the recipients of spawn and young fish are thirty-two in number. The extension of the benefit to other States, and its amplification in all, is simply a question of time and expenditure. The subject of fish culture is one of general popularity, as is evinced by the appointment of fish-commissioners in nineteen States, in most instances for the purpose of direct co-operation with the United States Commission.

The importance of the subject may be inferred from the fact that it may be stated, without exaggeration, that the waters bordering our shores can be made to yield a larger percentage of nutriment, acre for acre, than the land. Indeed, fish-culture is the only efficient means by which the fertilizing ingredients of the soil, which are constantly carried into the ocean by sewage, can be reclaimed for the reproduction of nutriment to organized beings. By want of a reclamation of this kind, certain portions of the earth thickly inhabited in ancient times have become sterile and almost deserted.

For the purpose of giving an idea of the nature and extent of the operations of the United States Fish Commission, Professor Baird gives the following statement, showing the distribution of fish during the years 1874 and 1875 :

Of young shad...	18,689,550
Of Penobscot salmon.....................................	2,294,565
Of California salmon	4,581,340
Total young fish	25,565,455

To this is to be added the hatching and distribution, during the winter and spring of 1875-'76, of California salmon, Penobscot salmon, landlocked salmon, and lake white-fish, not yet completed, amounting to at least fourteen million fish, thus making a total of forty million fish supplied by the United States Fish Commission in three years. This, at the assumed ratio of 1 to 200, would represent the proceeds of eight thousand million of eggs laid in the natural way, and subject to all the perils of natural spawning.

Polaris expedition.—Dr. Emil Bessels during the year has continued his labors at the Institution on the scientific materials which were saved from the Polaris expedition to the Arctic regions in the years 1871-'73, with the exception of two months in the summer, which were devoted to an attempt to make an exploration of Alaska in the United States steamer Saranac. He was, however, unfortunately shipwrecked and lost all his outfit. The first volume of the scientific results of the Polaris Expedition, relating to astronomy, pendulum experiments, temperature, winds, psychrometer, solar radiation, terrestrial radiation, ozone, face of the sky, meteorology, those taken at sea, &c., has been printed, and makes 793 pages. The volume will contain 960 pages, 14 plates, 2 maps, and 40 wood-cuts. Volumes II and III are under preparation, the former being devoted to natural history, comprising zoölogy, botany, geology, palæontology, mineralogy, containing about 250 pages, 10 plates, and 30 wood-cuts; the latter will comprise a complete monograph on the Eskimo, illustrated by a hundred plates and 300 wood-cuts. Of the former, 35 are ready to be engraved; of the latter 122 are drawn and 74 are engraved. The expense of preparation of this work and of the illustrations is defrayed by an appropriation of $15,000 by Congress at its last session.

NATIONAL MUSEUM.

The National Museum was established by the Government in 1842, and consisted of the specimens collected by the Wilkes exploring expedition. It was transferred from the Patent Office to the care of the Smithsonian Institution in 1858, where it has been enlarged by all the collections made by exploring and surveying parties of the several bureaus of the War, Navy, Treasury, and Interior Departments, and those of the Smithsonian Institution.

At first, $4,000 were allowed by Congress for the care and exhibition of the specimens. This sum has been gradually increased to $20,000. Nothing, however, has been allowed for the rent of the building, which was erected exclusively out of the income from the bequest of Smithson.

The following report from Prof. SPENCER F. BAIRD, Assistant Secretary, gives an account of the additions to the Museum and the various operations connected with it during the year 1875:

Increase of the National Museum.—The year 1875 constitutes a marked epoch in the history of this establishment, the increase in the number and comparative value of the specimens received, as also the work done in connection with the same, being much greater than that of any previous year. This is due partly to the natural increase year by year, which has been experienced since 1865, but more particularly as the result of special efforts made to prepare a suitable exhibition of the natural history and ethnology of the country at the International Exhibition of 1876.

For the purpose of enabling the Institution to exhibit a satisfactory display of the mineral, animal, fishery, and ethnological condition of the country, an appropriation was made by Congress of $67,000, subject, however, to a deduction for the erection of a building and the preparation of the surrounding grounds for that occasion. As this amounted to about $17,000, the sum actually available was $50,000. In addition to this, $5,000 was appropriated for the department of the food-fishes.

As many important gaps existed in the collection of American animals, speedy efforts were made to procure such as were wanting, or to replace such as were in bad condition.

The object of the exhibition in question was to present the industrial relations and applications of American natural history and geology; and as this had been entirely neglected previously, it became necessary to commence from the beginning and study out a plan of operations after determining the general character of the exhibit that was to be made. With this view, a series of circulars was prepared on the different subjects, and sent to all the correspondents of the Institution, accompanied with special directions for collecting, packing, and shipping, as also a schedule of classification.

The mineral department was first organized, and was placed in charge of Prof. William P. Blake, an experienced mining-engineer and geolo. gist. In this work he was assisted by Mr. Thomas Donaldson, who had charge of the collecting of the gold and silver ores of the West, and of which he secured a very complete and exhaustive representation.

The department of the animal products and of the fisheries was placed more particularly in Mr. Goode's charge; and that of ethnology assigned to Dr. Rau. For fuller details of what has been done in this and other branches, I refer to my special report to you.

As the general result of the agencies that have been set in motion, I may state that the contributions in 1875 amounted to over one thousand in number, embracing nearly two thousand packages, from four hundred and sixty-four different parties, this being, as already stated, far in excess of those of any previous year.

I present herewith a list of these donations, arranged alphabetically, and to which I refer for additional details, the aggregate being too great to permit the systematic plan of presentation of previous years.

Under the head of Mammals, the most important addition to the stock is that of the series of skins of the fur-seal and sea-lion, presented by the Alaska Commercial Company, twenty specimens of the former and five of the latter constituting the contribution. To this company the Smithsonian Institution is under many obligations, not only for securing and sending the skins, but for acting as its agent in San Francisco for the transaction of its business, connected with the transmission of supplies to its correspondents and the forwarding to Washington of their collections. From Mr. Charles E. Aiken, of Colorado, several specimens of mountain-buffalo and other animals have been received. Capt. James Gilliss has supplied the black-tailed deer; Colonel Brockett, a fine elk; Mr. P. T. Barnum, specimens of various animals that have died in his menagerie, such as the eland, giraffe, sea-lion, ostrich, &c. Rev. R. R. McLeod, of Houlton, Me., has furnished nearly all the mammals of Maine, such as the caribou, the beaver, the porcupine, the fisher, the marten, &c.

Of birds, the more especial contributions are a series of fine specimens from Mr. S. C. Bowman, a skin of the Honduras turkey from Mr. F. E. Sarg, and a collection of Alaskan species from Mr. Lucien M. Turner.

Numerous small lots of reptiles and amphibia have been received from various gentlemen, and will be found enumerated in the list.

Of fishes, the most important special collections are a series of the fishes of Norway from Mr. Robert Collett, and those gathered by the United States Fish Commission; types of South American fishes, from C. R. Lütken; collections from the vicinity of Newport, by Mr. Samuel Powel; and from Gloucester, by J. S. Whitman; from California and Oregon, by Mr. Livingston Stone, &c.

Of the fresh-water and land shells, all the collections were placed in charge of Dr. James Lewis for arrangement, and occasion was taken to issue a special circular, asking contributions to this department. Many responses were made to this invitation, and the collection thereby greatly increased.

Other invertebrates were secured by the efforts of the United States Fish Commission, and through correspondents.

The department of ethnology has been especially enriched in consequence of the desire to render the Centennial display a success. In this the co-operation of the Indian Bureau of the Department of the Interior has been of the greatest importance. Among the most valuable acquisitions in this department have been the collections of Mr. Paul Schumacher and his party on the mainlands and the islands adjacent to Santa Barbara, as also those of Rev. Stephen Bowers in the same neighborhood. Collections of less magnitude were also made by Mr. Schumacher in Oregon. The Alaska Commercial Company presented a series of nine mummies from Kagaymil Island of the Aleutian group, and one from Prince William's Sound, all of much ethnological interest, being the first specimens of the kind ever received from Alaska.

The traditions respecting the Aleutian mummies indicate that they are at least one hundred and fifty years old, antedating the discovery of the islands by the Russians. One of the bodies in a sitting posture was encased in a rude casket of raw-hide, lashed in a netting of sinews, all parts in an excellent state of preservation. Another body is without covering. Of these valuable ethnological specimens, three have been presented to other establishments, viz, the Peabody Ethnological Museum, Cambridge, Mass.; Yale College, New Haven, Conn., and the American Museum, New York City.

Col. William F. Arny has supplied a series of dresses and utensils of the Navajo Indians, and Maj. J. W. Powell an extensive series of similar objects from the Shoshone, the Bannock, and other tribes. Mr. James G. Swan, in the course of a special exploration for the Centennial, has furnished a vast number of interesting ethnological objects from Sitka, Queen Charlotte's Islands, British Columbia, and Puget Sound.

Mr. Stephen Powers visited Nevada and California, with the special object of obtaining collections for the Centennial, the results of which are of very great magnitude. A very valuable collection of pre-historic implements from New England was obtained from Mr. J. H. Clark, of New York, and a great number of contributions of a similar character, in small numbers, have been received, for which reference must be made to the appended list. From points outside of the United States the most important contribution is that of objects of stone and earthen ware, gathered by the late George Latimer in the island of Porto Rico, where, for many years a resident, he devoted himself to bringing together everything of antiquarian interest. This gentleman died in Paris in November, 1874, and bequeathed this collection to the Smithsonian Institution, and it was received in April last, and is, by far, the most complete series of the kind in existence, embracing as it does a number of peculiar forms, scarcely known elsewhere.

Mr. Hugo Finck, of Cordova, has furnished some very ancient American antiquities, and corresponding objects from Salvador have been supplied by Dr. Flint. Professor Gabb has contributed an extremely exhaustive and important collection of articles from Costa Rica, leaving but little to be desired in the line of ethnology from that country. Mr. Steinberg has sent some interesting specimens, models of boats, &c., from the Samoan Islands. Mr. J. B. Norton contributed a collection of antiquities from Peru, including quite a number of interesting articles in bronze.

From the University of Christiania has been received a very interesting group consisting of a life-size figure of a Laplander in his native costume seated in a sledge attached to a mounted reindeer, the whole forming an interesting ethnological illustration of the art of locomotion in Scandinavia.

The additions to the department of mineralogy have also been very great, and will be found detailed in the accompanying list.

The number of miscellaneous collections received during the year, covering more than one department of natural history, has been very great. These have been principally from Government expeditions, the collections of which were deposited with the Smithsonian Institution, in compliance with the law of Congress constituting it the custodian of the National Museum. Among the more important of these, we may mention the collections made by the party of Lieut. George M. Wheeler in the West, embracing a large variety of objects, including many skins of mammals, birds, eggs, reptiles, insects, &c. The collections of Major Powell, although principally ethnological, and referred to under that head, also embraced numerous animals and other objects.

In the report for 1874, reference was made to the preparations by the United States for the Transit of Venus expedition and the arrangements of the Institution to secure interesting objects of ethnology and natural history; and I am happy to say that the results have been far beyond all reasonable expectations. The most valuable collection of the kind was that made by Dr. J. G. Kidder, assistant surgeon on board the Swatara, and who, on the arrival of the vessel at Kerguelen Island, remained with the astronomical party, and devoted his energies to the investigation of the natural history of that little-known land. His collections made there embrace large numbers of birds, eggs, some mammals, and marine invertebrates and plants. A report on the results of his labors occupies two numbers of the lately commenced Bulletin of the United States National Museum. Dr. Kershner, the surgeon of the Swatara, also made large contributions somewhat similar in their general character to those of Dr. Kidder, and embracing species collected at ports that were visited by the vessel.

S. Mis. 115——4

The collections made by Mr. Russell, one of the photographers of the expedition, at Hobart Town and vicinity, were also very important, and included some specimens obtained from the Colonial Museum for transmission to the Smithsonian Institution.

From Mr. Edwin Smith, of the United States Coast Survey, in charge of the party on Chatham Island, have been received some interesting crania of the Maori and Moriori tribes.

As in previous years, the operations of the United States Fish Commission, under my charge, have furnished a rich yield of additions to the National Museum. Its headquarters for the season were established at Wood's Hole, Massachusetts, the same station as that of 1871; and the improved facilities for collecting were made use of to secure large numbers of marine animals, embracing a stock for distribution as duplicates to other establishments.

Work done in connection with the National Museum.—As might be expected, the increased number of contributions during the year has involved a corresponding amount of labor in the way of unpacking, recording, and general fitting for permanent preservation, taxing severely the efforts of the regular force and that enlisted temporarily for the purpose of meeting the exigencies of the Centennial Exhibition.

The actual number of entries made in the record-books of the Institution during the year was 12,578, carrying the total forward to 210,327.

A large amount of labor has been performed also upon the general collections. The reptiles and fishes have been put in excellent order by a transfer to suitable bottles, labeling and recording. The mammals and the skins of more or less birds have been re-arranged in new cases, and are now in excellent condition. The entire collection of duplicate birds' eggs has been overhauled, and a number of sets selected for distribution to scientific establishments.

The taxidermists have been diligently at work and have more than doubled the number of mounted animals of the collection, and greatly increased that of the birds. The work of preparing plaster-casts of fishes, reptiles, and cretaceans has also been continued, and this section is now believed to be entirely unique.

Outside of the building, as usual, much has been done on the Smithsonian collections. Dr. James Lewis, of Mohawk, N. Y., has continued his labors upon the fresh-water and land shells of the United States belonging to the Institution, having labeled the reserve series of *Unionidæ*, &c., and returned them to the Institution, the duplicates in large part being made up into sets for distribution.

Mr. J. A. Allen has had several groups of American mammals, especially the squirrels and the rabbits, from the Institution for the preparation of a series of monographs. Dr. Elliot Coues has continued his labors upon the collection of mice, and has also monographed the American carnivora.

A large number of specimens of insects has been turned over to the

Museum of the Agricultural Department, in accordance with the arrangement to render that establishment the depository of such objects; while to the Army Medical Museum many hundreds of human crania have been transmitted under a similar understanding. Several specialists, in addition to those mentioned, have received material for their investigation."

Tucson Meteorite.—Among the objects of special interest in the National Museum is a very large meteorite from Arizona, of which an account has been given in previous reports. For the possession of this specimen the Institution is principally indebted to Dr. B. J. D. Irwin, surgeon of the United States Army, who, although it had been seen by other travelers, was the first to conceive the idea of having it transferred to the Smithsonian Institution. In carrying out this proposition he was assisted by the generous co-operation of several persons and transportation companies. Owing to an imperfect history in regard to obtaining this interesting specimen, a label was affixed to it of which complaint was made by Dr. Irwin. After a review of all the facts of the case, and in accordance with his suggestion, the specimen is now labeled as follows: "The Tucson Meteorite presented to the Smithsonian Institution by Dr. B. J. D. Irwin, U. S. A., and transported from Tucson, Ariz., to Washington free of cost by S. Ainsa, the Flint & Halliday steamers, the Pacific Mail Steamship Company, and the Panama Railroad Company."

We hope this inscription will be satisfactory to Dr. Irwin and do justice to all concerned in furnishing the National Museum with one of its most interesting specimens.

GOVERNMENT EXPLORATIONS AND SURVEYS.

The following is a brief account of the principal explorations of the Government in 1875, from which specimens will be derived for increasing the collections of the National Museum.

The United States Geological and Geographical Survey, under the direction of Professor Hayden, during the season of 1875, continued its work of the two previous seasons in Colorado, completing the southern and southwestern portions, including a belt fifteen miles in width, of Northern New Mexico and Eastern Utah. The entire force of the survey was divided into seven parties for special duty, four of which were assigned to specific areas for the performance of topographical and geological work, one party attended to the primary triangulation, a second collected photographic views of the most interesting scenery and ancient ruins, while a third transported the supplies to the various districts.

The entire area surveyed during the summer of 1875 embraced about thirty thousand square miles. There now remains only the northwest corner of Colorado to be examined, prior to the completion of six sheets of the physical atlas which has been designed by the Department of the Interior. These maps will be engraved on a scale of four miles to one inch, and each sheet will embrace an area of about eleven thousand five hundred square miles. The districts explored during the past year were not so mountainous as those of the previous year, but were located in the most inaccessible regions of this continent. Much of the country is drained by the Colorado River and is mainly a plateau country, cut in every direction by deep gorges or cañons, the sides of which show, for geological investigations, admirable sections of the strata forming the earth's crust. The topography was elaborated in great detail by the use of the plane-table. The geological structure of the country was carefully studied and much material secured that will throw light on the various problems which have perplexed geologists for years past.

The exploration of the remarkable prehistoric ruins of Southern Colorado, glimpses of which were obtained the preceding season, was continued with great success. They were traced down the cañons of the Colorado River in New Mexico, Utah, and Arizona, and their connection established with the cliff cities of the Moquis of the latter Territory. Hundreds of cliff or cave dwellings of curious architecture and many miles from water were found in the sides of the gorges, and the ruins of extensive towns discovered in the adjacent plains, indicating the former existence of a people far more numerous and advanced in the arts of civilization than their supposed descendants of the present day. A good collection of pottery, stone implements, the latter including arrow-heads, axes, and ear ornaments, &c., some pieces of rope, fragments of matting, water-jars, corn and beans, and other articles were exhumed from the *débris* of these dwellings. Many graves were found, and a number of skulls and skeletons, that may fairly be attributed to the prehistoric inhabitants, were added to the collection. Of these ruins, many interesting sketches, plans, and photographs were made, and the materials were secured for an exhaustive report on this subject, which will be given to the public at an early day.

The photographer of the survey also obtained a series of mountain views on plates 24 inches long by 20 wide, or larger by several inches than any landscape photograph ever before taken in this country.

The publications of the survey during the year 1875 consist of "The Vertebrata of the Cretaceous Formations of the West," by E. D. Cope, 303 pages text, quarto, with 57 plates; third edition of "Lists of Elevations West of the Mississippi," much enlarged; second edition of "Catalogue of Photographs;" and "Bulletin of the Survey," in six numbers, comprising 500 closely printed octavo pages, with 26 plates of sections, maps, &c.

The work of the Second Division of the United States Geological and Geographical Survey of the Territories under the direction of Prof. J. W. Powell, had arrived at the beginning of the year 1875 at a stage at which it was deemed best that a review of the geology should be made for the purpose of establishing with greater accuracy the natural series of geological formations. A small party was organized for this purpose, and was led by Professor Powell himself The main party under Prof. A. H. Thompson, geographer of the division, continued the work during the past season in the Territory of Utah, over an area of nearly ten thousand square miles, stretching from the Henry Mountains, on the north, to the Kai-par-o-wits Plateau on the south, and from the Colorado River, on the east, to the Aquarius Plateau, on the west.

It was found that of the lands surveyed the past season, one-fourth of 1 per cent. can be utilized by irrigation; about 50 per cent. are pasture-lands; about 9 per cent. are of timber; 4 per cent. mineral-lands; and the remainder desert.

Mr. G. K. Gilbert studied the structural geology of the country, and collected the materials for a geological map.

A second and closely allied subject of study has been the eruptions that produced the Henry Mountains, a third has been the erosion by which the structure has been laid bare, and a fourth, the Salina Creek unconformity. The investigation at Salina Creek was of a special nature, and its bearings cannot be briefly stated. Its results establish a single point of geological history, namely, that an epoch of mountain-growth, of which evidences are found in the Sevier and Sanpete Valleys, and in the Pahvan Mountains, occurred at about the end of the Cretaceous period.

The stratified rocks examined range in age from Carboniferous to Tertiary. Upon the geological map the combined Trias and Jura will cover half the space. The volcanic area will come next in size, and after that the Cretaceous. The excellence of the topographic work will enable a very thorough delineation of their boundaries.

Fossils were found in numerous localities, but no large collections were made.

Coal of cretaceous age was seen, but no other valuable minerals.

Captain C. E. Dutton was engaged in the examination of a large tract consisting of igneous rocks. It lies in Southern Utah, its northern boundary being about one hundred and fifty miles south of Salt Lake City, extending thence southward about eighty-five miles, and having a breadth of about sixty miles. It consists of a series of long, narrow tables with intervening valleys, and is structurally a repetition of those features described by Professor Powell as characteristic of the whole of Southern Utah and Northern Arizona, and which have led him to call it the Plateau Province. The tables are cut from the platforms of the valleys by immense faults and uplifted from 2,000 to 5,500 feet above the valley-plains, presenting nearly vertical walls, fringed at their base by rugged foot-hills. The plateaus are composed of thick beds of igneous rocks well stratified and nearly horizontal; the foot-hills, on the contrary, are composed of beds much broken and disturbed and intermixed with lava. The southern portions are overlaid by a conglomerate which commences near the middle of the region, with a thickness of at least 2,300 feet, and diminishes southward to 700 or 800 feet. It is composed wholly of igneous fragments often of great size, inclosed in a matrix of sand and clay. In the southern portion it is underlaid by red sandstone and white marl of Tertiary Age; in the middle portion, by rocks of the porphyritic class. The northern and higher portion consists of well stratified rocks, having the mineral characteristics in some places of trachyte, in others of rhyolite, but with a structural habit, a texture and general mode of occurrence very unusual in that kind of rock. Lava-beds occur abundantly, but, so far as observed, are restricted to the foot-hills and valleys, and have evidently originated from the vicinity of the great faults.

Captain Dutton is also engaged in the investigation of the micro-structure of the rocks of that region, and has made considerable progress in the preparation of specimens for microscopic examination.

Prof. C. A. White, paleontologist of the division, visited many points in Northern Utah, a few in Northwestern Colorado, and a few in Southern Wyoming, making a re-examination of the sedimentary beds of that region, and the evidences upon which they had been previously separated into groups. Many localities where fossils had been obtained in previous years were visited, and other localities were discovered. The collections made were from the upper portions of the Carboniferous series through the whole series to near the summit of the Tertiary. The collections were chiefly of invertebrate fossils and are very full and satisfactory. Many new species, and also several types hitherto unknown in American strata, have been obtained. It is an interesting fact, also, that while the change from a salt or brackish water condition of the earlier Tertiary deposits to a wholly fresh-water condition took place without producing any perceptible physical change in the character of the strata, the species, mostly molluscan, were more numerous, and the differentiation of types much greater during the prevalence of salt in the water than at any subsequent time after the waters became wholly fresh. Indeed, in all the purely fresh-water strata of the Tertiary groups the species and genera are few, and there is a remarkable uniformity of type throughout. Both branchiferous and pulmonate mollusks range through all the Tertiary strata, except that thus far none of the latter have been found associated with brackish-water forms. The Green River group has furnished several species of insects. Of vertebrate remains, some massive fragments of bones of a very large saurian, found in Jurassic strata five miles west of Vermilion Cañon, are worthy of remark. Scales and detached bones of teleost fishes were found in considerable abundance in dark shales at the very base of the Cretaceous groups at Vermilion Cañon, and also at various other points at the same horizon. Teleost fish remains, mostly very perfect, were obtained from the Green River group, and also some from other Tertiary strata. Throughout the whole Tertiary series more or less vertebrate remains have been found, but it is the Bridger group that has furnished the greatest profusion of mammalian, beside many reptilian and a few ganoid remains.

Part of a skeleton of a Passerine bird has been obtained from the Green River group.

Large collections of plants have been made at numerous localities. Besides samples of silicified exogenous wood from numerous horizons throughout the Mesozoic and Tertiary series, leaves, stems, &c., have been collected from the Upper Cretaceous and Tertiary strata. These are mostly exogenous, but both ferns and palms were found associated with them in the Upper Green River group at Alkali Stage Station, twenty miles northward from Green River City.

Professor Thompson's party discovered the ruins of many prehistoric dwellings similar to those found in former years, and their position will be indicated on the ethnographic map. They also discovered on the cañon-walls and escarpments of the country many Shi′-nu-mo etchings, which were copied to scale. They will make a valuable addition to the collections of former years.

While on his travels, Professor Powell met with certain tribes of Shoshoni Indians whose arts were unrepresented in the National Museum, and the opportunity was seized to make collections of their implements and clothing, &c. In all departments, except that of food-plants, these Indians are now as fully represented as the Utes, Pai Utes, and Shi′-nu-mos by his former collections. Some additions were made to his Shoshoni vocabulary and to his mythologic tales.

During the past years of the survey, vocabularies have been collected of all of the above languages and dialects with the exception of the Ko-man′-tsu. These are far from being complete, but contain many hundred words each, some of them two or three thousand each.

The grammatic structure of these languages has also been studied to some extent, and while no structural principles have been found which have not been discovered in other Indian languages, much of value has been obtained.

Mr. L. F. Ward was attached to the division as botanist, and made very large collections from a region but hitherto little studied. He also collected a large suite of wood sections of the various shrubs and trees found in that region.

Mr. J. K. Hillers, the photographer, made a series of negatives, 101 in number, for topographic and geological purposes, and a series of 10 for ethnographic purposes.

The operations of the geographical surveys west of the one hundredth meridian, First Lieut. George M. Wheeler in charge, for the season of 1875 were confined to areas in Colorado, New Mexico, California, and Arizona, and were prosecuted in pursuance of a special project approved by the Chief of Engineers and the honorable Secretary of War.

The working force for the season was organized as follows: (1.) The

California section, under the command of Lieut. George M. Wheeler, Corps of Engineers; (2.) The Colorado section, under the command of Lieut. William L. Marshall, Corps of Engineers; and (3) the office-force in Washington, temporarily in charge of George M. Lockwood, assistant.

The two sections were constituted with a view to a systematic prosecution of the geodetic and allied work, and the office force was kept continuously employed upon the reductions of observations. From the California section a special party under Lieut. Eric Bergland, Corps of Engineers, was detached to make certain preliminary examinations and surveys as to the practicability of diverting the Colorado River. These labors have been accomplished so far as the past field-season would permit, and Lieutenant Bergland is now engaged in the preparation of his report. When received, with the maps and sketches, it will be forwarded, with additional information bearing upon the general subject of irrigation.

Four other parties from the California section were busily employed during the working summer months; one, under Lieut. Rogers Birnie, jr., moving to the south and east of the lower or southern limit of the Sierra Nevadas; another, under Lieut. C. W. Whipple, Ordnance Corps; and a special party under Dr. H. C. Yarrow for a brief period in the vicinity of Santa Barbara, Cal. The command of the latter party was afterward transferred to Dr. J. T. Rothrock, U. S. A., and was finally merged with the main party commanded by the officer in charge.

The results accomplished were of a highly satisfactory character, and the improvements introduced noted the transfer to a completely connected geodetic survey. Connection was had with the base-line measured by Captain, now Brig. Gen. E. O. C. Ord, near Los Angeles, Cal., in 1854. The developed base and measured triangles in a triple tier were carried eastward approximately as far as the one hundred and twentieth meridian of longitude. For the first time the correct latitude and longitude of what is probably the highest measured peak in the United States in the southern Sierras were obtained. The preliminary reductions show an altitude of 14,900 feet.

The Colorado section was composed of three principal parties: one under its commanding officer; the second under Lieut. W. L. Carpenter, Ninth Infantry; and the third in charge of Lieut C. C. Morrison, Sixth Cavalry. Their operations were in continuation of the organized work begun by the establishment of a series of main astronomical points along the east base of the Rocky Mountains, and the development therefrom of a series of measured bases and triangles so as to envelop completely the area entered and occupied, and which finally was to be connected through from the plains to the Pacific. Their labors were conducted with skill, energy, and success.

The office-force, engaged in computations, map-drawing, and other reductions, have succeeded in completing three additional atlas-sheets on a scale one inch to eight miles, and are advancing toward completion the work of five others.

The condition of the work up to June 30, 1875, appears more fully set forth in the annual report of Lieutenant Wheeler, submitted to the Chief of Engineers.

A portion of the field-force is now busily employed in the preparation of the final results at the office of the survey in Washington.

CONCLUSION.

From the foregoing statements I trust it will be evident to all interested in the prosperity of the Institution that it is successfully prosecuting the plan best adapted for realizing the intentions of its founder; that its funds are in a good condition and that its reputation and usefulness since the date of the last report have suffered no diminution.

Respectfully submitted.

JOSEPH HENRY,
Secretary Smithsonian Institution.

WASHINGTON, *January*, 1876.

APPENDIX TO THE REPORT OF THE SECRETARY.

SMITHSONIAN INSTITUTION,
Washington, January 3, 1876.

Sir: I have the honor to present herewith an account of the proposed plan of exhibition by the Smithsonian Institution at the International Centennial Exhibition, and the extent to which the work has been carried on.

History of the movement.—On the 23d of January, 1874, the President of the United States called upon the various Departments of the Government, including the Smithsonian Institution, to nominate one member each, to constitute a board, in behalf of the Executive Departments, to which should be committed the preparation and adoption of a plan for a collective exhibition, at the International Exhibition of 1876, " of such articles and material as will illustrate the functions and administrative faculties of the Government in time of peace and its resources as a war-power, and thereby serve to demonstrate the nature of our institutions and their adaptation to the wants of the people."

The persons designated, in response to the call of the President, were the following :

By the Secretary of the Treasury, F. M. Sawyer.
By the Secretary of War, Col. S. C. Lyford, U. S. A.
By the Secretary of the Navy, Admiral T. A. Jenkins, U. S. N.
By the Secretary of the Interior, John Eaton.
By the Postmaster-General, Dr. Charles F. McDonald.
By the Department of Agriculture, William Saunders.
By the Smithsonian Institution, S. F. Baird.

On the 25th of March, 1874, the nominations were accepted by the President for the board referred to, and Col. S. C. Lyford was designated as chairman. Subsequently, on the retirement of Mr. Sawyer, Mr. R. W. Tayler was appointed in behalf of the Treasury Department.

The first business before the board being that of preparing a general plan of the exhibition and estimates of the cost of carrying this out for each Department, the following estimates were made, after a careful consideration of the subject, as being absolutely necessary to accomplish the work on a proper scale:

Interior Department	$211,000
Treasury Department	5,000
Post-Office Department	5,000
Agricultural Department	50,000
Smithsonian Institution, (National Museum)	100,000
War Department	200,000
Navy Department	150,000
Add for show-cases, shelving, incidentals, &c	50,000

For a separate building, capable of removal to Washington after the close of the Exhibition, to be used as a National Museum at the capital of the nation $200,000

971,000

These estimates were reduced by the Committee on Appropriations, which presented to Congress the following, which was passed without opposition from any quarter:

War Department $133,000
Navy Department 100,000
Interior Department 115,000
Treasury Department 5,000
Post-Office Department 5,000
Agricultural Department 50,000
Smithsonian Institution 67,000
United States Commission of Food-Fishes.... 5,000
For show-cases, shelving, stationery, postage, telegrams, expressage, and incidentals 25,000

505,000

Authority was also given in the enactment to erect any building or part of a building that might be necessary ; to be " paid for *pro rata* out of the sums appropriated to the several Departments, the United States Commission of Food-Fishes, the Treasury and Post-Office Departments excepted, the cost of the building not to exceed one hundred and fifty thousand dollars ; said building to be sold at the close of the Exhibition and the proceeds covered into the Treasury as miscellaneous receipts."

Authority was given to the heads of the several Executive Departments to display at the Exhibition, under such conditions as they might prescribe, all such articles in store or under the control of such Departments as might be necessary or desirable to render the collection complete and exhaustive ; but the board were forbidden to expend any larger sum than was set down for each Department, or to enter into any contract or engagement that should result in any such increased expenditure.

The next question presented to the board for its consideration was that of the space required by the several Departments, and whether it would be necessary to erect a special building. Of course it was quite impossible at so short notice to decide as to the space needed, and approximate estimates only could be presented. Indeed, in all cases it has proved that the area originally decided upon was far below what has since been found necessary, and almost daily demands for increased accommodations are made by some branch or other of the Government.

In regard to the matter of accommodations, inquiry was first directed to the Centennial authorities in Philadelphia as to whether a building would be erected by them for the Government board; or, if not, whether space could be had in the main building. The board was informed, in response, that it would be impossible to put up a special building, but that space might be had in the general buildings of the Exhibition, provided the objects could be divided and classified according to the plan adopted by the commission. This, however, would have involved the separation of the various elements of the Government display and prevented its exhibition as a whole, and it was finally concluded to erect a building on ground assigned by the Centennial Commission, and in a very excellent situation.

After discussing the various plans for buildings submitted to the board, contracts were entered into for the erection of an edifice to cover 102,000 square feet of surface, and the work being put in hand, it has been prosecuted so rapidly as to be now nearly completed. Of the space in this building, 20,000 feet have been assigned to the Smithsonian Institution and 6,000 feet to the United States Fish Commission.

Plan of exhibition proposed by the Smithsonian Institution.—After a careful consideration of the subject, it was concluded that the most suitable exhibition on the part of the Smithsonian Institution should embrace, in the first place, the history, condition, functions, workings, and general results of the Institution itself; in the second, a display of the mineral and animal resources, as well as of the ethnology, of the United States, the Agricultural Department proposing to include the various subjects connected with the vegetable kingdom in its division. As the Interior Department desired to make a very exhaustive exhibition of everything relating to the Indian tribes of the United States, an arrangement was made with the Indian Bureau by the Smithsonian Institution, to join in a single display of the ethnology and archæology of the United States, to be held in the space assigned to the Indian Department and credited to the Indian Bureau. As the National Museum, in charge of the Smithsonian Institution, already embraces very large collections of this character, it was proposed to confine the action on the part of the Indian Bureau to explorations, investigations, and collections in those parts of the United States which were not already properly represented. In this way any duplication would be avoided.

The display of the United States Fish Commission, although named as a separate division in the bill appropriating funds for the purpose of exhibition, naturally belongs to that of the Smithsonian Institution, and was arranged to form a special division of "the fisheries" in the scheme already referred to; so that finally five divisions were provided for: first, the Smithsonian Institution; second, the mineral wealth of the United States; third, the animal resources; fourth, the fisheries; and, fifth, the ethnology of the country.

Progress of the work.—I now proceed, in accordance with your instructions, to present some fuller details of the proposed exhibition, and an account of what has been done in these several divisions.

I.

The display by the Smithsonian Institution of what pertains to its own operations, apart from anything connected with the National Museum, will consist of a series of tables illustrating some of its more important branches, such as its system of international exchanges, its publications, its explorations and researches, its twenty-five-year period of meteorological observations, &c. This will include its series of twenty quarto volumes of Smithsonian contributions to knowledge, thirteen volumes of miscellaneous collections, and thirty volumes of annual reports.

Mr. W. L. Nicholson, of the Post-Office Department, has been engaged in constructing a large map of the United States, in twenty sheets, covering a space of sixteen by twelve feet, on a scale of 16 miles to the inch. Upon one or more of these maps will be shown the temperatures, the rain-fall, the barometric pressure, the winds, &c., of the United States for the twenty-five years' mean.

II.

A display of the *mineral resources* of a country like the United States, so varied in character, was necessarily a very laborious undertaking, and the Institution was fortunate enough to secure the aid, as director of this part of the exhibition, of Prof. William P. Blake, a gentleman of much experience as a geologist, mining engineer, and mineralogist, and one who, by his official connection with the Expositions at Paris and Vienna, and as having had much to do with the original organization of the Centennial Commission in Philadelphia, was able to render very valuable service. He entered upon his duties on the 1st of May, 1875, and commenced by organizing a general plan of exploration, and establishing correspondence, preparing blank instructions, circulars, &c. Of these the following were prepared and published: First, a general circular, stating the proposed plan of the mineral exhibition, and giving an invitation to contribute specimens; second, sketch of the proposed character of the display to be made and its systematic arrangement; third, a list of prominent gentlemen in different States from whom aid might be expected, and whose co-operation was formally requested; fourth, instructions for packing collections for shipment; fifth, labels for the specimens; sixth, labels of address for the boxes; seventh, blank invoices for enumerating the contents of the boxes. Many thousands of these were printed and circulated throughout the country with very excellent results. Mr. Blake himself, after his preliminary work was accomplished, visited many parts of the country in the interest of the Institution, and especially the mining regions of Pennsylvania, New Jersey, New York, Connecticut, Massachusetts, Ohio, Missouri, Michigan, Wisconsin, and other States.

As far back as 1873 the Board of Finance of the Centennial Commission made an arrangement with Mr. Thomas Donaldson, one of the Centennial commissioners of Idaho, to visit the principal mining regions west of the Rocky Mountains, at its expense, for the purpose of collecting illustrations of the resources of the country in gold, silver, and mercury. Fortified by letters of credit from the commission, Mr. Donaldson proceeded on his mission, and was enabled to secure many valuable collections at little or no cost; the proprietors of mines especially manifesting a desire to be appropriately represented in the Exhibition and presenting many specimens not only interesting in a scientific point of view, but of much intrinsic value.

A concession, at the same time, was obtained by Mr. Donaldson from the railroad companies between Philadelphia and San Francisco by which they agreed to transport a given number of tons of these minerals free of charge, and thus greatly to reduce the cost of the enterprise.

After the organization of the Government board on Executive Departments, the Board of Finance came to the conclusion that it was not expedient for the Centennial Commission to undertake a separate display of minerals, and an arrangement was, therefore, made to turn over the collections made by Mr. Donaldson to the Smithsonian Institution on payment of the expenses incurred and its agreement to continue the engagement with Mr. Donaldson to the end of the year 1875. This was done to the satisfaction of all parties, so that since the 8th of May Mr. Donaldson has been in the employ of the Institution, and the collections made by him are in Philadelphia or on the way thither.

The State geologists of a number of the States have also co-operated in the efforts toward a mineral exhibition, and also a large number of proprietors of mining establishments and others who had it in their power to render any aid.

The present prospect in regard to the mineral display is entirely satisfactory. It is believed that no important interest in this direction will be unrepresented, and that the general exhibition, to consist of ores and their metals, with their slags and by-products, the crude and refined metals, the building-stones, the clays, the marbles, the coals, slates, &c., will be quite a perfect picture of the industries as at present developed throughout the United States. There will be also a series of the simple applications of the different substances, such as the petroleum products, the coal-tar products, specimens of terra-cotta, pottery, and porcelain as illustrating the clays, some manufactured articles of the metals, polished slabs of the marbles, &c.

Care has been taken to obtain the various specimens in sufficient size to make an imposing feature; the metals and coals, as far as possible, having been selected in cubes of two feet each way; the building-stones are in cubes of twelve and six inches, the latter size having been adopted for most of the ores also.

It is proposed to exhibit on the large Smithsonian map the geological features of the country, as also the general distribution of the valuable minerals and the extent to which mines of the same have been opened and prosecuted. Arrangements have been made for a display of the choice minerals of the country, principally as a loan from several private cabinets in Philadelphia and elsewhere.

III.

The display of the *animal resources* of the country will also be very extensive and interesting, as embracing, in the first place, an exhibition of all the species capable of any economical application to the wants of mankind, and, secondly, such forms as have special interest to the naturalist. This will have three divisions: first, the representations of the animals themselves, either living, stuffed, molded in plaster, or photographed; secondly, the applications of these animals in whole or in part; and, third, the apparatus by which they are pursued, captured, and utilized. This division will naturally fall into the primary classification of the mammals, the birds, the reptiles, the fishes, and the invertebrates, land and marine.

Among the mammals, mounted in the best manner, and in their stages of age, sex, and season, will be shown those of most importance as food, such as the different species of deer, including the moose, elk, and cariboo, the musk-ox, the buffalo, &c. The fur-bearing species will be represented by the bears, grizzly, brown, black, white, &c.; the foxes, black, cross, gray, kit, &c.; wolves, fur-seals, sea-lions, sables, minks, &c. Those furnishing oil will be the whales, the porpoises, and other cetaceans. The other species, furnishing leather, bone, &c., will also be represented.

The birds will include all the forms that are appreciated as being eatable and as supplying feathers, plumes, &c., for purposes of ornament or domestic utility. The kinds specially beneficial or injurious to the farmer will also be exhibited.

Among the reptiles will be included the edible frogs, terrapins, sea-turtles, the alligator, as furnishing food, leather, oil, &c.

The fishes will be shown in very great variety, to include, for the most part, plaster-casts, colored from nature, of the most important species. Some specimens will be shown in alcohol, while others will be represented by photographs. Of the casts, including the cetaceans, over five hundred are more or less complete, some of them fifteen feet long.

Among the objects of the fifth division will be the eatable mollusks, such as the oyster in its different varieties, the clams, the eatable crabs, lobsters, sponges, and many other forms, both land and aquatic.

The second series of the animal display will consist of a systematic presentation of the applications of these animals, such as the different preparations of food, whether as dried, smoked, salted, pickled, or canned; second, of the various applications of the teeth, bones, horn, &c., for ornaments or other uses; third, of the preparations of fur, hides, leather, and the like; fourth, of the different varieties of oils; fifth, miscellaneous applications.

Under the head of furs will be shown dressed skins of all the varieties of fur-bearing animals of the United States, in their different grades, as occurring in different seasons of the year and from different parts of the country, as well as some simple applications of some of these furs to articles of dress or ornament. In this series will also be included dressed skins of birds and ornamental feathers.

The divisions of the bones and teeth will embrace the various forms of carving, knife-handles, umbrella-handles, &c. In this division will be included whalebone and its applications.

The oils will be exhibited in sufficient quantity for comparison, including those of all the different species of whales, cetaceans, alligators, crocodiles, the various fishes, &c.

The third series, that of apparatus, will represent the dress and equipment of the hunter and fisherman, whether savage or civilized, while pursuing their game, together with the different forms of boats, sledges, snow-shoes, &c., made use of for the same purpose. There will also be the various arms and implements in the way of rifles, guns, pistols for hunting, nets, traps of every kind, fire-jacks, &c., for the sportsman and trapper, and for the fisherman fish-hooks, lines, floats, rods, reels, nets, pounds, models of fishing-smacks of various kinds, &c.

IV.

The preparations for an exhibition illustrating the *fisheries* of the United States have involved a great deal of labor, in consequence of the want of experience in this country of displays of this character, so that the general plan and classification had to be almost entirely improvised as a whole. It is, however, to be hoped that the measures that have been taken will result in showing the general nature and extent of our interests in this direction. It is, of course, evident that the display of animals of the country must have the inhabitants of the water as a prominent feature, as also their application for food, oils, glues, &c., and they cannot well be separated.

The apparatus, however, by which they are followed, captured, and applied to the purposes of life will represent satisfactorily this portion of the programme. It is much more difficult to present attractive exhibition of the fishes of the country than the mammals or birds, as they are generally only shown as alcoholic specimens, which are always more or less unsightly; and, at any rate, only the smaller can be thus preserved. On this account, the plan of a display of plaster-casts of the actual fish, colored from nature, has been adopted. The work of making these casts has been prosecuted with quite a large force of assistants ever since the passage of th appropriation, specimens in the best procurable condition having been sent to Washington, mostly packed in ice, where a colored sketch is at once taken of them. They are next photographed, and then a mold taken in plaster of Paris. The casts are finally made either in papier-maché or plaster and colored from the sketches referred to.

This work was also prosecuted during a four months' residence at Wood's Hole, on Cape Cod.

The series of casts thus taken is very extensive, embracing nearly six hundred specimens, illustrating the fishes of the ocean, the lakes, and the rivers of the United States, and including nearly all the species known to the professional or the amateur fisherman. In this collection, also, is embraced the seals, and the different species of cetaceans, such as the porpoise, the black-fish, grampus, white whale, &c., the whole display being, it is believed, far in advance of anything that has ever been attempted heretofore.

It is also proposed to make an exhibition of such living species as can conveniently be procured. This feature will probably be shown in the agricultural building, under the charge of the agricultural branch of the United States Centennial Commission, and I propose to render whatever assistance lies in my power in supplying the specimens.

Another interesting feature of this division will be the exhibition of the fish themselves in a fresh state in a refrigerator, covered with a glass top, and under the special direction of Mr. E. G. Blackford, a well-known fish-dealer in New York. This gentleman has undertaken not only to put up the refrigerator, but to keep it stocked every day with various fishes from all portions of the United States. He will arrange with some of the restaurants on the grounds to take the fish at the close of the day and to serve them up to those calling for them.

The second division, that of the applications of the fish, will consist, in the first place, of food-preparations, whether smoked, dried, salted, pickled, canned, or otherwise treated. Next will come the glues, gelatines, sizings, &c.; then the economical or ornamental applications of the scales; and, finally, the oils and the guanos and miscellaneous uses. In this same exhibition will be included the vegetable and mineral products of the sea, such as the infusorial earths, greensand, the various algæ, &c., the latter with their application as manures, and also in the manufacture of soda, iodine, and other substances.

The third division of this subject will consist of as complete a series as possible of the apparatus used in connection with the fisheries, and will embrace models or full-size specimens of the various ships, steamers, smacks, boats, canoes, smoke and curing-houses, nets, traps, pounds, rods, reels, hooks, lines, artificial baits, &c., and a variety of other articles too numerous to mention. A prominent idea will be the exhibition, either separately or in collective divisions, of whatever illustrates the different classes of the fisheries. Taking the whale-fishery as an illustration, there will be shown skeletons of several species of whale, together with the whalebone, occupying its natural position in the mouth. Wooden models of the large whales, and plaster-casts of the smaller ones, will also be exhibited. The different kinds of oil, sper-maceti, ambergris, sperm-whales' teeth, &c.,will be presented, with their application, such as the purified oils and candles ; the different uses of the whalebone, for domestic, surgical, or other purposes; the sperm-whale's teeth, as carved into various articles of ornament or utility; the sperm-whale's jaw-bone, as used for knife-handles and other purposes, &c. There will also be models of whale-ships of different varieties, everything being made to a scale ; a full-sized whale-boat, with all its equipments of harpoons, bomb-lances, spades, lances, lines, tubs, &c., together with small models of the same, and several groups, representing scenes connected with the whale-fishery, as well as several separate drawings made expressly for this exhibition.

The menhaden-fishery will be exhibited also by figures, photographs, and casts of fish themselves, and by a working-model of the factory in which the fish are steamed and pressed for their oil and scrap, and a model of the Wood's Hole factory, where this menhaden scrap or refuse is converted into an important fertilizer; a model of the establishment where first they are scaled and prepared as sardines; as also the dif-ferent kinds of nets used, with a model of the kind of steamer by which these fish are pursued. The different preparation of the fish will also be shown.

The oyster industry will be also represented by all the varieties of oysters known on both coasts of the United States, with their trade or local name, with specimens of the animals that prey upon them. This will also embrace specimens of the eastern oyster transported to the western coast as undergoing certain known modifications. The various oyster sloops, rakes, and other devices, will also be shown.

The other fisheries illustrated will be those of the cod, the mackerel, the herring, shad, salmon, the sponge, coral, &c.

The fourth division of the fisheries will be the illustrations of pisci-culture or artificial propagation. Here will be shown the models of the United States establishments for securing and hatching the eggs of the salmon and shad ; illustrations of the various boxes, spawning-races, &c., and the fish-ways or fish-ladders, all in full-size representations, or in models.

The actual process of hatching out the eggs of fish and rearing the young will also be exhibited, in connection with the Agricultural Bureau division of the centennial display. It is expected that for a consider-able part of the time of the exhibition the eggs of the California salmon can be secured, this being a species well suited to illustrate the changes undergone in actual incubation, the egg being as large as a common currant, and permitting the various stages of development to be readily observed.

In connection with this exhibition of the fisheries, steps have been taken toward securing complete reports of the past and present history of many of our important industries. Among them that of the whale-fishery, the menhaden, the mackerel, &c. The report on the whale-fishery will include a list of all the vessels, as far as practicable, that have ever been fitted out from the several whaling ports of the United States, together with the yield of oil, bone, and sperm for each year, and their respective prices.

The menhaden report will contain similar data for that fish, together with an exhaustive account of the yield in 1874 and 1875. Steps have also been taken to obtain a list of all the vessels used in these fisheries, arranged as to their tonnage, names of owners, captains, and the nature of the service performed by them.

V.

The fifth division of the exhibition of the National Museum is intended to illustrate the past and present condition of the native tribes of the United States, or its *anthropology*, and in view of the very great interest in subjects of this character, it was determined to make a special effort to render the display exhaustive and complete. As, how-ever, the Indian Bureau of the Interior Department contemplated a somewhat similar exhibition, it was thought best to unite the two, and to conduct the efforts of each upon a systematic plan, and so as to avoid duplication. This was specially proper, as any collections made by the Indian Bureau would, under the law of Congress, be turned over to the Smithsonian Institution for safe-keeping, as soon as their temporary functions had been fulfilled.

For the better presentation of the subject to collectors and corre-spondents, Prof. O. T. Mason, of Columbian University, was requested by you to draw up a systematic schedule of the various articles of clothing, ornaments, household utensils, implements of agriculture, weapons of war and the chase, tools of trade, the apparatus used for the pursuit and capture of game, &c., and a pamphlet was accordingly prepared by this gentleman, embracing over six hundred subjects. Copies of this pamphlet were then sent by the Indian Bureau to all its agents, and by the Smithsonian Institution to its correspondents, with the request that they would indicate by a mark on the list the articles that could be obtained, and return them to Washington. This was done to a considerable extent, and authority was given in many cases to proceed in making the collection. Several gentlemen of much experi-ence in ethnological researches were also employed by the Bureau to secure complete collections from the tribes within their reach. Among those appointed for this purpose were Mr. James G. Swan, for the Alaska and Puget Sound tribes; Maj. J. W. Powell, for those of Utah and Wyoming; and Mr. Stephen Powers, for those of Nevada and Cali-fornia, all of whom have been diligently occupied in carrying out their instructions.

Researches in the department of archæology proper, or the ancient implements of stone, metal, and earthenware, were also prosecuted on a large scale, especially on the south coast of California, where, within the historical period, the tribes were numerous and intelligent. These, however, have long since been exterminated, and their history is only to be read from the articles buried in their graves.

For the purpose of properly working this field, arrangements were made jointly by the Smithsonian Institution and the Indian Bureau with Mr. Paul Schumacher to proceed with a party and prosecute his explorations. The Treasury Department authorized the transportation of the party to the islands on a revenue-cutter, and the War Department furnished rations at cost-price, as well as tents, &c., while the United States Coast Survey extended the courtesy of one of its surveying-vessels, under Captain Taylor. With these facilities, Mr. Schumacher gathered a large number of articles, some tons in weight, and representing a great variety of very choice specimens, such as stone mortars, pestles, ornaments of stone, shell, bone, &c.

Simultaneously with this labor of Mr. Schumacher, Lieutenant Wheeler, of the Engineer Bureau, had a party in the vicinity of Santa Barbara, in charge of Dr. H. C. Yarrow, which also made important collections. In the same field and with satisfactory results, Rev. Stephen Bowers has also been occupied in behalf of the Centennial display.

Understanding that there were numerous remains of a similar character in Oregon, Mr. Schumacher, with a small party, proceeded there in September last, and obtained some articles of interest.

The many correspondents of the Smithsonian Institution were also invited, by means of a circular, to make contributions to the same department. The returns have already been very great, amounting to many thousands of stone implements of every kind and character.

In some instances gentlemen who were not willing to present their collections permanently, have consented to lend them for the Exhibition, and these will be carefully kept separate and returned at its close.

The labors of Mr. Swan, like those of Mr. Schumacher, were greatly facilitated by the action of the Treasury Department in placing the revenue-cutter Oliver Wolcott at his disposal, by means of which he was enabled to visit many Indian tribes on Puget Sound and elsewhere, otherwise inaccessible.

In addition to what has already been acknowledged, the War Department has also rendered much assistance by instructing quartermasters to receive and forward packages delivered to them for the purpose of the Centennial display. The amount of material thus obtained from all sources has been very great, and is continually increasing, so that there is little question that, so far as inanimate objects are concerned, scarcely anything will be wanting in the elements of a satisfactory exposition. This will contain several hundred lay figures, of life size, properly dressed, with the clothing and ornaments of their own tribe, illustrating their various grades of rank as well as ages and sex, as also models or actual representations of their dwellings, their boats, snow-shoes, horses and dogs, and their trappings, implements of hunting and fishing, agricultural tools, and indeed everything else that can be thought of.

Among the more conspicuous objects already collected by Mr. Swan are a Haidah canoe, 60 feet long, 8 feet wide, and 4 feet high, cut from a single log of cedar, profusely ornamented with carvings and paintings in the manner of the natives, with several other canoes 30 feet long; also several carved posts, 60 feet high, such as are set in front of the dwellings of the Haidah chiefs; materials for a complete dwelling, 100 feet long by 20 wide, and many other things not necessary to enumerate.

The selection of ethnological objects for exhibition at the Centennial has been intrusted to Dr. Charles Rau, one of the most eminent of American ethnologists, who is preparing an elaborate report upon the subject, with numerous illustrations, which will shortly be printed.

One feature which promised to be of very great interest, but which the reduction of the estimates for the Government display rendered impracticable, was that of an exhibition of living representatives of the principal Indian tribes, each series to embrace from four to eight persons, of different sexes and ages, to be brought to Philadelphia with their native clothing, implements, utensils, apparatus, and dwellings; the whole to be grouped on a reservation of the Centennial grounds, where they could carry on their various occupations, including the practice of their aboriginal arts; the Navajoes to show their methods of weaving blankets and belts; the Pueblos, their manufacture of pottery; the Piutes, the construction of their stone implements; other tribes their basket-work; the Blackfeet their method of dressing buffalo and other skins, &c. The plan embraced the presentation of some twenty or more tribes, from the Esquimaux of Northwestern Alaska to the Seminole, and from the Passamaquoddy Indians of Maine to those of San Diego, California. The expense of such an enterprise would, of course, be very great, involving not only the transportation of the Indians and an agent and interpreter to and from Philadelphia, but also their subsistence during the exhibition. There is reason, however, to believe that no feature on that occasion would be more interesting to our own people and to foreign visitors than the one referred to; and it is to be hoped that authority may be granted by Congress, in season for the purpose. In anticipation of such action the Indian agents have been instructed to make their selections of families and be in readiness to act when notified by telegraph or otherwise.

I have thus presented a sketch of the displays that are considered desirable for the Smithsonian Institution and the United States Fish Commission to make in the International Exhibition, although, to carry it out to its utmost completeness, so as to be a credit to the nation, will require the appropriation by Congress of the remainder of the sum originally estimated as necessary for the purpose. A work of such magnitude, of course requires the employment of a great many persons, as well as much expense for the acquisition of objects and their preparation for exhibition.

A large force of taxidermists is at present engaged at the Smithsonian Institution in doing the necessary work, and sufficient progress has been made to warrant the belief that with sufficient means everything will be completed in time for the opening of the Exhibition. The cost of putting these articles in attractive cases will, however, be very considerable, and must be provided for.

An important consideration in connection with these displays is the fact that their service will not be limited to the period of the Centennial year; but, as the material all belongs to the Government and to the National Museum, it will all be brought back to Washington, where, with proper facilities to be furnished by Congress, it will be displayed to interested visitors, it is to be hoped for centuries to come.

So far as the ethnological display is concerned it is quite reasonable to infer that by the expiration of a second hundred-year period of the life of the American republic, the Indians will have entirely ceased to present any distinctive characters, and will be merged in the general population. It is more than probable that the ethnological collection now being made by the Government will be the only exposition of the past; and with each succeeding year these specimens will become more valuable and more highly appreciated.

The permanent exhibition, too, so complete and exhaustive, of the mineral wealth of the country will also be a matter of great importance. It is proposed to arrange these collections by States, and even by mining districts, and as new mines are opened to have them properly exhibited in their series. Nowhere else than in Washington could such a collection be brought together, and nowhere else would it be of so great service in furnishing the means for a proper appreciation of the mineral wealth of the Territories and of the different States. The same reasoning, of course, applies to the other departments of the animal resources of the United States, and of the fisheries; and the whole, when combined, may be made to constitute a perpetual exhibition of the resources of the country, as derived from the animal and mineral kingdoms, as well as from its ethnology.

In this connection it must not be forgotten that the expense of preparing the special anthropological collection for the Centennial has been borne almost entirely by the Indian Bureau, from its portion of the Centennial fund given by Congress to the Interior Department. The direction, however, of the work has been intrusted by the Commissioner of Indian Affairs to the Smithsonian Institution, as the collections made will, under the law of Congress, become ultimately a portion of the National Museum under its charge.

It will, however, be readily understood that the Smithsonian Building will be entirely inadequate to accommodate this collection on its return from Philadelphia, especially as even now it is overcrowded and packed from top to bottom with thousands of boxes, for the proper exhibition of the contents of which there is no space or opportunity at the present time. It is to be hoped that action at an early day will be taken by Congress looking toward a proper provision for this emergency, especially when it is realized that the materials are thus available for a National Museum that shall be equal, in its extent and completeness and in its educational advantages, to that of any nation in the world.

The collections made directly through the Government appropriations will also be very largely supplemented by the donation of series of American and foreign exhibitors, a very large proportion of which will be placed at the disposal of the United States Government.

Another subject which will require early consideration will be the best mode of distributing the duplicate specimens, of which vast numbers will be on hand at the close of the Exhibition, and it is probable that an appropriation by Congress will be needed for the arrangement, labeling, packing, and boxing of these specimens. Several hundred sets of these objects can be made up for the principal educational, literary, and scientific institutions throughout the country.

It may be remembered that several years ago Congress appropriated $10,000 for the expenses of distributing the duplicates then in the National Museum, with the proviso that the freight be paid by the recipients. Under this enactment nearly a quarter of a million of labeled specimens were supplied to several hundred institutions throughout the country, and have doubtless answered an excellent purpose in furnishing the means of instruction. The surplus available for such a distribution at the close of the International Exhibition, even after all exchanges have been made, will be very much greater than on the occasion referred to.

Respectfully, yours,

SPENCER F. BAIRD,
Representative of the Smithsonian Institution
and of the Department of Food-Fishes in
Government Centennial Board.

Prof. JOSEPH HENRY,
Secretary Smithsonian Institution.

Table showing the number of entries in the record-books of the United States National Museum at the close of the years 1874 and 1875, respectively.

Class.	1874.	1875.
Mammals	12,294	12,462
Birds	68,361	70,378
Reptiles and amphibians	8,293	8,410
Fishes	13,808	16,649
Skeletons and skulls	14,408	15,363
Eggs	17,062	17,249
Crustaceans	2,204	2,210
Annelids	100	100
Mollusks	25,757	26,757
Radiates	3,142	3,148
Invertebrate fossils	7,727	7,905
Minerals	9,178	9,394
Ethnological specimens	16,415	20,000
Add for centennial volume, 24751–25052		302
Total	197,749	210,327
Increase for 1875		12,578

ADDITIONS TO THE COLLECTIONS OF THE SMITHSONIAN INSTITUTION (UNITED STATES NATIONAL MUSEUM) IN 1875.

Abbott, Dr. C. C.　Cast of prehistoric mask; box and package of arrow-points from New Jersey.

Abert, General J. T.　Skin of albino cedar-bird, (*Ampelis cedrorum.*)

Adam, Joseph S.　Specimens of marble from Canaan, Conn.

Adams, George R.　Three skins of fur-seal (*Callorhinus ursinus*) and skin of arctic fox (*Vulpes lagopus*) from Saint George's Island, Prybilov group, Alaska.

Aiken, Charles E.　Skin of Abert's squirrel, (*Sciurus Abertii;*) eggs of rufous owl, (*Scops flammeola,*) Woodhouse's jay, (*Cyanocitta Woodhousii,*) blue partridge, (*Callipepla squamata;*) skins of Rocky Mountain sheep, (*Ovis montana;*) 5 skins of mountain-buffalo, (*Bison americanus;*) and specimens, in flesh, of coyote, (*Canis latrans,*) 2 lynxes, (*Lynx rufus,*) and jack-rabbit, (*Lepus callotis,*) from Colorado.

Akhurst, John.　Stone pestle from Croton Lake, N. Y.

Alaska Commercial Company, San Francisco, Cal.　Nine mummies from Kagemil group, Aleutian Islands, Alaska, and one from Prince William's Sound; 20 skins of fur-seal, (*Callorhinus ursinus,*) from Alaska, 5 of sea-lion, (*Eumetopias stelleri,*) and many other objects.

Aldrich, Charles. Specimens of wood cut by stone ax, from Colorado; clay pipe from San Juan River, N. Mex.

Ambler, R. C. Specimens of minerals from West Virginia.

American Sardine Company, New York City. One dozen boxes of "American sardines," (*Brevoortia menhaden,*) preserved in oil.

American Whip Company, Westfield, Mass. Collection illustrating manufacture of whips from whalebone.

Ames, James T. Barrel and box of emery specimens from Chester, Mass.

Anderson, William. Arrow-heads, polished stones, &c., from Roseville, Ohio.

Anderson, W. F. Specimens of galusite from Virginia City, Nev.

Angel, Dr. Manuel Uribé y, and Luis Johnson. Earthenware from Indian graves in Manizalez, Colombia, S. A.

Aquarial Gardens, Boston, Mass., (W. E. Baker.) Two specimens, in flesh, of common seal, (*Phoca vitulina.*)

Arny, General W. F. M. Specimens of implements and clothing of Navajo and Apache Indians of Arizona; insects from Bonito Cañon, Arizona.

Babcock, Dr. W. H. Alligator eggs and oil from Central Florida.

Bagot, Samuel O. Specimens of rock from St. Michael's Cave, Mediterranean.

Bailey, W. B. F. Specimens of stone implements and quartz; 1 box ethnological specimens from Griffin, Ga.

Baird, G. W., Passed Assistant Engineer, U. S. N. Wooden image representing a "frog-tamer," made by Indians of Sitka, Alaska.

Baird, Prof. S. F. Sioux clay pipe. See under *Washington, D. C.*

Baker, W. E. See under *Boston, Aquarial Gardens.*

Ballou, W. H. Small stone implement from Niagara River, N. Y.

Baltimore, J. D. Interspinous process of fish.

Banks, Montague. Specimen of hell-bender (*Necturus lateralis*) from Manitoba.

Barker, W. P. Specimen of giant beetle (*Dynastes hercules*) from Alabama.

Barnes, G. W. Specimens of jumping seeds from San Diego, Cal.

Barnum, Hon. P. T. Skeletons of eland, (*Oreas camma,*) giraffe, (*Giraffa camelopardalis,*) sea-lion, (*Zalophus Gillespii,*) and specimens, in flesh, of ostrich, (*Struthio camelus,*) Malayan tapir, (*Rhinochœrus sumatranus,*) and manatee, (*Trichechus manatus ;*) 2 black-neck swans, (*Cygnus nigricollis.*)

Bartlett, Dr. E. H. Living specimens of golden eagle (*Aquila chrysaëtos*) from Maryland.

Batty, Joseph H. Skins of rabbit, (*Lepus americanus,*) weasels, (*Putorius vison, noveboracensis,* and *longicauda,*) and squirrel, (*Sciurus hudsonius,*) and skeletons.

Bauermeister, Rev. W. G. C. Minerals from Indiana.

Bausett, S. P. Specimens of herring (*Clupea harengus*) and of sardines from lower St. Lawrence, Canada.

Bean, T. H. Specimen of lesser red-poll (*Ægiothus linaria*) from Virginia; collection of fresh-water fishes; twenty-five bird-skins and squirrel (*Sciurus hudsonius*) from Pennsylvania; skeleton of cow (*Bos taurus*) from Virginia; stone dish from Pennsylvania; ovaries and spermaries of black bass, (*Micropterus salmoides,*) and kettle from Indian grave in Pennsylvania.

Bechler, G. R. Skull of boar (*Sus scrofa*) from Colorado.

Bendire, Capt. Charles, U. S. Army. Eggs of double-crested cormorant, (*Graculus dilophus ;*) skins of gray-crowned finch, (*Leucosticte littoralis ;*) Bohemian waxwing (*Ampelis garrulus*) from Oregon.

Bernary, Dr. F. F. Polished stone from Missouri.

Berthoud, E. L. Box of ethnological specimens; two boxes minerals from Colorado.

Berthoud, W. B. Specimen of giant beetle (*Dynastes hercules*) from Louisiana.

Blackford, Eugene G. Specimens of red snapper, (*Lutjanus aya ;*) barracuda, (*Sphyræna picuda ;*) toothed herring, (*Dorosoma cepedianum ;*) haddock, (*Melanogrammus æglefinus ;*) head of salmon, (*Salmo quinnat ;*) crabs and lobsters; snapper. (*Epinephelus ;*) albino haddock, (*Melanogrammus æglefinus ;*) Spanish mackerel, (*Cybium maculatum ;*) pompanos, (*Trachynotus carolinus ;*) terrapin, (*Ptychemys decussata,*) and young, one year old; three turtles, (*Chelonia mydas ;*) grenadier, (*Macrurus rupestris ;*) leather-back turtle, (*Sphargis coriacea ;*) loggerhead-turtle, (*Thalassochelys caunna ;*) sturgeon, (*Acipenser ;*) long-tailed file-fish, (*Alutera cuspicauda ;*) spiny box-fish, (*Chilomycterus geometricus ;*) sheep's-head, (*Archosargus probatocephalus ;*) king-fish, (*Menticirrus nebulosus ;*) big-eyed herring, (*Elops saurus ;*) cobia, (*Elacate canadus ;*) horse-fish, (*Vomer setipinnis ;*) cero, (*Cybium caballa ;*) dolphin, (*Coryphæna seueri ;*) mud-fish, (*Amia calva ;*) drum, (*Pogonias chromis ;*) sturgeon, (*Acipenser ;*) flasher, (*Lobotes surinamensis ;*) mullet, (*Mugil lineatus ;*) carangids; silver gar, (*Belone longirostris ;*) goose-fish, (*Lophius americanus ;*) sole, (*Achirus lineatus ;*) eel, (*Anguilla bostoniensis ;*) egg-capsules of periwinkle, (*Sycotypus ;*) pike, (*Esox ;*) common flat-fish, (*Pseudopleuronectes americanus ;*) moon-eye, (*Hyodon tergisus ;*) shiner, (*Stilbe americana ;*) whitefish, (*Coregonus* sp.;) large mouth black bass, (*Micropterus nigricans ;*) catfish, (*Noturus flavus ;*) toad-fish, (*Batrachus tau ;*) sucker, (*Catostomus* sp.;) yellow perch, (*Perca flavescens ;*) cusk, (*Brosmius americanus ;*) white perch, (*Morone americanus ;*) rock-fish, (*Roccus lineatus ;*) brook-trout, (*Salmo fontinalis ;*) sea-robin, (*Prionotus evolans ;*) bluefish, (*Pomatomus saltatrix ;*) salmon, (*Salmo salar ;*) fresh-water cusk, (*Lota maculosa,*) from Fulton Market, N. Y.

Blake, Prof. W. P. Eleven boxes of minerals from various localities.

Boardman, George A. Four eggs of ring-neck duck (*Fulix collaris*) from Milltown, Me.

Boehmer, George H. Quartz-crystals from Maryland.

Booth, G. W. Specimens of minerals from Talladega County, Ala.

Boston, Mass., Aquarial Gardens, (W. E. Baker.) Two specimens, in flesh, of common seal, (*Phoca vitulina.*)

Bourse, C. J., jr. Collection illustrating mineral resources of Columbia, Lancaster County, Pa., and Carroll County, Md.

Bowman, Peter. Arrow-heads from Savannah, Ohio.

Bowman, S. C. One box of bird-skins; two boxes of mounted birds from Illinois.

Boyd, C. R. Collection illustrating mineral resources of Wythe County, Va.

Boyd, Dr. Specimen of pike-perch (*Stizostedium americanum*) from Tennessee.

Brackett, Lieut. Col. A. G. Specimens of gray-crowned finch, (*Leucosticte tephrocotis* var. *littoralis ;*) skins of porcupine, (*Erethizon dorsatus*) and woodchuck, (*Arctomys monax ;*) ferrugineous buzzard, (*Archibuteo ferrugineus ;*) sparrow-hawk, (*Tinnunculus sparverius ;*) hawk, (*Buteo*) bittern, (*Botaurus ;*) sandpiper, (*Tringa ;*) long-billed curlew, (*Numenus longirostris ;*) spermophiles, (*Spermophilus tridecemlineatus* and *S. richardsonii* var. *elegans ;*) elk, (*Cervus canadensis*) in flesh, from Fort Saunders.

Bradley, Prof. F. H. Collection illustrating mineral resources of East Tennessee, North Carolina, and Georgia.

Brand, C. C. Whaling-gun and bomb-lances.

Bransford, Dr. J. T., U. S. N. Alcoholic fishes, shells, and minerals from Isthmus of Panama.

Breck, Prof. Robert L. Cast of prehistoric medallion found near Richmond, Ky.

Briggs, Ulysses. Oriole's nest made of flax from Iowa.

Broadhead, Prof. G. C. Collection illustrating mineral resources of Missouri and western part of Illinois.

Brown, H. Felt from bottom of U. S. gunboat "Isaac P. Smith," sunk during the rebellion in Charleston Harbor.

Brown, Dr. J. J. Specimens of shells from Gulf Stream.

Bryan, O. N. Specimens of fishes from Akocheek, St. Georges County, Md.

Bryan, R. B. Specimen of meteorite from Mound City, Kans.

Bryant and Warker. Specimens of shells from Detroit, Mich.

Buck, Stuart M. Specimens of coal from Coalburgh, W. Va.

Burchard, Miss Sophia. Specimens of birds (*Falco tinnunculus, Cuculus canorus, Turdus torquatus, Coccothraustes vulgaris, Saxicola œnanthe, Pratincola ruberta, Fringilla montifringilla, Emberiza schnœniclus, Parus cristatus, Phyllopneuste trochilus, Sternus vulgaris, Rallus aquaticus, Rallus porzana*) and fishes and insects from Rostock, Germany.

Byrne, Surgeon G. C., U. S. N. Indian pestle from Willet's Point, New York Harbor.

Calkins, W. W. Box of fresh-water and land shells from Chicago, Ill.

Calvin, William. Two boxes of shells from Cincinnati, Ohio.

Canfield & Co. Specimens of quartz-crystals.

Capron, General Horace. Lay figures of Japanese farmer and his wife. Screens with colored drawings of Japanese fishes.

Carley, B. J. M. Specimens of oysters, clams, and razor-clams from numerous localities in the vicinity of New York, illustrating the New York oyster-trade.

Carlisle, Amos M. Specimens of galena from Tallahassee.

Carpenter, R. C. Specimens of British birds' eggs.

Carpenter, Lieut. W. L., U. S. A. Specimens of birds' eggs; invertebrate fossils; box of zoological collections; teeth of *Brontotherium;* insects; invertebrate fossils.

Casey, J. Stone hatchet, hammer, sinker, pestles, picks, &c., from Pennsylvania.

Central Virginia Manufacturing Company. Copper-ores from the vicinity of Tolersville.

Chace, William. Three stone axes, three stone chisels, and one quartz arrow-head from South Carolina.

Chapman, George W. Two specimens of septaria; fragment of an aerolite from Waconda, Kans.

Chase, A. W. Two boxes of ethnologica, one box of birds, and one box of fossils from California. (Deposited.)

Chester, Capt. H. C. Wooden anchor used on coast of Connecticut; model of Noank sharpey.

Chicago, Ill., Academy of Sciences of. One box of fish-skins.

Chiraz, Mirza Mohammed Aly Persan. Persian coins from Poul.

Christchurch, New Zealand, Canterbury; Museum of. A collection of moa bones from New Zealand.

Christiania, Norway; Royal University of Norway. Mounted reindeer; model of Laplander and sledges; mosses and lichens; carved-wood articles of Norwegian industry; medals of Norway; stone paper-weights; diadem made from fish scales and eyes; and basket from boiled roots of pine-tree.

Clark, George. One keg of salted whitefish (*Coregonus albus*) from Michigan.

Clark, J. H. Eight boxes and one bale of fossils and ethnologica of New England; implements carved from whale's teeth, (*Physeter macrocephalus.*)

Clark, Wilson H. Minerals from Connecticut for examination.

Clark, Dr. W. M. Three boxes of human bones, carved figures, (idols?) mound-pipes, earthen vessels, shell-beads, gorgets, chisels, sinkers, chumkee-stone, &c., from Tennessee.

Clark, William S. Rubbing-stone and arrow-points from Iowa.

Clendennin, Frank. Three Arapaho scalps.

Collett, Prof. Robert. A collection of marine fishes from Norway.

Cox, Prof. E. T. Specimens of Lake Tippecanoe sisco (*Argyrosomus sisco*) from Indiana.

Cox, John F. Specimens of gypsum from Little Rock, Ark.

Crittenden, A. R. Thimble made from jaw-bone of sperm-whale, (*Physeter macrocephalus.*)

Crufts, W. H. Skin of snake from California.

Curley, Rev. James. Eskimo bows, arrows, harpoons, and fishing-lines from Alaska.

Currier, George H. Mounted badger (*Taxidea americana*) from Wisconsin.

Currier, J. M. Ethnological specimens, quartzite, bones of various animals, and earth from Indian camping-ground near Bristol, Vt.

Cushing, Frank H. Implements from Indian grave, bone-perforators, arrow-heads, &c., from Northern New York.

Dabney, William C., M. D. Carved stone head from Monticello.

Dall, Rev. C. H. Eleven terra-cotta figures, Parsee hat, and sacred Brahminical thread from Calcutta, India.

Dall, William H., U. S. Coast Survey. Two sea-lion teeth from Pacific ocean; cones of fir, (*Abies* sp.) 300 species exotic, 75 species east coast, and 25 species fossil mollusca.

Davis, O. W., jr. Specimens of graphite, limonite, cinder, pig-iron, &c., from Katahdin Iron-Works, Me.

Dawson, Dr. J. W. Ten species of arctic shells and Post-Pliocene fossils.

De Frece, A. B. Box of articles manufactured from American pearl-bearing shells.

Delano, George, & Co., New Bedford, Mass. Samples of whale-oils and sperm-candles.

Derry, Charles W. Skin of pine-grosbeak (*Pinicola enucleator*) from Colorado.

Dexter, Mr. Specimen of spear-fish sucker (*Rhombochirus osteochir*) from Vineyard Haven, Mass.

Dick, Dr. F. N. Skin and skull of black-footed ferret (*Putorius nigripes*) from Nebraska.

Dickeson, M. W. Two " security-medals."

Dillingham, Joseph R., and Sumner J. Plumner. Specimen of land-locked salmon (*Salmo sebago*) from Maine.

Dodge, R. F., Boston, Mass. Series of oars and paddles.

Douglas, Thomas and William G. Collection illustrating mineral resources of Virginia.

Dozier, Dr. G. R. Osseous growth from jaw of mule.

Dunedin, New Zealand, Otago Museum, (Capt. F. W. Hutton.) Two boxes of fossil bones and birds.

Eaton, D. H. Box of Indian implements from Peotone.

Edes, Lieut. B. Long. Seeds of camelia (*Camelia japonica*) from Japan.

Edwards, Daniel. Two specimens of bay lynx (*Lynx rufus*) from Allegany County, N. Y.

Edwards, Vinal N. See under *Washington, U. S. Commission Fish and Fisheries.*

Edwards, William H. Specimens of cannel-coal from Coalburgh, W. Va.

Elliott, Henry W. Phonolithic rock with spinel, and *Mytilidæ* from Saint George's Island, Alaska.

Evans, W. W. Birds and Indian antiquities of Peru, &c.

Ferguson, Maj. T. B., Maryland Commissioner of Fisheries. Young black bass, (*Micropterus salmoides,*) specimens of golden carp, (*Cyprinus carpio,*) and tench, (*Tinca vulgaris;*) three crates for packing fish-eggs; models of oyster-boats used on Chesapeake Bay.

Finick, Dr. Hugo. Collection of pestles, mortars, mullers, carved stone heads of animals, stone images, (very ancient,) stone balls, obsidian cores, flakes, spear and arrow heads, pottery, spindle-whorls, handles to pottery vessels, &c., from near Cordova, Mexico.

Fitch, F. A. Specimens of coral, insects, and spear-heads from Randolph, N. Y.

Fithian, Dr. W. Stone ax from Kentucky.

Flint, Dr. Earl. Two cases containing stone idols, mortars, chisels, pottery, earthen vases of different kinds, and stone implements from Nicaragua.

Flynt, W. N., & Co., Monson, Mass. Specimens of granite, in the form of cubes, from Monson, Mass.

Foote, George B. Specimens of mineral from Montana.

Fouch, F. W. Specimens of fossil teeth, shells, bones, &c., from Badito, Colo.

Fowler, W. H. Living otter (*Lutra canadensis*) from Maryland.

Fox, W. H. Skin of pine-creeping warbler (*Dendroica pinus*) from New Hampshire.

Friel, Joseph. Stone and iron axes from Cloverport, Ky.

Fryer, C. G. Six boxes Cornish sardines.

Fuller, C. B., Curator of Portland Society Natural History. Box of shells from Portland, Me.

Gabb, Prof. William M., Director of Talamanca Expedition. Specimens of stone chisels, lancets, ancient pottery, pots, dishes, images of animals, dogs, horses, &c., box of shells from Talamanca, Costa Rica.

Galvin, Thomas. Stone pestle from Rhode Island.

Garrett, A. Land and fresh-water shells from Tahiti.

Gattunger, Dr. August. Specimens of European mosses, (*Musci.*)

Gianque, Florien. Specimens of celt bark-peelers from Ohio.

Gibson, J. P. Calcareous rocks from Concord, N. C.

Gilchrist, James. Specimen of mineral from Wheeling, W. Va.

Gill, Herbert A. Specimens of bats (*Scotophilus fuscus*) from the District of Columbia.

Gilliss, Capt. James, U. S. A. Black-tailed deer (*Cariacus macrotis*) and black-footed ferret (*Putorius nigripes*) from Cheyenne, Wyo.

Glover, Townend. Specimen of malformed carp (*Cyprinus carpio*) from the District of Columbia.

Golden, H. W. Three specimens of land-locked smelt (*Osmerus* sp.) from Belgrade, Me.

Goode, G. Browne. Specimens of shad, (*Alosa sapidissima;*) mullet, (*Mugil lineatus;*) spotted squeteague, (*Cynoscion carolinensis;*) yellow perch, (*Perca flavescens;*) sun-fish, (*Pomotis aureus;*) sucker, (*Catostomus;*) cat-fish, (*Amiurus atrarius;*) "smelts," (*Hybopsis;*) 10 specimens of carp, (*Carassius auratus;*) pike, (*Esox,*) from Washington market; 8 alligator-skins, Indian-tanned deer-skins, from Indian River, Fla.; collection of fishes and reptiles of East Florida; specimens of columbite and molybdenite; 30 mallard-ducks, (*Anas boschas;*) 2 rabbits, (*Lepus sylvaticus;*) 130 living animals from Florida, transmitted to Zoological Gardens of Philadelphia.

Grant, M. N. Soda from a soda lake, Laramie Plains, Wyo.

Grant, William. Specimen of harlequin-snake (*Elaps* sp.) from Couralitas, Chihuahua, Mexico.

Gray, Arthur F. Box of shells from Cedar Keys, Fla.

Green, H. A. Copper spear from Livingston County, New York.

Green, Monroe A. Sturgeon, (*Accipenser* sp.) 8 days old, from Hudson River.

Gregory, S. S. Hornet's nest from Berea, Ohio.

Griswold's (B. B.) School. Indian relics from Maryland.

Gruber, F. Skull and skin of head of young sea-lion (*Eumetopias Stelleri*) from California.

Gunnell, T. M., Medical Director U. S. N. Feather-coat from Bering's Strait.

Haigh, Dr. A. V. Indian implements from Wellborn, Ark.

Hale, Dr. Specimens of orthoptera from Middle Park, Colo.

Hamilton, R. J. Indian arrow-straightener from Chapurito, Mexico.

Hanley, Sylvanus. One hundred and five species of mollusks from England.

Hardenburgh, A. R., surveyor-general of California. Specimens of gold, silver, quicksilver, and lead ores from various mines in California.

Hardenburgh, G. R. Skins of six species of birds from New Brunswick, N. J.

Harkness, James. Frontal bone of human skull.

Harper, G. W. Specimens of shells from Ohio.

Hart, J. P. Crystals from Kansas.

Harvey & Holden. Specimen of Virginia rail (*Rallus virginiana*) from Virginia.

Hathaway, G. W. Samples of ore from Tioga, Pa.

Haven, Williams & Co. Skins of fur-seal from Antarctic Ocean and samples of oils.

Hazard, Joseph P. Minerals from North Carolina, South Carolina, and Virginia.

Hempstead, G. S. B.   Box of ethnologica from Portsmouth, Ohio, and vicinity.

Henderson, J. H.   Shoes made from rattlesnake and chicken-snake skins, tanned deer-skin, and antidote for rattlesnake's bite from Alabama.

Hering, Dr. C. J.   Skull of tapir, horns of deer, stone implements, and bird-skins from Paramaribo, Mexico.

Herran, Thomas V., President University of Medellin, Colombia, S. A.   Living orchids from Colombia.

Herrendean, Captain.   Specimen of *Pseudopriacanthus altus* from Wood's Hole, Mass.

Heyman, Isaac.   Mineral from Alabama.

Hill, A. F.   Fragments of pottery from Masontown, Pa.

Hill, Dr. H. H.   Casts of stone implements from Cincinnati, Ohio.

Hoderman, Henry.   Malformed hen's egg.

Holmes, F. S.   Ancient pottery from Charleston, S. C. ; bust of Osceola.

Holston Salt and Plaster Company.   Box of salts and plasters from Saltville, Va.

Hooper, W. E., & Sons, Baltimore, Md.   Fyke, trammel, and seine nets, and specimens of twine used in manufacturing fish-nets.

Hoskinson, R. M.   Five univalve shells from Kansas.

Hough, Daniel.   Cast of stone implement from Indiana.

Hough, Dr. R. B.   Box of Indian relics, arrow-points, Indian dresses, and ethnologica from New York.

Hough, Lewis S.   Stone pestles from Maryland.

Houston, Edward.   Stone implements from Irish Grove, Mo.

Hoy, Dr. P. R.   Specimens of whitefish (*Coregonus* sp.) and burbot (*Lota maculosa*) from Racine, Wis.

Hoyt, B. F.   One box of *Unionidæ* from Iowa.

Hoyt, I. H.   One box of shells from Iowa.

Howe, H. M.   Thirteen boxes of minerals, illustrating the mineral resources of parts of New Hampshire, Massachusetts, Vermont, New York, Maine, Rhode Island, &c.

Howland, J. S.   Bull-whip used on the plains.

Hunt, J. H.   One box *Unionidæ* and one box stone implements from Ohio.

Huston, Lieut. J. T., U. S. A.   Specimen of beetle, (*Monohammus titillator.*)

Hutchinson, S. G., Johnstown, N. Y.   Series of skins and gloves illustrating processes of glove-manufacture.

Hutchinson, H. M.   Chinese dog, in flesh, (*Canis familiaris.*)

Hyatt, H. O., M. D.   Specimens of alcoholic fishes from Tarboro, N. C.

Janeway, John H.   Two specimens of gophers in alcohol from Fort Wallace.

Jewell, Hon. Harvey.   Specimens of brook-trout (*Salmo fontinalis*) and land-locked salmon (*Salmo sebago*) from Sysladobsis Lake, Me.

Johnson, Luis. See under *Angel, Dr. Manuel Uribé y.*

Johnston, F. H. Specimens of cod, (*Gadus morrhua,*) haddock, (*Melano-grammus æglefinus,*) and hake, (*Phycis chuss,*) from Massachusetts.

Jones, W. H., passed assistant surgeon, U. S. N. Four skulls of natives of Honolulu.

Jones, Rev. C. M. Wing of hawk from Iowa.

Kaehler, F. Skull (partial) and teeth of horse, (*Equus caballus.*)

Kaucher, William. Specimens of minerals from Oregon, Mo.

Keim, M. Insects from Danville, Va.

Kempton, C. W. Specimens of galena, quartz, copper, auriferous pyrites, &c., from Essex County, Mass.

Kercheval, A. W. Specimen of cannel-coal from Romney, W. Va.

Kershner, Dr. Edward, U. S. N. Sixteen boxes of birds, fishes, woods, minerals, mammals, &c., from Australasia.

Kidder, Dr. Jerome H., U. S. N. Fifteen boxes, one barrel, one keg, natural-history specimens from Kerguelen Island.

King, C. J. Skin of porcupine (*Erethizon dorsatus*) from Mount Washington, N. H.

Kinnett, White. Miner's wooden shovel from shaft in Washington County, Mo., used sixty years ago.

Kinney, Thomas W. Photographs of Indian relics from Maysville, Ky.

Kirkby, W. W. One box of natural-history specimens, birds' eggs, and mammal from Hudson's Bay.

Kjerulf, Dr. Lava-dust from Tryssil, Norway.

Knapp, Dr. James. Paint-cups and stone implements from Louisville, Ky.

Knight, Joseph. Specimens of minerals from Mount Union, Pa.

Koberlin, Frederick, M. D. Map of "Nova Belgica et Anglia Nova."

Kratachoil, Dr. J. Pottery from Chiriqui, Panama.

Laing, Dr. J. M., U. S. A. Specimen of bat-fish (*Malthe cubifrons*) from Florida.

Langille, Rev. J. H. Specimens of insects.

Lapham, Dr. I. A. Box of shells from Wisconsin.

Lapham, I. G. Model of animal mounds of Wisconsin.

Latham, James H. Specimens of fishes and invertebrates; eel-pot from Noank, Conn.

Latimer, W. H. Ten barrels and sixteen boxes stone and other relics from Porto Rico and elsewhere.

Le Baron, J. Francis. Twenty specimens of red-poll, (*Ægiothus linaria;*) shells; skin of snipe, (*Pelidna americana;*) and insects in alcohol, from Massachusetts.

Leavenworth, J. H. Specimen of Virginian deer, albino, (*Cariacus virginianus,*) from Peshtigo, Wis.

Ledyard, L. W. Pottery from shell-heap mounds, Florida; two stone sinkers from Oneida Lake, and other stone implements from Western New York.

Lewis, Albert E.   Pottery from old Indian village, site of Hochelaga.

Lillard, John B.   Stone pestle; box of bones of Indian children, teeth, &c., (supposed "pigmies,") and costal segment of tortoise, from Tennessee.

Lindheimer, Dr. F.   Stone spear and arrow heads, perforator, &c., from New Braunfels, Tex.

Lindstrohm, Dr. G.   Thirty-one species of invertebrates from the Baltic Sea.

Lloyd, C.   Minerals, fossils, bones, &c., from Missouri.

Lloyd, L. W.   Specimens of lignite from Marshall, Texas.

Loew, Dr. Oscar.   Steatite from Fichtelgebirge, Germany.

Louderback, W. H.   Arrow-points from Kentucky.

Lucas, David.   Seeds of *Nelumbium luteum.*

Ludington, C.   Three bottles of young shad and herring from the Potomac River.

Lull, Comr. E. P., U. S. N.   One box of pottery from Newport, R. I.

Lütken, Prof. C.   Box of alcoholic fishes from South America.

Lüttwitz, Lieut. A. H. von., U. S. A.   Skin of golden eagle (*Aquila chrysaëtos*) from Wyoming.

Lyford, Dr. William H.   Hematite axe; bear's tooth from Illinois.

McAdoo, W. G.   Indian relics from Milledgeville, Ga.

McChesney, Charles E.   Specimens of ducks (*Spatula, Aix, Bucephala,* and *Lophodytes*) from Dakota.

McClellan, Dr. E., U. S. A.   Deformed skull of woodchuck (*Arctomys monax*) from Kentucky.

McClintock, Frank.   Earth from bottom of Great Salt Lake, Utah.

McCrary, Dr. E. W.   Minerals and ethnologica from Arkansas.

McIlvaine, A. R.   Stone implement from Raleigh, Iowa.

McKenzie, Dr. N. K.   Indian implements from Wellsville, Ohio.

McKinley, William.   Three boxes of ethnologica from Milledgeville, Ga.

McLeod, Rev. Robert R.   Two caribou (*Rangifer caribou*) in flesh; Canada lynx, (*Lynx Canadensis ;*) (*Vulpes alopex* var. *fulvus ;*) skins of pine-grosbeak, woodpecker, Canada jay, &c.; cross-fox and birch-bark canoe, from Maine.

McMahon, James.   Specimen of tabulate coral from Indiana.

McWilliams, Dr.   Skin of silver clarion (*Myiadestes unicolor*) from Mexico.

Macy, S. W.   Box of wooden and stone implements from Polynesia.

Malone, D. R.   Package of ethnologica from Indiana.

Maltzan, Baron von.   Sixty-five species of shells from Norway.

Manigault, Dr. G. E.   Skeletons of oldwife (*Balistes vetula*) and rattlesnake (*Crotalus adamanteus*) from South Carolina.

Mann, A. S.   Specimens of sea-horses (*Hippocampus* sp.) and porcupine-fish (*Diodon* sp.) from Florida.

Marcy, J. E.   Specimen of turtle in alcohol.

Martin, Dudley A.   Package of Indian relics from Pennsylvania.

Martin, Horace. Box of pottery from Corning, Mo.

Mather, Fred. Box of fresh grayling (*Thymallus tricolor*) and spawn and embryos of same from Honeoye Falls, N. Y.

Matulé, Juan Ygnacio. Specimens of the 1, 2, 3, 4, and 5 eruptions of the volcano of Ceboruco, Mexico.

Maury, M. F. Twelve boxes illustrating the coal resources of West Virginia.

Mazyck, William G. One package of unios from South Carolina.

Meek, Prof. F. B. One box and one barrel of reptiles, echinoderms, &c., from Florida.

Meigs, Gen. M. C. Geological specimens from Indian Territory.

Meigs, Mrs. M. C. Collection of Central American birds.

Mercer, Dr. F. W. Box of stone implements from Anna, Ill.

Mercer, R. W. Box of stone implements from Ohio.

Merrill, Dr. J. C., U. S. A. Four skins of European tree sparrow (*Passer Montana*) from Saint Louis, Mo.

Middleton & Carman. Specimens of dolphin, (*Coryphœna Seuerii,*) butterfish, (*Poronotus triancanthus,*) and black rudderfish, (*Palinurichthys perciformis,*) from Fulton Market, N. Y.

Middletown, Conn., Wesleyan University. Three mounted specimens of *Buteo polysomus*, and *Phalcobœnus montanus*, from Ecuador and Peru; specimens of black-walnut bird-stands.

Mills, Clark. Cast of fossil shark's tooth.

Milner, James W. See under *Washington, U. S. Commission of Fish and Fisheries.*

Moffat, E. S. Five boxes of iron-ores from Morris County, N. J.

Monroe, Charles E. Two boxes of fossils from Annapolis, Md.

Moore, N. B. Skin of Harlan's Hawk, (*Buteo Harlani.*)

Moores, H. Box of shells from Columbus, Ohio.

Moran, Dr. George H., U. S. A. Mounted specimen of Virginia rail (*Rallus Virginianus*) from Charleston, S. C.

Morgan, S. B. Specimen of coal from Tennessee.

Morley, J. R. Box of Rocky Mountain locusts, from Fort Scott, Kans.

Morris, S. F. Two boxes of iron-ores from Quinnimont, W. Va.

Morse, Charles H. Book illustrating punishments 25 years ago in China.

Munn, J. Box of oils and bone from whale's head from Newfoundland.

Newberry, Dr. C. Chest of bird-skins; zoological collection from Black Hills, Wyo.

New Jersey Zinc Company, Passaic, N. J. Specimens of zinc and minerals.

Newton, Dr. Box of fossils from Kansas.

Nickell, G. W. Specimens of minerals.

Nickerson, George Y. Seal-skin buoy from Greenland, and various articles illustrating whale-fishing.

Nimrod Furnace Company.   Box of minerals from Youngstown, Ohio.

Norton, John V.   Box of ancient pottery and other ethnologica from Peru.

Owen House, Washington, D. C.   Specimen of "oyster-fish," (*Batrachus tau.*)

Orvis, Charles F.   One "Orvis fishing-reel."

Otis, Colonel.   Skull and fossil wood from California.

Oudeslys, Charles L.   One bottle of asbestos-oil.

Ourley, J. B.   Box of flint hatchets and fossils from Ohio.

Pacific Guano Company, Wood's Hole, Mass.   Materials for making guano.

Palmer, Dr. E.   One box of ancient pottery; 2 boxes birds from Guadalupe; 7 boxes and 1 package ethnologica from California.

Palmer, F. W.   Stone beads from Brockport, N. Y.

Pardon, W. P.   Package of ethnological specimens from Maryland.

Parish, Grant.   Double egg of hen.

Parrott, R. D. H.   Box of "mineral wood."

Patterson, Holmes A.   Indian stone implements from Flint River, Miss.

Patterson, Dr. D. C.   Specimen of lignite found 65 feet below the surface, Washington, D. C.

Pease, Harper.   Collection of mollusca from Sandwich Islands.

Phillips, William.   Box of stone implements and specimens of natural history, alcoholic, from Georgia.

Phœnix Mines.   Box of minerals.

Pierce, E. G.   Piece of Sir William Pepperell's house, &c., in Kittery, Me.

Pierce, ———.   Small arrow-points from Maysville, Ky.

Pike, R. G.   Two young specimens of salmon (*Salmo quinnat*) from Branford, Conn.

Plummer, Sumner J.   See under *Dillingham, Joseph R.*

Poey, Prof. Felipe.   Specimen of *Sarothrodus amplexicollis* from Cuba.

Pomeroy, Mrs. Mary H.   Indian clothing from western plains.

Potter, Elihu H.   Albino eel (*Anguilla bostoniensis*) from Noank, Conn.

Powell, Samuel.   Stone ax; 2 cans of alcoholic fishes from Newport, R. I.

Powell, Maj. J. W., Washington, Interior Department.   Five boxes of fossils; skull of bison, (*Bison americanus;*) 10 boxes of ethnological specimens; 4 boxes of general collection.

Powers, Stephen.   Box of Indian implements from Susanville, Cal.; 3 boxes of Indian implements from Pyramid Lake, Nev.; 2 boxes ethnologica from Colorado.   See *Washington, D. C., Smithsonian Institution.*

Price, Henry M.   Specimens of amethystine quartz from Antioch, Va.

Prior, William, jr., & Co., Boston.   Specimens of haddock and hake.

Providence, R. I., Brown University, of.   Skin of file-fish (*Balistes vetula*) from Rhode Island.

Pulsifer, Sidney.   Three stone axes and 2 pieces of pottery (deposited) from Illinois.

Pybas, Ben. Box of stone implements and specimen of coal-plant from Alabama.

Quail, William. Two moths (*Samia cecropia*) from Pennsylvania.

Randle, Mrs. E. H. Box of Indian relics from Tennessee.

Rawson, Governor. Eleven Carib shell-chisels from Barbadoes.

Raymond Coal Company. Box of coal from Raymond, W. Va.

Renfrew, G. R., & Co., Quebec. Series of marketable furs from Labrador coast, moccasins, &c.; shark, (*Somniosus brevipinnis ;*) white porpoise, (*Delphinapterus catodon,*) from Labrador.

Reuss, Dr. A. Skulls of foxes (*Vulpes* sp.) and other mammals from Belleville, Ill.

Rhea, Maj. Alexander. Indian relics from Tennessee.

Ricksecker, E. Skin and egg of wren (*Catherpes mexicanus*) from Texas.

Ried, James H., M. D. Box of skulls and Ute arrows from Colorado.

Ridgway, C. W. Collections of bird-skins and living fox (*Vulpes*) from Mount Carmel, Ill.

Ridgway, Robert. Collection of vines from Illinois.

Robertson, Augusta. Fragment of fossil fern (?) from Arkansas.

Robertson, J. L. Specimen of mineral from Arkansas.

Robertson, W. S. Specimens of sediment of Arkansas River, Ark.

Robertson, Capt. Zephaniah. Sperm-whale's jaw from Congo River, Africa.

Roessler, F. E. Three boxes and one package ethnological material from Saint Louis, Mo.

Roney, C. J. Box of geological specimens from Illinois.

Ropes, E. E. Indian pottery from Florida.

Rudasilk, J. M. Specimen of mineral from Virginia.

Russel, Benj. Specimens of fishes, in alcohol, from Massachusetts.

Ryder, Stephen A. Seal (*Phoca vitulina*) in flesh from Princeton, Mass.

Sacramento, Cal., Agassiz Institute. Box of stone implements from California.

Salvin, Osbert. Box of birds and specimen bird-case from England.

Sanborn, J. K. Silurian fossils from Williamsport, Pa.

San Diego Cal., Academy of Sciences of. Photographs of Indians of San Diego; bird-skin; skin of badger, (*Taxidea americana ;*) and skull and ears of black-tailed deer, (*C. columbianus.*)

Sargent, Hon. A. A. Box of gold and silver ores from Sitka, Alaska.

Sarg, F. Specimen of Honduras turkey (*Meleagris ocellata*) from Coban.

Savoy, Louis. Specimen of petrified wood from Brightwood.

Scarborough, J. V. B. ·Collection of reptiles and fresh-water shells from Ohio.

Schayer Bros., Boston, Mass. Articles made from alligator-leather.

Schneck, J. Stone and iron implements, &c., from Ohio.

Schuermann, Carl W. Skin of barred owl (*Syrnium nebulosum*) from Virginia.

Schumacher, Paul. Fifty-one boxes of ethnological specimens from Santa Babara, Cal.

Scupham, J. R.   Specimens of spermophile (*Spermophilus harrissii*) and crawfish from California.

Seeds, O. H.   Skull of Comanche chief from Texas.

Sevey, J. A., Boston.   Collection illustrating the manufacture of whale-bone.

Shardlow, Joseph.   One box of carvings from American ivory and bone.

Shearer, J. S.   Specimen of aerolite from Forks of Solomon River.

Shepard, C. U.   Box of minerals from Massachusetts.

Shepard, E. W.   Indian relics from Poughquay, N. Y.

Sherman, J. M.   Specimen of mineral.

Shirley & Son.   Fish-hatching apparatus.

Shotwell, J. R.   One box of smelts, &c., from Raritan River, N. J.

Shute, J. G.   Stone sinker from Jamaica Plains.

Sibley, P. B.   Box of stone implements from Missouri.

Slagle, J. W.   Stone implements from South Carolina.

Slater, W. F.   Ammonite from Cow Island, Upper Missouri.

Slocum, George.   Specimen of billfish (*Euleptorhamphus longirostris* from Newport, R. I.

Smith, A. F.   Specimens of silver-ore supposed from Texas.

Smith, Rev. C. D.   Specimens of minerals from Macon County, N. C.

Smith, E. J.   Chain made from cherry and peach pits.

Smith, Edwin, U. S. Coast Survey.   Two Maori and one Moriori skulls from Chatham Islands, South Pacific.   See under *Washington.*

Snyder, Dr. J. F.   Box of stone disks; box of Indian implements from Illinois.

Southwick, J. M. K.   Models and samples of fishing-tackle, &c., used about Newport, R. I.

Spangler, George.   Arrow-heads and fossils from Madison, Ind., quartz-crystals from Warm Springs, Ark.; trilobites, fossil, and brachiopods from Indiana.

Sprague, Stephen.   Specimen of ore from Mason, Texas.

Spring, J. A., and *H. Buschman.*   Birds' nests and eggs; collection of plants; mutilated specimen of chaparral-cock (*Geococcyx californianus*) from Arizona.

Spur Mountain Iron Mining Company, Henry M. Walker, President.   Box of minerals.

Stanago, S. W.   Box of shells from Ohio.

Stanforth, Richard.   Specimens of catfish from Maryland.

Stanton, Clarence L.   Diminutive arrow-points; box of ethnological specimens from Maysville, Ky.

Steinberger, Col. A. B.   Specimen of Palolo mats, canoes, utensils for cooking, &c., from the Samoan Islands.

Stephens, F.   Skin of sparrow (*Coturniculus passerinus*) from Colorado Springs, Colo.

Sternberg, Charles W.   Eggs and birds' nests from Kansas; box of fossils from Nebraska.

Stevens, H. A.   Specimens of decoy ducks.

Stevens, D. W. Specimen of sucker (*Leptecheneis naucrateoides*) from Vineyard Haven, Mass.

Stevenson, James. Skin and skeleton of Little Chief hare, (*Lagomys princeps.*)

Stone, Livingston. (See under *Washington, U. S. Commission of Fish and Fisheries.*) Collection of fishes from California; two boxes of alcoholic fishes from McCloud River, California; can of alcoholic fishes from California; four packages of Indian implements from McCloud River Indians.

Stratton, Lorenzo. Box of ethnological specimens from Tennessee.

Strode, Stephen. Supposed silver-ore from Texas.

Summerhayes, Lieut., U. S. A. Scorpion from La Paz, Ariz.

Sutro, Adolph. Cast-iron model of "Sutro" tunnel.

Swan, J. G. Two boxes of Indian curiosities, Northwestern coast.

Sweeney, R. O. Box of alcoholic specimens.

Swift, E. E. Baleen of fin-back whale from Provincetown, Mass.

Taber, Frank. Two birds' nests from Ohio.

Taylor, Lewis H. Fresh-water fishes from Susquehanna River; one jar of brook-trout (*Salmo fontinalis*) from Luzerne County, Pa.

Thompson, John A. Box of stone disks from burial-mounds in Jersey County, Ill.

Thomson, John H. Arrow-head; specimens of yellow mackerel, (*Paratractus pisquetus;*) banded rudder-fish, (*Halatractus zonatus*) file-fish, (*Alutera cuspicauda*) &c.; whale-boat gear, from Massachusetts.

Throckmorton, S. R. Specimens of salmon from San Francisco Bay, Cal.

True and Sutton. Head of buffalo (*Bos americanus*) from Colorado.

Tune and Graham. Specimen of fish-hawk (*Pandion carolinensis*) from Fauquier County, Virginia.

Turner, Lucien M. Box of bird skins and eggs from Saint Michael's, Alaska.

Turner, Samuel. Specimen of mud pup, (*Menopoma alleghaniensis*) lampreys, and snakes from Mount Carmel, Ill.

Twitchill, R. W. Box of fossils from Indiana.

Underwood, William, & Sons. Box of canned meats.

Vance, Hon. Robert B. Leaves of plants from Macon, N. C.

Van Fleet, Walter. Skin of muskrat (*Fiber zibethicus*) from Watsontown, Pa.

Van Nostrand, J. Box of stone implements from Texas.

Velie, Dr. J. W. Stuffed specimen of curlew, (*Limosa hudsonica*) two specimens of white-fronted geese (*Anser gambelli*) from Chicago, Ill.

Waggaman, J. H. Mounted specimen of red-head duck (*Aythya americana*) from Washington, D. C.

Walker, Mrs. Dora H. Two boxes of fossils from Texas.

Walker, Dr. R. L. Package of arrow-heads and two living menopomas from Mansfield, Pa.

Wallace, Charles M. Package of supposed infusorial earth from Richmond, Va.

Wallace, John. Brazilian head-dress made of beetle-wings; head of black-tailed deer, (*Cariacus columbianus*) carcass of bird.

Wasson, John, surveyor-general, Arizona ; collection of minerals from Arizona; collection of iron ores from Arizona.

Webb, J. G. Two barrels of shells from Florida.

Webber, Mrs. F. P. Specimens of arrow-heads from Georgia.

Webber, Mrs. Mary C. Fossils from Alabama.

Webster, Colonel. Specimen of little blue heron (*Florida cærulea*) from Potomac River.

Weeks and Potter. Sample of ambergris from Indian Ocean.

Welfley, D. P. Virginia deer in flesh (*Cariacus virginianus*) from Cumberland, Md.

Wells, S. H. Dried potatoes from La Junta, N. Mex.

Welsher, H. W. One bottle of alcoholic fishes from Ferry Landing, Va.; one sturgeon (*Acipenser*) and four gar-fishes, (*Lepidosteus osseus.*)

Wendt, A. F. Box of minerals from New York.

› *Wesleyan University.* See under *Middletown, Conn.*

Wheeler, Lieut. Geo. M. Collection of skins and alcoholic collection of mammals; two boxes of fossils and minerals; eight hundred and ninety bird-skins, six nests, eleven eggs, seven hundred and sixty coleoptera, forty-three lots of hemiptera, one hundred and ninety-four hymenoptera, one hundred and forty-five lepidoptera; botanical collection of 1874; Indian blankets, quivers, &c.; six skins of gray fox (*Vulpes littoralis*) from Santa Cruz, Cal.; two boxes of type fossils.

Wesche, Charles E. Specimen of beetle from New Mexico.

Wetherby, A. G. Stone implements from Ohio.

White, Dr. C. A. Cast of fossil tooth from Iowa; fragment of the " great Iowa meteorite."

White, W. E. Nest and eggs from Mebanesville, N. C.

Whiteaves, J. S. Sixteen bottles of alcoholic fishes from Saint Lawrence River and Gulf; forty-five species of shells from Gulf of Saint Lawrence.

Whitman, G. P. Specimens of crevalle and crab; sea-mouse, (*Aphrodite*) from Massachusetts.

Whitney Armory. Two rifles and one shot-gun, breech-loading.

Wicks, George T. Fossil ore and (?) brown hematite.

Wiggans, John B. Steatite pyramid from Chula, Amelia County, Va.; unfinished stone implement from same place.

Williams, Haven & Co. Fur-seal skins from Patagonia.

Williamson, Hon. George, U. S. minister, Guatemala. Ethnological collection from Guatemala.

Wilson, A. D. Nest and four eggs of white-tailed ptarmigan (*Lagopus leucurus*) from Colorado. (Dr. Hayden's expedition.)

Wilson, Rev. C. W. Two copper beads from Wisconsin.

Woodforth, Philip R. Specimen of horns and hoofs of domesticated bovines.

Wooster, A. F. Specimen of marble from Connecticut; arrow-points, and old Continental newspapers and Continental sixty-five-dollar note, 1779; specimen of salamander (*Plethodon erythronotus*) from Connecticut.

Wright, J. W. A. Fossil fish from Wyoming Territory.

Yarrow, Dr. H. C. Collection of foreign shells; fossils and celt; collection of alcoholic fishes, reptiles, and insects.

Zoological Society of London. Fragment of "new marine animal" from Northwest coast United States.

Washington, D. C.:

Department of State. See under the name of *George Williamson, U. S. minister, Guatemala.*

Treasury Department, United States Coast Survey. See under the names of *A. W. Chase, W. H. Dall,* and *Edwin Smith.*

War Department:

United States Army. See under the names of *General M. C. Meigs, Col. A. G. Brackett, Capt. Charles Bendire, Capt. A. W. Corliss, Capt. James Gilliss, Lieuts. W. L. Carpenter, J. F. Huston,* and *George M. Wheeler.*

Surgeon-General's Office, United States Army Medical Museum, (Dr. G. A. Otis in charge.) Tonto Apache; medicine-stick; clay-pipe from Virginia; feathered bonnet of Cheyenne medicine-man from Kansas. See also under the names of *Drs. G. C. Byrne, E. McClellan, Elliott Coues, J. M. Laing,* and *George S. Moran, medical officers United States Army.*

Surveys west of the one hundredth meridian, Lieut. G. M. Wheeler in charge. General zoological collections made by *Drs. H. C. Yarrow, J. F. Rothrock,* and *Mr. H. W. Henshaw.*

Signal-Service U. S. Army. See under the name of *Sergeant Lucien M. Turner.*

Navy Department, U. S. A.:

U. S. Navy. See under the names of *Commander E. P. Lull, Lieut. B. Long Edes,* and *F. M. Gunnell, Medical Director U. S. N.;* also under *Passed Assistant Engineer G. W. Baird.*

Bureau of Navigation, Commodore Daniel Ammen. Specimens of ocean-bottom between San Francisco and the Sandwich Islands; dredgings by *United States Steamer Narragansett* in Gulf of California, *Commander George Dewey;* natural-history specimens from Pacific Ocean, *United States Steamer Tuscarora.* See also under names of *Drs. Kidder, Kershner, Coues, W. H. Jones, T. H. Streets,* and *Bransford.*

Interior Department, U. S. A.:

General Land-Office. See under the names of *Surveyors-General L. Hardenburgh* and *John Wasson.*

United States Geological Survey of the Territories, (Prof. F. V. Hayden in charge.) One stone; nine mammal-skins; ten skulls of mammals; two skins of birds from Colorado.

United States Commission of Fish and Fisheries, (*Prof. Spencer F. Baird, Commissioner.*) One hundred and fifty-four boxes of general zoological collections from Wood's Hole, Mass., and vicinity, by *Prof. A. E. Verrill, G. Brown Goode*, and *Tarleton H. Bean*; two large tank reptiles and fishes from Kinston, N. C.; specimen of redfish (*Sciænops ocellatus*) from North Carolina; collection of insects from Kinston, N. C.; two boxes of insects from Waukegan, Ill., and collection of fishes from Potomac River, by *James W. Milner*; three boxes collection of fishes from California, box of alcoholic specimens from McCloud River, Cal., and case of ethnological collections from California, by *Livingston Stone*; alcoholic fishes from Mississippi, by *Frederick Mather*; one bottle of natural-history specimens from Ferry Landing, Va., specimens of sturgeon and gar, (*Lepidosteus osseus*,) by *H. W. Welsher*; skeleton of black-fish, (*Globicephalus melas*;) box of fish from Wood's Hole, Mass.; baleen and chin of hump-back whale, specimen of young sea-salmon, (*Salmo salar*,) baleen of finback whale, conger-eel, box of fishes, invertebrates, &c., eight boxes of fresh fish, specimens of *Scomberesox* and *Pomolobus*, two skeletons of cow-fish, and skeleton *Grampus*, by *Vinal N. Edwards*; models of boats, &c.

Survey of the Colorado, (*Maj. J. W. Powell in charge.*) Five boxes of fossils; skull of bison, (*Bison americanus*;) ten boxes of ethnological specimens; four boxes of general collection.

Department of Agriculture, (*Hon. Frederick Watts, Commissioner.*) Cocoons, &c., of B. mori; 200 living fire-flies, *Photinus* (*Elliperlampis*) pyralis, for introduction into Bermuda, &c.

STATISTICS OF LITERARY AND SCIENTIFIC EXCHANGES IN 1875.

BOXES SENT ABROAD.

Agent and country.	No. of boxes.	Cubic feet.	Weight in pounds.
To Royal Swedish Academy of Sciences, Stockholm............	4	30	900
To Royal Danish Society of Copenhagen......................	3	21	600
To Royal University of Norway, Christiana....................	2	15	400
To L. Watkins & Co., St. Petersburg, Russia..................	9	65	1,800
To Fr. Müller, Amsterdam, for Belgium......................	6	45	1,200
To Prof. von Baumhauer, Bureau Scientifique Néerlandais, Harlem.	4	30	900
To Dr. Felix Flügel, Leipzic:			
Germany, Austria, Switzerland, and Greece......	46	325	10,000
To Gustave Bossange, Paris.................................	18	130	3,600
To U. Hoepli, Reale Istituto Lombardi di Scienze e Lettere, Milano.	8	60	1,600
To William Wesley, London:			
Great Britain, British possessions in Asia, &c...............	43	325	8,600
To Academia Real das Sciencas, Lisbon.......................	2	15	400
To Real Academia de Ciencias de Madrid.....................	2	15	400
To Cuba, Real Universidad de la Habana.....................	1	7	200
To Chili, University......................................	2	14	400
To Mexico, Sociedad Mexicana de Geografia y Estadisca......	1	7	200
To Prof. Burmeister, Buenos Ayres..........................	1	7	200
To Georgetown, British Guiana	1	5	150
To Peru..	1	7	200
	154	1123	31,800
To Foreign governments...................................	54	380	13,500
	208	1503	45,300

Besides these, 1 box was sent to Turkey by favor of the American Board of Commissioners for Foreign Missions in Boston, and smaller boxes to Nicaragua, Costa Rica, Guatemala, Bogota, Kingston, (Jamaica,) Trinidad, (Port of Spain,) St. Pierre, Martinique, Cape Town, Natal, St. Helena.

Government exchanges.

	Boxes.
To Government of Ontario, Toronto, Canada	2
To Parliamentary Library, Ottawa, Canada	1
To France, Portugal, Sweden, Turkey, set of 6 boxes	24
To Mexico, Brazil, Argentine Republic, set of 6 boxes each	18
To Belgium and Chili, 4 boxes each	8
To Japan	1
Total......	54

PACKAGES RECEIVED BY THE SMITHSONIAN INSTITUTION FROM EUROPE, ETC., IN 1875, FOR DISTRIBUTION IN AMERICA.

CALIFORNIA.

Oakland:
University of California............ 1

Sacramento:
California Institution............... 1
Geological Survey of California...... 7
Sacramento Agricultural Society..... 1
State Library....................... 3

San Francisco:
California Academy of Natural Sciences 79
Historical Society.................. 1
Mayor of the City of San Francisco.. 1
Mercantile Library Association...... 2

Stockton:
California Insane Asylum............ 1

CONNECTICUT.

Hartford:
Connecticut State Board of Agriculture 1
Young Men's Institute............... 2

New Haven:
American Journal of Science and Arts 54
American Oriental Society........... 26
Connecticut Academy of Arts and Sciences............................... 107
Sheffield Scientific School.......... 1
Yale College........................ 11
Yale College Observatory............ 8
Young Men's Christian Association... 1
Young Men's Christian Association, (German)............................ 1

DISTRICT OF COLUMBIA.

Georgetown:
Georgetown College.................. 6

Washington:
Board of Indian Commissioners...... 1
Bureau of Education................. 7
Bureau of Navigation................ 1
Bureau of Ordnance and Hydrography 1
Bureau of Statistics................ 20
Census Bureau....................... 9
Chief of Engineers.................. 2
Coast Survey........................ 54
Columbian College................... 1
Commissioners of the District of Columbia 1
Department of Agriculture........... 105
Engineer Department................. 1
General Land-Office................. 4
Geological Survey of the Territories. 44
Hydrographic Office................. 6
Interior Department 1
Library of Congress 29
Medical Society of the District of Columbia.............................. 1
National Academy of Science......... 47
Nautical Almanac.................... 3

DISTRICT COLUMBIA—Continued.

Washington:
National Deaf-Mute College......... 1
Naval Observatory................... 58
Navy Department..................... 2
Ordnance Bureau..................... 1
Patent-Office....................... 134
Public schools...................... 1
Signal Office....................... 30
State Department.................... 3
Surgeon-General's Office............ 127
Swedish and Norwegian Legation.... 1
Treasury Department................. 2
War Department...................... 6
Young Men's Christian Association... 1

ILLINOIS.

Chicago:
Botanical Garden.................... 1
Chicago Academy of Science......... 63
Chicago Historical Society.......... 1
Chicago Public Library.............. 3
Dearborn Observatory................ 4
Mayor of the City of Chicago........ 1
Young Men's Association Library.... 1

Jacksonville:
Illinois State Hospital for Insane.... 1

Peoria:
Mercantile Library.................. 1

Rantoul:
Rantoul Literary Society............ 2

INDIANA.

Indianapolis:
Geological Survey of Indiana........ 16
Indiana Institution for the Blind 2
State Library....................... 1

IOWA.

Des Moines:
State Library....................... 3

Iowa City:
Geological Survey of Iowa........... 1
Iowa State University 20
Laboratory of Physical Science...... 1

KANSAS.

Leavenworth City:
Young Men's Christian Association... 1

Topeka:
Kansas Academy of Science.......... 1

KENTUCKY.

Cambridge:
College............................. 1

Frankfort:
Geological Survey of Kentucky...... 1

Lexington:
Agricultural College................ 1
Young Men's Christian Association... 1

Packages received by the Smithsonian Institution, &c.—Continued.

KENTUCKY—Continued.	No.
Louisville:	
Richmond and Louisville Medical Journal	1

LOUISIANA.

New Orleans:	
Mayor of the City of New Orleans	1
New Orleans Academy of Natural Sciences	42
State Library	7
University of Louisiana	1

MAINE.

Augusta:	
State Library	1
Brunswick:	
Bowdoin College	3
Historical Society of Maine	1
Portland:	
Commissioner of Fisheries	2
Portland Society of Natural History	40
Waterville:	
Colby University	1

MARYLAND.

Annapolis:	
State Library	1
United States Naval Academy	1
Baltimore:	
Maryland Historical Society	2
Mayor of the city of Baltimore	1
Mercantile Library	2
Peabody Institute	4
Young Men's Christian Association	1

MASSACHUSETTS.

Amherst:	
Agricultural College	1
Amherst College	2
Geological Survey of Massachusetts	1
Boston:	
American Academy of Arts and Sciences	172
American Social Science Association	1
American Statistical Association	11
Board of Agriculture	4
Board of Education	2
Board of State Charities	2
Boston Art Club	1
Boston Athenæum	1
Boston Hospital Library	1
Boston Medical and Surgical Journal	7
Boston Society of Natural History	240
Bowditch Library	2
Gynæcological Society	1
Massachusetts Historical Society	3
Mayor of the City of Boston	1
Mercantile Library Association	1
Perkins Institution for the Blind	1
Prison Discipline Society	1
Public Library	16
State Library	9
Young Men's Christian Association	1

MASSACHUSETTS—Continued.	No.
Cambridge:	
Cambridge Entomological Club	1
Harvard College	26
Harvard College Observatory	31
Harvard College Herbarium	4
Museum of Comparative Zoölogy	111
Jamaica Plain:	
Bussey Institution	7
Northampton:	
State Lunatic Hospital	1
Salem:	
American Association for the Advancement of Science	41
American Naturalist	2
Essex Institute	94
North Church and Society	1
Peabody Academy of Sciences	72
Worcester:	
American Antiquarian Society	14

MICHIGAN.

Ann Arbor:	
Observatory	6
University of Michigan	1
Detroit:	
Michigan State Agricultural Society	7
Museum	1
Public Library	1
Lansing:	
Agricultural College	1
Michigan State Board of Health	1
State Library	1

MINNESOTA.

Minneapolis:	
Minneapolis Academy of Natural Sciences	6
Saint Paul:	
Minnesota Historical Society	8
State Hospital for Insane	1

MISSOURI.

Jefferson City:	
Governor of the State of Missouri	1
Saint Louis:	
Geological Survey of Missouri	20
Mayor of the City of Saint Louis	1
Public School Library	1
Saint Louis Academy of Sciences	117
State Board of Agriculture	1
University of Saint Louis	3

NEBRASKA.

Omaha:	
Young Men's Christian Association	2

NEW HAMPSHIRE.

Concord:	
New Hampshire Asylum for the Insane	1
New Hampshire Historical Society	1

Packages received by the Smithsonian Institution, &c.—Continued.

NEW HAMPSHIRE—Continued.	No.
Concord :	
State Prison	1
Young Men's Christian Association	1
Hanover :	
Dartmouth College	3
Observatory of Dartmouth College	1
Manchester :	
City Library	1

NEW JERSEY.

New Brunswick :	
Geological Survey of New Jersey	2
Princeton :	
College of New Jersey	3
Halstead Observatory	1

NEW YORK.

Albany :	
Albany Institute	22
Dudley Observatory	23
New York State Agricultural Society	19
New York State Library	41
New York State Museum of Natural History	9
New York State University	6
Young Men's Christian Association	1
Brooklyn :	
Mayor of the City of Brooklyn	1
Mercantile Library Association	1
Young Men's Christian Association	1
Buffalo :	
Buffalo Society of Natural Sciences	31
Medical and Surgical Journal	1
Young Men's Christian Association	1
Clinton :	
Hamilton College Observatory	3
Hoboken :	
Stevens Institute of Technology	4
Ithaca :	
Cornell University	2
New York :	
American Bible Society	1
American Chemist	4
American Geographical and Statistical Society	54
American Institute	25
American Museum of Natural History	10
American Society of Civil Engineers	13
Anthropological Institute of New York	5
Apprentices' Library	1
Astor Library	10
Board of Health	2
Board of Missions of the Protestant Episcopal Church	1
Chamber of Commerce	3
Columbia College	2
Cooper Institute	1
Dermatological Society	1
Engineering and Mining Journal	17
International Review	1

NEW YORK—Continued.	No.
New York :	
Institute for the Blind	1
Lyceum of Natural History	105
Manufacturer and Builder	8
Mayor of the City of New York	1
Medical Journal	1
Mercantile Library	3
Metropolitan Museum of Art	2
Microscopical Society	1
Numismatic and Archæological Society	1
New York Academy of Medicine	2
New Yorker Handels-Zeitung	1
New York Herald	1
New York Historical Society	1
New York Hungarian Society	1
Observatory, Central Park	3
Sanitarian	12
School of Mines	6
Superintendent of Insurance Department	3
Swedish and Norwegian Consulate	1
Torrey Botanical Club	1
United States Sanitary Commission	7
University	6
Young Men's Christian Association	1
Young Men's Christian Association, (German)	1
Poughkeepsie :	
Vassar College	1
Sing Sing :	
State Lunatic Asylum	1
State Prison	1
Ward's Island :	
Emigrants' Refuge and Hospital	1
West Point :	
President of the Committee of Engineers	1
Willard :	
Willard Asylum for Insane	1

OHIO.

Cincinnati :	
Astronomical Observatory	26
Historical and Philosophical Society	1
Longview Asylum for Insane	1
Mayor of the City of Cincinnati	1
Medical College of Ohio	1
Mercantile Library	2
Ohio Mechanics' Institute	1
Public Library	3
Columbus :	
Geological Survey of Ohio	4
Ohio State Board of Agriculture	59
State Library	13
North Bend :	
Ohio State Horticultural Society	1

PENNSYLVANIA.

Alleghany :	
Alleghany Observatory	4

Packages received by the Smithsonian Institution, &c.—Continued.

PENNSYLVANIA—Continued.   No.

Danville:
State Hospital for the Insane......... 1
Easton:
American Institute of Mining Engi-
neers................................. 1
Lafayette College..................... 1
Harrisburgh:
State Library......................... 2
State Lunatic Hospital............ 1
Philadelphia:
Academy of Natural Sciences......... 194
Agricultural Society of Philadelphia. 1
American Entomological Society 12
American Institute of Architects 3
American Journal of Conchology.... 2
American Pharmaceutical Association 25
American Philosophical Society...... 136
Board of Public Education........... 4
Central High School 1
College of Physicians................. 1
Eastern State Penitentiary........... 1
Franklin Institute.................... 29
Girard College....................... 1
Historical Society..................... 6
Jefferson Medical College 1
Library Company...................... 2
Mayor of the City of Philadelphia.... 1
Medical Society of Pennsylvania..... 1
Medical Times........................ 13
Pennsylvania Hospital Library....... 1
Society for Alleviating the Miseries of
Public Prisons...................... 1
University of Pennsylvania.......... 1
Wagner Free Institute of Science.... 15
Zoölogical Society 2
Pittsburgh:
Western Penitentiary................. 1

RHODE ISLAND.

Providence:
Athenæum 1
Brown University..................... 2
Rhode Island Historical Society 2

SOUTH CAROLINA.

Charleston:
Charleston Library Society.......... 2
Elliott Society of Natural History... 7
Columbia:
University of South Carolina........ 1

TEXAS.

Austin:
State Lunatic Asylum................. 1
Chappell Hill:
Soulé University...................... 3

VERMONT.
Bristol:
Orleans County Society of Natural
Science............................. 24

VERMONT—Continued.   No.

Burlington:
University of Vermont................ 1
Montpelier:
State Library......................... 2
Young Men's Christian Association... 1

VIRGINIA.

Charlottesville:
University of Virginia 4
Lynchburgh:
Young Men's Christian Association... 1
Richmond:
State Library......................... 2
Young Men's Christian Association... 1
Williamsburgh:
Eastern Lunatic Asylum............. 2

WISCONSIN.

Janesville:
Wisconsin Institution for the Blind.. 1
Madison:
State Board of Agriculture.......... 1
Wisconsin Academy of Sciences, Arts,
and Letters........................ 14
Wisconsin State Agricultural Society. 32
Young Men's Christian Association... 1
Milwaukee:
Young Men's Christian Association... 1
Neenah:
Scandinavian Library Association.... 1
Oshkosh:
Northern Hospital for the Insane..... 1

BRITISH AMERICA.

Charlottetown, Prince Edward Island:
Lunatic Asylum....................... 1
Fredericton, New Brunswick:
Geological Survey of New Brunswick. 2
Halifax, Nova Scotia:
Nova Scotian Institute of Natural Sci-
ences.............................. 4
Kingston, Ontario:
Botanical Society of Canada......... 2
Queen's College...................... 1
London, Ontario:
London Asylum for Insane.......... 1
Montreal, Quebec:
Geological Survey of Canada........ 5
McGill College 1
Meteorological Observatory.......... 1
Natural History Society............. 27
Quebec, Quebec:
Astronomical Observatory........... 3
Literary and Historical Society...... 11
Ottawa, Ontario:
Library of Parliament................ 3

Packages received by the Smithsonian Institution, &c.—Continued.

BRITISH AMERICA—Continued.	No.	INDIVIDUALS—Continued.	No.
St. John's, New Brunswick:		Coffin, Prof. J. H. C	3
Natural History Society	8	Colvin, V	1
St. John's, Newfoundland:		Cope, Prof. E. D	9
Geological Survey of Newfoundland	2	Coues, Dr. E	10
Toronto, Ontario:		Cox, E. T	5
Canadian Entomological Society	1	Cummings, M	1
Canadian Institute	10	Curtis, Dr	2
House of Assembly	1	Da Costa, Dr	1
Literary and Historical Society	1	Dall, W. H	24
Magnetical and Meteorological Obser-		Dana, Prof. J. D	32
vatory	9	Davies, H. C	1
Toronto Globe	1	Davis, Miss J. N	1
University of Toronto	4	Dawson, Prof. J. W	01
		Delaney, J	1
INDIVIDUALS.		Dike, C	1
		Dobson, James	1
Abbe, Dr. C	7	Dobson, John	1
Agassiz, Prof. A	18	Dodge, C. R	1
Agnew, Dr. E. A	1	Dow, Capt. J. M	5
Allen, H	1	Dowler, B	1
Allen, J. A	2	Doyle, Lieut.-Gen. Sir H	4
Althorf, Dr. H	1	Draper, Dr. H	8
Alvord, B	1	Dutton, Capt. C. E	4
Ames, Miss M. E. Pulsifer	2	Eads, J. B	1
Angerer, A. W	4	Eaton, Prof. D. C	2
Anthony, J. C	1	Eaton, Hon. J	1
Appleton & Co	1	Eastman, Prof. J. R	1
Atlee, Dr. W. D	1	Edwards, W. H	2
Austin, C. F	1	Egleston, Prof. T	1
Baird, Prof. S. F	81	Elliott, D. G	4
Ballard, J	2	Elliot, E. B	1
Bancroft, Hon. G	1	Elliott, H. W	1
Barnard, H	1	Ellis, F. B	1
Barnes, Surgeon-General J. K	1	Emerson, Prof. B	1
Barnes, Hon. W	1	Emmet, Dr	1
Barrick, Dr	1	Endlich, Dr. F. M	1
Bartlett, Hon. J. R	1	Engelman, Dr. G	3
Bebb, M. S	2	Evans, Prof. E. P	1
Bell, R	1	Fay, S	1
Bessels, Dr. E	6	Ferrel, W	4
Bethune, Rev. C. J. S	1	Fisher, Dr. G. J	1
Billings E	2	Fiss, G. W	1
Billings, Dr. J. S	1	Foreman, H. L	1
Binney W. G	2	Gale, Dr. L. D	1
Bland, T	2	Gardner, Prof. J. F	1
Bliss, R	1	Gibbons, Dr. W. P	1
Blodget, L	1	Gill, Dr. T	11
Boardman, G. A	1	Gnauvold, Dr	1
Boehmer, G. H	1	Goode, G. B	1
Bolander, H. A	1	Gray, Prof. A	25
Broadhead, G. C	3	Greene, Rev. E. L	3
Brennan, S. A. L	1	Gross, Dr. S. D	2
Brewer, Dr. T. M	2	Grote, A. B	1
Brewer, Miss C. M	1	Guyot, Prof. A	9
Brewster, Mrs. J	1	Hagen, Prof. H	2
Brown, A. D	1	Hall, Prof. A	3
Brown, J. C	1	Hall, Dr. C	1
Brown, S. G	4	Hall, Prof. J	13
Brush, Prof. G. J	2	Hamilton, Dr. F. H	1
Bucknell, R. E., Lieut	2	Hammond, Dr. W. A	2
Canby, W. M	2	Harding, C. L	1
Carpenter, P. P	1	Harding, E	1
Chandler, Dr	1	Harding, G. W	1
Chickering, Prof. J. W	1	Harkness, Prof	1
Clift, H. A	1	Harper & Brothers	2

Packages received by the Smithsonian Institution, &c.—Continued.

INDIVIDUALS—Continued.	No.	INDIVIDUALS—Continued.	No.
Hart, Prof. J. M.	1	Mitchell, Dr. S. Weir	1
Hawkins, R. C.	1	Morgan, W	1
Hayden, Dr. F. V	97	Morris, Prof. G. S	1
Hedrick, Dr. S	1	Munn, A	1
Henry, Prof. J	27	Myer, Brevet Brig. Gen. A. J	16
Henry, Dr. M. H	1	Newberry, Dr. J. S	1
Higgins, D. F	1	Newcomb, Dr	1
Higgins, E. S	1	Newcomb, Prof. S	10
Hilgard, Dr. E. W	1	Newton, H. A	4
Hilgard, Prof. J. E	2	Oliphant, L	1
Hill, G. W	1	Olmstead, Rev. L	1
Hinrichs, Prof. G	13	Osborne, J. W	1
Hettinger, J. W	1	Packard, Dr. A. S	6
Hitz, J	2	Palmer, Dr. E	1
Hodges, Dr	1	Palmer, J	1
Hough, Dr. F	1	Pancoast, Dr. W. H	1
Holden, Prof. E. S	3	Parker, Dr. P	1
Homans, Sheppard	1	Patterson, T. W	1
Hoppin, Prof. J. M	1	Pearson, J	1
Horn, Dr. G. H	1	Peirce, Prof. B	3
Horn, J	1	Peters, Prof. C. H. F	6
Hough, F. B	1	Pettersen, F	1
Humphreys, Gen. A. A	3	Philbrick, J	1
Hunt, Dr. Sterry	2	Phillips, Dr. W. A	1
Hyatt, Prof. A	2	Poole, H. S	1
Jackson, Lieut. H	1	Poole, W. F	1
Jarvis, Dr. E	38	Pourlier, Dr.	1
Jewett, Col. E	2	Powell, J. W	1
Kennedy, J. C. G	1	Prime, T	1
King, Clarence	3	Putnam, Prof. F. W	4
Kingston, G. T	4	Riley, C. V	2
Knapp, Dr. H	1	Rittler, Dr. J	1
Krout, A. F. K	7	Roberts, G	2
Koistendahl, Rev. C	2	Ridgway, Robert	8
Langley, Prof	1	Robinson, R. W	1
Lawrence, G. N	3	Rogers, W. A	1
Lawson, Prof. E	1	Rosenthal, A	1
Lea, Isaac	15	Ross, A. M	1
Le Conte, Dr. J. L	7	Ruggles, S. B	1
Lee, Admiral S. P	1	Rutherford, L. M	4
Lee, Capt. T. J	1	Safford, T. H	2
Lees, J. S	1	St. John, O	1
Leidy, Prof. J	8	Salisbury, Prof. E. E	2
Lesley, Prof. J. P	2	Sargent, Prof	1
Lesquereux, Prof. L	9	Sayre, Dr. L	1
Lewis, A	1	Schaff, P	1
Loomis, Prof. E	10	Schott, Dr. A	1
Lovering, Prof. J	5	Schott, Prof. C. A	2
Lyman, B. S	8	Schuster, M	3
Lyman, T	4	Scudder, S. H	1
McAlpine, M	3	Seaman, W. H	1
McLean, F. P	1	Senborn, Baron	1
McMaster, A	1	Selwyn, A. R. C	2
McMurtrie, W	1	Shepard, Prof. C. V	1
Marcou, Prof. J	13	Silliman, Prof. B	12
Marsh, Prof. F. A	3	Sims, Dr. M	1
Marsh, Prof. O. C	8	Slater, H. N	2
Mason, Prof. O. T	1	Smith, Alex	2
Matile, Prof. G. A	1	Smith, Prof. Hamilton L	6
Matthew, G. F	1	Smith, Prof. S. I	1
Meek, Prof F. B	24	Snow, Dr. E. M	5
Meigs, Dr. J. A	3	Spofford, A. R	1
Meigs, Gen. M. C	1	Squier, E. G	4
Milner, J. W	2	Stirling, Prof. C	1
Mitchell, Miss M	2	Stone, Prof. O	1

Packages received by the Smithsonian Institution, &c.—Continued.

INDIVIDUALS—Continued.	No.	INDIVIDUALS—Continued.	No.
Strong, Hon. W	1	Wheeler, Prof	1
Taft, R. E	2	White, Dr. C. A	12
Taylor, Dr. I	1	White, Lieut. H. C	1
Taylor, Dr. R. W	1	Whitney, Prof. J. D	7
Thomas, Prof. Cyrus	2	Whitney, Prof. W. D	15
Thomson, J. H	3	Wilkes, Admiral C	1
Tietze, Dr. E	2	Wilson, D	1
Toner, Dr. J. M	1	Winlock, Prof. J	1
Tryon, G. W	3	Wood, Dr. H. C	1
Tuckerman, Prof. E	9	Woodward, Dr. J. J	2
Uhler, Dr. P. R	1	Woodworth, Dr. J. M	1
Vasey, G	1	Worthen, A. H	1
Verrill, Prof. A. E	5	Wylie, W	1
Watson, Prof. J. C	2	Wyman, Commodore R. H	1
Watson, S	1	Yates, L. G	1
Weeden, W. B	2	Yarrow, Dr. H. C	8
Westermann, B	1	Young, Prof. C. A	4
Weston, H. C	1	Young, C. B	10
Wheeler, Lieut. G. M	5		

RECAPITULATION.

Total addresses of institutions	329
Total addresses of individuals	281
	610
Total number of parcels to institutions	3,619
Total number of parcels to individuals	1,042
	4,661

JOURNAL OF PROCEEDINGS OF THE BOARD OF REGENTS OF THE SMITHSONIAN INSTITUTION.

WASHINGTON, D. C., *January* 19, 1876.

In accordance with a resolution of the Board of Regents of the Smithsonian Institution, fixing the time of the beginning of their annual meeting on the third Wednesday in January of each year, the Board met to-day, at 7 o'clock p. m.

Present, Chief-Justice Waite, Chancellor of the Institution; Hon. T. W. Ferry, acting Vice-President of the United States; Hon. J. W. Stevenson, Hon. A. A. Sargent, Hon. H. Clymer, Hon. B. H. Hill, Hon. G. W. McCrary, Rev. Dr. John Maclean, Hon. Peter Parker, Hon. George Bancroft, and Professor Henry, the Secretary.

The Chancellor took the chair.

The Secretary presented the following communication:

FORTY-FOURTH CONGRESS, FIRST SESSION.

CONGRESS OF THE UNITED STATES,
In the House of Representatives, December 14, 1875.

The Speaker appointed the following-named members Regents of the Smithsonian Institution on the part of the House:

Mr. Hiester Clymer, of Pennsylvania.
Mr. Benjamin H. Hill, of Georgia.
Mr. George W. McCrary, of Iowa.

Attest: GEO. M. ADAMS, *Clerk.*

A letter was read from Hon. H. Hamlin, stating that he was unavoidably detained from attendance at this meeting.

The Secretary stated that he had the painful duty to announce the death, since the last session of the Board, of the Hon. Henry Wilson, Vice-President of the United States.

On motion of Dr. Parker, it was

Resolved, That a committee of three be appointed to prepare resolutions expressing the sentiments of the Board in regard to the death of Hon. Henry Wilson.

The Chancellor appointed Hon. Dr. Parker, Hon. T. W. Ferry, and Hon. J. W. Stevenson.

The Secretary presented a general exhibit of the condition of the fund, and the receipts and expenditures for the year 1875; which was referred to the Executive Committee.

Dr. Parker, from the Executive Committee, stated that, in order to save time, the committee had already examined all the vouchers and accounts of the Institution and of the National Museum, with the exception of eleven, which had been paid since the first of January, and was prepared to make a partial report, and that a full report would be made at the next meeting. He accordingly presented a statement of the receipts and expenditures, of the accounts examined, and a history of the funds, reserving until the next meeting the remainder of the report.

The Secretary gave an account of the method of keeping the accounts, drawing checks, &c., and showed the necessity of making up the annual statements of receipts and expenditures to include the semi-annual interest due on the 1st of January, but which this year had not been received from the Treasury Department until the 16th of January.

The Secretary also presented, for the information of the new members, a general account of the operations of the Institution, and the plans which had been adopted to carry out the will of Smithson " to increase and diffuse knowledge among men."

The Board then adjourned to meet on Wednesday, 26th January, at 7 o'clock.

WASHINGTON, D. C., *January* 26, 1876.

A meeting of the Board of Regents was held this day, at 7 o'clock p. m., in the Regent's room of the Smithsonian Institution.

Present, Chief Justice Waite, Chancellor of the Institution; Hon. T. W. Ferry, acting Vice-President of the United States; Hon. H. Hamlin, Hon. A. A. Sargent, Hon. H. Clymer, Hon. B. H. Hill, Hon. Peter Parker, Hon. George Bancroft, Professor Asa Gray, Professor Henry Coppée, and the Secretary, Professor Henry.

The minutes of the last meeting were read and approved.

Excuses for non-attendance were presented from Hon. J. W. Stevenson, Hon. G. W. McCrary, and Professor J. D. Dana.

Dr. Parker, from the special committee to prepare resolutions on the death of the late Vice-President, Hon. Henry Wilson, presented the following report and resolutions, which, he stated, had the approval of all the members of the committee :

Since the last annual meeting of the Board of Regents of the Smithsonian Institution, HENRY WILSON, Vice-President of the United States, and an honored member of the Regency, having departed this life, the Board deem it suitable that a just tribute to his memory and worth be entered upon the records of the Institution : Therefore,

Resolved, That among the distinguished men of the first century of our national existence who have been prominent for patriotism, practical wisdom, statemanship and high moral and Christian character, impartial history will assign Henry Wilson a distinguished rank ; and as a representative man of the class of " *self-made men*" to which the verdict of mankind assigns exalted positions, the late Vice-President of the United States will long be remembered and highly appreciated by posterity.

Resolved, That the Secretary cause a copy of these resolutions to be transmitted to the relatives of the deceased.

Dr. Parker then made the following remarks:

Mr. Chancellor: Fitting encomiums upon the late Vice-President have already been pronounced, both in the Senate and House of Representatives of the United States, and, so far as I am informed, with an unanimity of appreciation, irrespective of all lines of demarkation, truly remarkable; and the pen and the press, not only in this but also in every civilized country, will set forth his just merits in appropriate panegyric. Besides, this is neither the place nor the occasion for extended eulogy, yet I desire brief indulgence.

The late Vice-President was my personal friend, and the proximity of our summer residences facilitated the exchange of social and friendly intercourse. It was my privilege also to see him in his last illness.

The prominent characteristics of Mr. Wilson, his humble origin, indigence, limited means of early education, the resolute determination by which he surmounted difficulties and rose to great distinction; his success in the attainment of lofty aspirations, even surpassing some of his contemporaries who had the greater advantages of classical and professional learning, are too well known to require repetition.

I wish, however, to recall very concisely only two of his distinguishing traits.

As a means to an end, Mr. Wilson was emulous of high positions that he might render it promotive of the best interests of the country, and of all classes composing it, especially the poor and the enslaved.

Whilst sincere in his practice and advocacy of *temperance,* in his denunciation of *slavery,* and his expressions of sympathy for the *laborer,* he had the sagacity to use these as means to the attainment of the coveted positions of high office and national influence. He was emulous also of distinguished place not only for its utility in the present, but still more so in reference to the future. I remember well his emphatic remark when the intelligence was received of the death of the eminent historian Prescott: "*I had rather live, as Prescott will live, in history, than be President of the United States.*"

Here may be found, I think, the predominating influence that urged him on in the completion of his historical work; with an all-absorbing devotion that far exceeded his physical and mental strength, and but for which, humanly speaking, he might be with us still.

The other prominent characteristic to which I wish simply to advert is, in his later years, his truly religious life. No one intimately acquainted with Mr. Wilson subsequently to his public profession of religion can doubt the genuineness of his Christian faith.

The hymn which he rose from his sick-pillow to mark at three o'clock in the morning, only a few hours before breathing his last, as though preadmonished his end had come, entitled " *The Christian and his echo*," may be regarded as a true exponent of his religious character, and as his last legacy to the country and the world—

" *True faith producing love to God and man.*"

The resolutions submitted by the committee were then adopted unanimously by a rising vote.

Dr. Parker, in behalf of the Executive Committee, presented the annual report of the receipts, expenditures, estimates, &c.; which, on motion of Mr. Sargent, was adopted.

The Secretary presented his annual report of the operations of the Institution for the year 1875; which was read, and various suggestions contained in it were discussed at some length by the members of the Board.

On motion of Dr. Gray, it was

Resolved, That a special committee of three be appointed to take into consideration the connection of the Smithsonian Institution and the National Museum, and to recommend such action as may be thought proper in relation to the matter.

The Chancellor appointed Messrs. Gray, Clymer, and Sargent as the committee.

The report of the Secretary as to what the Smithsonian Institution was doing and had done in relation to the Centennial Exhibition in Philadelphia was read.

On motion of Mr. Hamlin, it was

Resolved, That the annual report of the Secretary be accepted, and be transmitted to Congress, as usual.

On motion of Mr. Sargent, it was

Resolved, That the salary of the chief clerk of the Institution be twenty-five hundred dollars per annum, commencing with the present year.

On motion of Mr. Clymer, it was

Resolved, That the Secretary be authorized to procure a carriage for the use of the Institution, for a sum not to exceed four hundred dollars.

The Board then adjourned to meet at the call of the Secretary.

REPORT OF THE EXECUTIVE COMMITTEE.

The executive committee of the Board of Regents respectfully submit the following report in relation to the funds of the Institution, the appropriations by Congress for the support of the National Museum, the receipts and expenditures for both of these departments for the year 1875, and the estimates for the year 1876:

FINANCES.

Statement of the condition of the funds at the beginning of the year 1876.

The amount originally received as the bequest of James Smithson, of England, deposited in the Treasury of the United States in accordance with the act of Congress of August 10, 1846	$515,169 00
The residuary legacy of Smithson, received in 1865, deposited in the Treasury of the United States, in accordance with the act of Congress of February 8, 1867	26,210 63
Total bequest of Smithson	541,379 63
Amount deposited in the Treasury of the United States, as authorized by act of Congress of February 8, 1867, derived from savings of income and increase in value of investments	108,620 37
Amount received as the bequest of James Hamilton, of Carlisle, Pa., February 24, 1874	1,000 00
Total permanent Smithson fund in the Treasury of the United States, bearing interest at 6 per cent., payable semi-annually in gold	651,000 00
In addition to the above there remains of the extra fund from savings, &c., in Virginia bonds and certificates, viz: consolidated bonds, $58,700; deferred certificates, $29,375.07; fractional certificate, $50.13; total, $88,125.20, now valued at	42,000 00
Cash balance in the United States Treasury at the beginning of the year 1876, for current expenses	20,555 82
Amount due from First National Bank, $2,056.22, (value unknown)	
Total Smithson funds 20th January, 1876	713,555 82

103

Statement of the receipts and expenditures during 1875:

RECEIPTS.

Interest on $650,000 from the United States, 6 per cent., gold	$39,000 00
Premium on above June 30, 1875, at $116\frac{1}{16}$, $3,107.81; and January 1, 1876, at $112\frac{13}{16}$, $2,474.07, (less commission)..	5,581 88
Interest on Virginia bonds, coupons sold June 14 and December 31, 1875.....................................	4,750 11
Dividend from First National Bank, 10 per cent., May 5, 1875, $822.48; and 15 per cent., December 27, 1875, $1,233.73...	2,056 21
Amount..	51,388 20

EXPENDITURES.

Total expenditure from the Smithson income in 1875.....	46,809 98
Balance unexpended of the annual income, which is included in the cash balance in the Treasury, ($20,555.82)..	4,578 22

HAMILTON BEQUEST.

By the will of the late James Hamilton, of Carlisle, Pa., the sum of one thousand dollars was left to the Institution, the interest of which was to be expended biennially for the advance of knowledge. This bequest was received on the 24th of February, 1874, from the executors of Mr. Hamilton, and to secure its safe investment the money was immediately deposited by Professor Henry in the Treasury of the United States, (see Smithsonian Report for 1873, page 159,) on the same terms as the original bequest of Smithson, in accordance with the act of Congress of February 8, 1867, which authorizes the increase of the permanent fund to a sum not exceeding one million dollars.

The following is a statement of the interest received on the Hamilton bequest, which will be appropriated in accordance with the terms of the will:

Interest on $1,000 from February 24, 1874, to December 31, 1874		$50 88
Interest from January 1, 1875, to December 31, 1875, 6 per cent. in coin....................................	$60 00	
Premium at $112\frac{13}{16}$, less commission	7 61	
		67 61
		118 49

VIRGINIA BONDS.

Previous to the year 1867, the savings from the income of the Institution were invested in State stocks, as shown in the following table:

	Amount.	Rate.	Cost Jan., 1857.	Sold Feb., 1867.	Gain.	Loss.
Indiana 5 per cent. bonds...............	$75,000 00	84	$63,000 00	$68,906 25	$5,906 25	....
Tennessee 6 per cent. bonds...........	15,000 00	94	11,167 50	9,586 78	....	$1,580 72
Georgia 6 per cent. bonds	500 00	100	500 00	358 71	....	141 29
Washington 6 per cent. bonds	100 00	100	100 00	100 00	....	....
	90,600 00	......	74,767 50	78,951 74	5,906 25	1,722 01
Net gain......................	....	......	....	....	4,184 24	....
Virginia 6 per cent....................	53,500 00	93	49,832 00	....	....	....

In accordance with the authority given in the act of Congress of February 8, 1867, to increase the Smithson fund in the United States Treasury, the regents disposed of all the State stocks held by the Institution as shown above, with the exception of the Virginia bonds, which were at the time so low that it was thought advisable to retain them, with the expectation that they would enhance in value, which expectation has been realized. The following table, however, shows that the value of these bonds has fluctuated:

1867	$31,565	1872	35,500
1868	30,000	1873	37,000
1869	40,018	1874	33,000
1870	42,200	1875	35,000
1871	48,000	1876.	42,000

Under the provisions of an act of the legislature of Virginia, of 30th March, 1871, the accumulated interest on these bonds was funded by the State; that is, the interest was added to the principal, and for two-thirds of the increase new bonds were issued, and certificates of indebtedness were given for the remaining one-third.

These funds are, therefore, of two classes, one known as " consolidated bonds," due from the State of Virginia, and the other as " deferred certificates," the payment of which is reserved until an adjustment is made between the States of Virginia and West Virginia as to the settlement of the State debt prior to their separation.

The income which the Institution has received from this source is entirely from the sale of the coupons of the consolidated bonds.

The bonds and certificates now belonging to the Institution are as follows:

Consolidated bonds.

58 bonds, Nos. 11521 to 11578 inclusive, for $1,000 each... $58,000 00
1 bond, No. 1380, for $500 .... 500 00
2 bonds, Nos. 4191 and 4192, for $100 each.............. 200 00

58,700 00

(These bonds are deposited in the Treasury of the United States.)

Deferred certificates.

No. 4543, dated July 1, 1871...............................	$29,375 07
No. 2969	50 13

(These certificates are in charge of Messrs. Riggs & Co.)

Total par value of Virginia securities 88,125 20

The State of Virginia has made only partial provision to pay the interest on its debt, but, as the coupons of the consolidated bonds are receivable for taxes, they have a commercial value, and were sold, by direction of the Institution, during the year by Messrs. Riggs & Co., as follows:

Coupons on $58,700, due July 1, 1874, and January 1, 1875; sold June 14, 1875:

$3,000, at 89½	$2,685 00	
510, at 89¾	457 73	
	3,142 73	
Less ½ per cent. commission	17 55	
	3,125 18	
12, at 89½, less commission	10 68	$3,135 86
3,522		

Coupons on $58,700, due July 1, 1875; sold 31st December, 1875:

$1,761, at 84½...................................	$1,488 04	
Less ½ per cent. commission....	8 80	
		1,479 24

In addition to the above, the Institution had in its possession coupons for one-third the interest due on the 1st of January and 1st of July, 1872, amounting to $1,174, the remaining two-thirds ($2,348) having been collected by Riggs & Co. and sold for the Institution, according to their statement of November 9, 1872. (See Smithsonian Report for 1872, page 81.) This amount, $1,174, above referred to, was sold by Riggs & Co. on the 14th June, 1875, with the following result:

$1,174, at 12	$140 88	
Less commission	5 87	
		135 01

Total amount realized from sale of Virginia coupons in 1875 ....   4,750 11

There still remain unsold the coupons on the $58,700 bonds due 1st January, 1876.

Provisional appropriations.

For building..	$2, 000
For general expenses.............................	14, 000
For publications and researches	20, 000
For exchanges.....................................	7, 000
For books and apparatus	1, 000
For contingencies	1, 466
	$45, 466

NATIONAL MUSEUM.

The National Museum still continues to be in charge of the Smithsonian Institution, Congress making an appropriation annually of $20,000 for the care and preservation of the collections.

The number of specimens is, however, every year increasing from the public surveys and explorations, and the sum appropriated by Congress has never been sufficient to meet the demand for their proper care and exhibition. During the past year it has been found necessary to erect an additional building for the use of the Museum taxidermists and photographer, toward the expense of which $2,614 have been advanced from the Smithson income. In addition to this, $1,908.45 were also required to meet the current expenses of the Museum, making a total of $4,522.45 expended during the present year from the Smithson income beyond the appropriation by Congress for the Museum.

The appropriation made by Congress for fitting up the halls has been expended in the construction of additional walnut table-cases with glass tops and sides, for the exhibition of ethnological specimens.

At the session of the Board of Regents, January 23, 1875, a resolution was adopted to request Congress to make an appropriation of $2,500 to increase the heating capacity of the apparatus used to warm the rooms occupied by the Government collections.

The subject was presented to the appropriate committees of Congress and the desired appropriation was granted without dissent. After estimates had been procured, a contract was made with the firm of Baker, Smith & Co., of New York, to substitute larger boilers and pipes for those then in use, and the work has been satisfactorily accomplished for the amount of the appropriation.

The following is a tabular statement of the condition of the Museum funds:

Balance unexpended of appropriation for preservation of the Government collections, for the fiscal year ending 30th June, 1875. (Statutes for 1874, p. 216)................. $7, 988 62
Expenditure from January 1, 1875, to July 1, 1875. (Museum Journal A, p. 130).. 7, 988 62

Appropriation for the fiscal year ending 30th June, 1876.
(Digest of Appropriations, 1876, p. 105.)

For preservation of collections................. $20, 000 00
For fitting up new halls 10, 000 00
For completing heating apparatus............ 2, 500 00
                                                            $32, 500 00

Expenditure from July 1, 1875, to December 31, 1875. (Museum Journal A, p. 163) 22, 881 32

Balance unexpended..................................... $9, 618 68
Required for the six months ending 30th June, 1876.

The estimates submitted by the Institution to Congress for appropriations for the fiscal year ending 30th June, 1877, were as follows:

For preservation of the collections of the surveying and exploring expeditions of the Government $25, 000 00
For fitting up apartments for mounting and photographing
specimens....................................... 5, 000 00
                                                            30, 000 00

This sum is $5,000 less than the amount asked for the previous year.

All the payments on account of the National Museum have been made, during the past year, directly by the disbursing-officer of the Department of the Interior on the presentation of vouchers approved by the Secretary of the Smithsonian Institution.

SUMMARY.

The Executive Committee have examined five hundred and ninety-eight vouchers for payments made from the Smithson income during the year 1875, and three hundred and forty-six similar vouchers for payments made from the Congressional appropriations for the National Museum, making a total number of nine hundred and forty-four vouchers.

All of the vouchers have the approval of the Secretary of the Institution, and a certificate setting forth that the materials and property and services rendered were for the Institution, and to be applied to the purposes specified.

As authorized by a resolution of the Board of Regents, 26th May, 1874, the committee have also examined the account-books of the National Museum and find the balance of $9,618.68 to the credit of the appropriation for the "preservation of the collections" remaining on the 1st of January, 1876, to correspond with the certificate of the disbursing-clerk of the Department of the Interior.

The quarterly accounts current, bank-book, check-book, and ledger have also been examined and found to be correct, showing a balance in the charge of the Treasurer of the United States 19th January, 1876, of $20,555.82.

Respectfully submitted.

PETER PARKER,
JOHN MACLEAN,
GEO. BANCROFT,
Executive Committee.

WASHINGTON, *January* 24, 1876.

GENERAL APPENDIX

TO THE

SMITHSONIAN REPORT FOR 1875.

The object of this appendix is to illustrate the operations of the Institution by reports of lectures and extracts from correspondence, as well as to furnish information of a character suited especially to the meteorological observers and other persons interested in the promotion of knowledge.

EULOGY ON ALEXANDER VOLTA.

[Translated for the Smithsonian Institution.]

GENTLEMEN: When amber is rubbed it immediately attracts light bodies, such as the down of feathers, fragments of straw, and sawdust. Theophrastus, the Greek, and Pliny, the Roman, had both noticed this property, but attaching apparently no importance to it, treated it simply as an accident of form and color. They little suspected they were touching the first link of a long chain of discoveries, and did not appreciate the value of an observation which, at a later date, was to furnish assured means of disarming the thunder-cloud and conducting the electricity concealed in its bosom to the earth without danger and sometimes even without explosion.

From *electron*, the Greek for amber, is derived "electricity," a term applied originally to the attractive property of rubbed bodies, but now to the cause of a great variety of effects and to all the details of a brilliant science.

Electricity long remained in the hands of physicists, the almost exclusive result of complicated combinations, which nature rarely presented. The man of genius whose works we are about to analyze was the first to transcend these narrow limits. With the aid of microscopic apparatus, he found electricity everywhere, in combustion, in evaporation, and in the simple contact of dissimilar bodies. He therefore assigned to this powerful agent a wide-extended domain, which, in terrestrial phenomena, scarcely gives precedence to that of gravity.

The development disclosing the connection of these important discoveries appears to me deserving of being traced with some degree of extension. It seems to me also that, since definite knowledge is so much desired, academic eulogies may become introductory chapters of a general history of the sciences. The following is an essay, on my part, which I frankly submit to the rigid and enlightened criticism of the public.

BIRTH OF VOLTA—HIS YOUTH—HIS FIRST WORKS—LEYDEN JAR—
PERPETUAL ELECTROPHORUS—IMPROVEMENTS IN THE ELECTRI-
CAL MACHINE—CONDENSING ELECTROMETER—ELECTRIC PISTOL—
PERPETUAL LAMP—EUDIOMETER.

Alexander Volta, one of the eight foreign members of the Academy of Science, and son of Philip Volta and Madeleine de Conti Inzaghi, was born at Como, on the 18th of February, 1745. His early education

115

was carried on at the public school of his native place under his father's watchful care. Great aptitude, steady application, and a well-regulated mind soon placed him at the head of his fellow-students. At eighteen, he was already in correspondence with Nollet on the most recondite questions of physics. At nineteen, he composed a Latin poem never given to the public, in which he described the phenomena discovered by the most celebrated experimentalists of the time. It has been said that at this period, Volta's vocation was undetermined, but I beg to differ from this assertion, for a young man would scarcely hesitate about exchanging the poetic art for a retort, if he had the singular taste to select chemistry as the subject of his literary compositions; and, in fact, with the exception of several of his poems, including that describing Saussure's ascent of Mont Blanc, we shall find the long career of this distinguished physicist devoted solely to the study of nature.

Volta, at the age of twenty-four, had the temerity to assail, in his first essay, the delicate question of the Leyden jar. This apparatus had been invented in 1746. The singularity of its effects would have amply sufficed to justify the curiosity it excited throughout Europe; but this curiosity was also due, in a great measure, to Musschenbroeck's extravagant exaggeration of the unaccountable terror he experienced on receiving a very feeble discharge, in regard to which, the physicist emphatically exclaimed, he would not again expose himself for the proudest kingdom of the universe. The numerous theories of the jar which were successively offered are scarcely worthy of being enumerated. Franklin has the honor of having solved this important problem, and, it must be acknowledged, Volta has added little to the labors of the illustrious American physicist.

The second essay of the physicist of Como appeared in 1771. In this, observation is the only guide of the author in the researches undertaken to determine the nature of the electricity of bodies covered with different coatings; to ascertain the circumstances of temperature, color, and elasticity causing the phenomena to vary; to study the electricity produced by rubbing, percussion, or pressure; or finally, the properties of a new kind of electrical machine in which the movable plate and the insulating supports were of dried wood.

On this side of the Alps, the first two essays of Volta were scarcely read at all. In Italy, on the contrary, they produced a lively sensation. Public authority, which is usually unfortunately partial, and which in its blind love of absolute power often even refuses the modest request of reference to competent judges, hastened itself to encourage the youthful experimentalist. He was nominated by it as regent of the Royal School of Como, and soon after professor of physics.

The missionaries to Pekin in 1755 communicated to the savants of Europe an important fact made known to them by accident, respecting electricity by induction, which, in certain bodies, is developed or dissipated as these bodies are separated or brought into immediate contact.

This fact gave rise to the interesting researches of Æpinus, Wilcke, Cigna, and Beccaria. Volta also made it the subject of special study and found in it the germ of the *perpetual electrophorus*, a wonderful instrument, which, however small, affords an inexhaustible supply of electricity, and which, without the necessity of resorting to friction of any kind, and whatever may be the state of the atmosphere, enables the physicist to command incessant charges of undiminished power.

The essay on the electrophorus was succeeded in 1778 by another very important production. It was known even at this time that a given body, hollow or solid, has the same electrical capacity, provided the surface remains the same. An observation by Lemonnier pointed out, moreover, that, besides equality of surface, the shape of the body is not without its influence. Volta was the first, however, to establish this principle on a solid basis. His experiments proved that of two cylinders having the same surface, the longer receives the larger charge, so that wherever the situation permits, it is an immense advantage to substitute for the large conductors of ordinary machines a system of very small cylinders, the total capacity of which is, however, not larger than the other. By combining, for example, sixteen rows of slender silver-plated rods, 1,000 feet in length each, a battery would be formed, according to Volta, capable of killing the largest animal.

Not one of the discoveries of the professor of Como was the result of accident. All the instruments with which he enriched science, before being formed by the mechanic, were thoroughly planned in his mind. There was no chance, for instance, in the changes made by Volta in the electrophorus in order to transform it into a *condenser*, a genuine microscope of a new kind which detects the presence of electricity where every other means would fail.

In 1776 and 1777, Volta devoted himself for some months to a subject of pure chemistry, in which, however, electricity, his favorite science, was involved in the most fortunate combinations.

At this epoch, chemists having as yet only discovered natural inflammable gas in coal mines and mineral salts, regarded it as belonging exclusively to mineral regions. Volta, whose attention had been directed to this subject by an accidental observation of P. Campi, showed they were mistaken. He proved that the putrefaction of both animal and vegetable matter is always accompanied by the production of inflammable gas; that if stagnant water and the slime of a marsh be stirred up, this gas will escape through the liquid, presenting the appearance of ordinary ebullition. Thus, the inflammable gas of marshes, which for several years so much occupied the attention of chemists, is, as to its origin, a discovery of Volta.

This discovery might lead to the belief that certain natural phenomena, such, for example, as burning marshes and burning springs, arose from a similar cause; but Volta knew too well how nature sports with our feeble understandings to be satisfied with mere analogy. In 1780 he hastened to visit the celebrated marshes of *Pietra Mala* and *Velleja*. He thoroughly examined all he could find in different travels in similar localities, and then succeeded in establishing, with complete proof, and contrary to received opinion, the fact that these phenomena did not depend upon the presence of petroleum, naphtha, or bitumen; he demonstrated, moreover, that it was caused alone by the disengagement of inflammable gas. But has Volta proved, with the same accuracy, that this gas has, in all places, its origin in the maceration of animal or vegetable matter? I think we may be allowed to question this. The electric spark had been, at an early date, used to inflame certain liquids, certain vapors, and different gases, such as alcohol, the smoke of a candle just extinguished, and hydrogen gas; but all these experiments were made in the open air. Volta was the first to make them in closed vessels, (1777.) He is therefore the originator of the apparatus used by Cavendish in 1781 for combining the separated elements of water by synthesis, so as to form anew the decomposed body from its two constituent gaseous elements.

Our distinguished associate possessed in the highest degree two qualities rarely found united, a creative genius and great powers of application. He never abandoned a subject without examining it in all its phases, without describing, or at least pointing out, the various aids which science, ingenuity, and even mere curiosity might bring to bear upon it. Thus several experiments on the inflammable nature of the air of marshes gave rise to the electrical *gun* and *pistol*, upon which it would be superfluous to dwell here, as they have passed from the hands of physicists into those of the showman, and, in public places, are daily exhibited to the admiring gaze of gaping idlers. Then the *perpetual hydrogen-gas lamp*, so generally known in Germany, which, by the most ingenious application of the electrophorus, lights itself when needed, and, finally, the eudiometer, the valuable instrument of analysis, which has been so useful to chemists.

The discovery of the composition of atmospheric air has given rise to this momentous question in natural philosophy: Does the proportion, in which the two component parts of air are found united, vary with the successive revolutions of ages, and according to locality and the changes of seasons?

When one reflects that all mankind, all the beasts of the earth and fowls of the air are constantly consuming, in the act of breathing, one of these two components, oxygen gas; that this same gas is the indispensable food of combustion in our homes, in workshops and vast factories; that a candle or lamp is not lighted without absorbing it; that, finally oxygen plays the chief part in the phenomena of vegetation, it may readily be imagined that in the long run the atmosphere varies sensibly in its composition; that at some future time it will become unfit for respiration; that then all the animal creation will be extinguished, not in consequence of one of those physical revolutions of which geologists have discovered so many vestiges, and which, notwithstanding their vast extent, may leave some chance of safety to a few individuals advantageously situated, but from an all-pervading and inevitable cause, in which case the frozen zones of the poles, the burning regions of the equator, the vastness of the ocean, and the snowy summits of the Cordilleras and Himalayas would be equally powerless to save. To study all that can be discovered of this great phenomenon up to the present time, to collect all the exact data with which the centuries to come will be teeming, is the task physicists are hastening to accomplish, especially since the eudiometer with the electric spark has supplied them with the means of so doing. To answer some of the objections to which the first trials of this instrument gave rise, Humboldt and Gay-Lussac sub- mitted it to the most scrupulous examination. When such judges declare that no known eudiometer approaches in accuracy that of Volta, doubt as to its value can no longer exist.

DILATATION OF THE AIR.

As I have abandoned the chronological order, before taking up the two most important works of our venerable fellow-member, before analyzing his researches on atmospheric electricity and describing his discovery of the pile, I will mention in a few words the experiments published by him in 1793 on the subject of the dilatation of air.

This important question had already attracted the attention of a great number of skillful physicists, who could not agree either on the total increase of volume that air undergoes between the fixed temperatures of melting ice and ebullition, or the rate of the expansions of the intermediate temperatures. Volta discovered the cause of these discordances. He showed that, by operating in a vessel containing humidity, the increase of expansion would be found ; that if there be in the apparatus no more humidity than the film ordinarily covering the sides of the glass, the apparent expansion of the air will be increasing in the lower part of the thermometric scale and decreasing in the upper part. He finally proved, by delicate measurements, that atmospheric air, if confined in a perfectly dry vessel, expands in proportion to its temperature, when this latter is measured by a mercurial thermometer divided into equal parts. Now, as D'Huc's and Crawford's works seemed to establish the fact that a similar thermometer gives the correct measurement of the amount of heat, Volta felt himself authorized to announce, in the new terms, whose importance all will appreciate, the very simple law resulting from his experiments, that the elasticity of a given volume of atmospheric air is in proportion to its heat.

When air, at a low temperature, and constantly containing the same amount of humidity, was heated, its elastic force increased as did that of dry air. Volta concluded from this that the vapor of water and air expand precisely in the same manner. Every one now knows that this result is accurate ; but the experiment of the physicist of Como did leave some doubts, since, at the ordinary temperature, vapor mingles with the atmospheric air in very small proportions. Volta regarded the work I have just analyzed as a mere rough draught.

Numerous other researches of the same kind to which he had applied himself were to form part of a treatise which has never seen the light. Besides, on this point science now seems complete, thanks to Gay-Lussac and Dalton. The experiments of these ingenious physicists, made at a time when Volta's treatise, though published, was known neither in France nor in England, included all the gases, whether permanent or ephemeral, in the law of the Italian scientist. They lead, moreover, in every case, to the same co-efficient of expansion.

ATMOSPHERIC ELECTRICITY.

I will not resume the subject of Volta's researches on atmospheric electricity until after having given a hasty sketch of the analogous experiments preceding them. In order to judge judiciously of a traveler's course, it is often necessary to view it at the same time from the starting and finishing points.

Dr. Wall, who wrote in 1708, should be here named as the first, for in one of his treatises is found this ingenious remark: "The light and crackling noise of electrified bodies seems, *up to a certain point*, to represent thunder and lightning." Stephen Grey published in 1735 a similar remark. "It is probable," said this distinguished physicist, "that in time some means of concentrating this electrical fire in larger quantities, will be discovered, and also of increasing the power of an agent, which, if it be allowable to compare small things with great, according to several of my experiments, seems to have the nature of thunder and lightning."

The majority of physicists saw merely comparisons in these passages. They did not suppose that in finding a resemblance between the effects of electricity and those of thunder, Wall and Grey claimed to infer from it an identity of causes. This doubt, however, would not be applicable to the sketch introduced by Nollet, in 1746, in his lectures on experimental physics. In that, for example, according to the author, a storm-cloud, far above the earth, is nothing more than an electrified body placed above a body which is not. *Thunder in the hands of nature is electricity in the hands of physicists.* Several striking resemblances are pointed out, and, in a word, nothing is wanting to complete this ingenious theory, except the only thing necessary to give it a definite place in science, the sanction of direct experiment.

Franklin's first views of the analogy between electricity and thunder were, like those entertained by Nollet, mere conjectures; the whole difference between the two physicists being then reduced to a plan for an experiment not mentioned by Nollet, and which seemed to promise definitive proofs for or against the hypothesis. The object of this experiment was to prove whether, during a storm, a metallic rod, insulated and terminating in a point, would give out sparks similar to those proceeding from the conductor of an ordinary electrical machine.

Without wishing to detract from Franklin's glory, I must remark that the projected experiment was quite unnecessary.* The soldiers of the Fifth Roman Legion had previously made it, during the African war—the day when, as related by Cæsar, the iron heads of their lances seemed on fire during a storm. The same was also noticed by numerous navigators, to whom Castor and Pollux appeared, either at the metallic points of the mast-head and yard-arms or other prominent parts of their vessels. Finally, in certain countries, in Frioul, for instance, at the Chateau de Duino, the sentry was strictly carrying out what Franklin would have desired, when, in conformity with his duty and to decide when it would be necessary, by ringing a bell, to warn the peasants of the approach of a storm, he examined with his halbert the iron head of a spear planted vertically on the rampart, to ascertain whether sparks had been given out. Besides, whether some of these circumstances were ignored, or whether they were not considered sufficiently demonstrative, direct experiments seemed requisite, and it is to Dalibard, our fellow-countryman, that science is indebted for this. On the 10th of May, 1752, during a storm, a long, pointed metallic rod, placed by him in a garden of Marly-la-Ville, gave out small sparks, like the conductor of an ordinary electrical machine in contact with a metallic wire. It was not until a month later that Franklin, in the United States, by means of a kite, realized the same experiment. Lightning-rods were the immediate result of this, and the distinguished American physicist hastened to announce it to the world.

That portion of the public which, in matters of science, is reduced to judge from hearsay, rarely decides by halves. It admits or rejects, if I may be allowed the term, impetuously. Lightning-rods, for example, became the object of a genuine enthusiasm, whose flights it would be curious to follow in the writings of the day. Here you find travelers who, in the open fields, suppose themselves able, sword in hand pointed toward the clouds, to exorcise the lightning, in the posture of Ajax threatening the gods; there, churchmen, whose garb forbids the sword, bitterly deploring being denied this talisman of safety; some, seriously proposing, as an infallible preservative, to place themselves under a rain-spout at the beginning of the storm, considering wet clothing good conductors of electricity; others invented certain head-gear, from which were suspended long metallic chains, which with great care must be kept constantly trailing on the damp earth. Some physicists, it must be acknowledged, did not share this infatuation. They

---

* We do not agree with Arago in this remark. The phenomena he mentions were the spontaneous productions of nature, and were not referred to atmospheric electricity. To fully establish the identity of electricity and lightning required such an experiment as that of Franklin's, in which electricity was actually drawn from the cloud in accordance with previously-established principles.

J. H.

admitted the identity of lightning and electricity, so conclusively proved by the experiment of Franklin and of Marly-la-Ville; but the small number of sparks proceeding from the rod, and their minuteness, created doubts as to the possibility of exhausting the immense amount of fulminating matter with which a storm-cloud must be charged. The frightful experiments made by Romas de Nerac did not overcome their opposition, because this experimentalist used a kite with a metallic cord, which rose several hundred feet, to draw down the thunder from the very regions of the clouds. Soon, however, the deplorable death of Richman, August 6, 1753, occasioned by a simple discharge from an ordinary insulated lightning-rod which this distinguished physicist had placed on his house in Saint Petersburg, threw new light upon the subject. The learned saw in this tragic death an explanation of the passage in which Pliny, the naturalist, relates that Tullus Hostilius was struck by lightning for not having been sufficiently careful in the performance of certain ceremonies by means of which Numa, his predecessor, forced the lightning to descend from the skies. On the other side, and this was of more importance, physicists, without prejudice, found in this same event a fact which had before been wanting, namely, that under certain circumstances a metallic rod, slightly elevated, draws down from a storm-cloud not only inappreciable sparks, but genuine torrents of electricity. Accordingly, from this time discussions relating to the efficacy of lightning-rods are without interest, not even excepting the animated debate as to whether lightning-rods should terminate in a point or ball, which for some time divided the English scientists. No one is ignorant now that George III was the promoter of this polemic—that he was in favor of rods terminating in balls, because Franklin, then his successful antagonist in political questions of vast importance, required they should terminate in points; but this discussion, taking all things into consideration, belongs rather, though a matter of much moment, to the history of the American Revolution than to that of science.

The results of the experiment of Marly were scarcely known, when Lemonnier, of this academy, placed in his garden at Saint-Germain-en-Lage a long vertical metallic rod, insulated by some newly invented precautions, and from this time clusters of electrical sparks (July and September, 1752) were produced, not only when the thunder rumbled, not only when the sky was overcast with threatening clouds, but even when it was perfectly serene. A beautiful discovery was thus the result of apparently the most insignificant modification of Dalibard's original apparatus.

Lemonnier discovered without much difficulty that this serene-day lightning, whose existence he had just revealed, was subject every twenty-four hours to regular variations of intensity. Beccaria delineated the laws of this diurnal periodicity by means of excellent observations. He, moreover, established the important fact that at all seasons, at all heights, whatever the direction of the wind, the electricity of a serene sky is invariably positive.

By thus following, in the order of their dates, the developments of atmospheric electricity, I gradually reach the works with which Volta has enriched this important branch of meteorology. The object of these works was by turns the improvement of the methods of observation and the minute examination of the different circumstances under which the electricity was developed, which pervaded all the regions of the air.

When a new branch of science has been discovered the experimentalists devote themselves almost exclusively to the discovery of new phenomena, reserving their numerical valuation for later times. In electricity, for example, several physicists made themselves in this way a well-merited reputation. The Leyden jar, we may add, was conspicuous in all the laboratories of Europe, but no one had yet invented a veritable electrometer. The first instrument of this kind was made in 1749, and was the work of Darcy and Le Roy, two members of this academy. Its want of sensibility in small charges prevented its being adopted.

The electrometer suggested by Nollet (1752) appeared at first sight simpler, more convenient, and especially as having infinitely greater sensibility. It was to consist of two wires, which after being electrified would open, like the two branches of a compass, from the effect of repulsion. The measure sought would thus be reduced to the observation of an angle.

Cavallo realized what Nollet had only suggested, (1780.) His wires were of metal, and had at their extremities small balls of the pith of elder. Volta finally abolished the elder and substituted dry straws at the end of the wires. This change might seem unimportant if it were not explained that the new electrometer alone possessed the valuable and unexpected property of giving, between 0 and 30°, the angular motions of the two straws exactly proportional to the electrical charges.

Volta's letter to Lichtenberg, dated 1786, in which he established by numerous experiments the properties of the straw electrometer, contained interesting views, no traces of which are to be found in more recent works. They relate to the means of rendering these instruments comparable in the measurement of the strongest charges, and to certain combinations of the electrometer and condenser. This letter cannot be too highly recommended to young physicists. It will initiate them into the very difficult art of investigating; it will teach them to mistrust first impressions and to constantly vary the form of the apparatus; if tempted by an impatient temper to abandon the slow but sure and beaten track of observation for seductive chimerical ideas, they may, perhaps, be arrested on this slippery ground by beholding a man of genius undaunted by the most minute details. And, moreover, at a time when, save in a few honorable cases, the publication of a book is a purely business operation, when scientific treatises, especially, modeled after the same pattern, do not differ from each other, except perhaps by a few slight shades in the compilation, often indeed imperceptible, when each author neglects most scrupulously all the experiments, theories, and instruments forgotten or ignored by his immediate predecessor, it is but a duty, it seems to me, to direct the attention of beginners to the original sources, and it is from these sources, and these alone, important subjects for research can be drawn, and where they will find a faithful history of discoveries, where they will learn to distinguish clearly the true from the doubtful, and finally to mistrust rash hypotheses adopted by compilers without discrimination and with blind confidence.

When Saussure, profiting by the wonderful power exercised by points on the electric fluid, succeeded, in 1785, by the simple addition of a rod eight or nine decimeters (about a yard) in length, in increasing the sensibility of Cavallo's electrometer, and consequently invoking a great number of minute experiments, the wires terminating in the elder-pith balls of the Neapolitan physicist being replaced by dried straws, this small apparatus might be supposed incapable of receiving any additional important improvement. Volta, however, in 1787, succeeded in considerably increasing its power, without at all changing its original construction. He had recourse to the strangest of expedients to accomplish this; he attached to the point of the metallic rod introduced by Saussure either a wax candle or simply a lighted match.

No one could assuredly have foreseen such a result. Experimentalists had discovered, at an early date, flame to be an excellent conductor of electricity; but would not that very fact have a tendency to divert the thoughts from considering it as a powerful collector? Besides, Volta, endowed with a strictly logical mind, did not thoroughly receive this strange fact until he could find for it an explanation. He found that the fact that a candle attracts to the point to which it is attached three or four times as much electricity as could be collected in any other way, is owing to the current of air induced by the flame, and to the increased communications established between the metallic point and the atmospheric molecules.

Since flame attracts the electricity of the air much better than pointed metallic rods, does it not follow, said Volta, that the best means of preventing storms, or rendering them less frightful, would be to light enormous fires in the fields, or, still better, on very elevated places. After reflecting on the grand effects of the very small flame of the candle of the electrometer, is there anything unreasonable in supposing that a large flame might, in a few moments, rob immense volumes of air and vapor of all their electricity?

Volta was anxious to submit this idea to the proof of direct experiment; but so far his wishes have been unsatisfied. Perhaps some encouraging ideas might be obtained with regard to this by comparing the meteorological observations of the counties in England, where the flames of so many high chimneys and factories convert night into day with those of the surrounding agricultural districts.

The *fiery lightning-rods* tempted Volta to throw aside the severe gravity in which he usually indulged. He tried to enliven the subject at the expense of the erudite, who, like the famous Dietens, always found, but after the event, the discovery of their contemporaries in some ancient author. He begged, then, in this instance, to go back to the fabulous times of the Greeks and Romans, and directed their attention to the sacrifices in the open air, the dazzling flames on the altars, the black columns of smoke which ascended into the air from the bodies of the victims; finally, to all the circumstances of those ceremonies which the ignorant believe were intended to appease the wrath of the gods, and to foil Jupiter's fulminating arm. All this could be but a mere experiment in physics, alone understood by the priests, and designed to restore silently to the earth the electricity of the air and clouds. The Greeks and Romans, during the most brilliant periods of their history, sacrificed, it is true, in closed temples; but, added Volta, this difficulty is not without its solution, as it may be said that Pythagoras, Aristotle, Cicero, Pliny, and Seneca were ignorant fellows, who, even according to simple tradition, did not possess the scientific knowledge of their predecessors. No criticism could be more cutting; but, to have any effect, it would be necessary to forget that the Zoileans, in all ages, who ransack musty books for the first rudiments, true or false, of great discoveries, are less eager to honor the dead than to bring discredit upon their contemporaries.

Nearly all physicists ascribe electrical phenomena to two fluids of different natures, which, under certain circumstances, accumulate separately on the surface of bodies. This hypothesis naturally led to an investigation into the source from which atmospheric electricity emanates. The problem was important. A delicate, though very simple, experiment led to its solution.

In this experiment, an insulated vessel from which the water could evaporate, gave, with the assistance of Volta's condenser, very manifest indications of negative electricity.

I regret my inability to announce, with any degree of certainty, to whom to ascribe this capital experiment. Volta relates in one of his treatises that he had been thinking of this since 1778, but various circumstances having prevented his attempting it, it was not until 1780, in Paris, in the month of March, *in company* with several members of the Academy of Science, that he was finally successful. On the other hand, Lavoisier and Laplace, in the last line of the treatise published by them on the same subject, merely remarked : *Volta was anxious to be present at our experiment and make himself useful to us.*

How shall we reconcile these two very contradictory statements? A historical note, published by Volta himself, is far from dispelling these doubts. This note, attentively examined, does not expressly state who originated the idea of the experiment, nor which one of the three physicists suggested that it might succeed with the aid of the condenser. The first attempt, in Paris, by Volta and the two French scientists unitedly, was unsuccessful, the hygrometrical state of the atmosphere not having been favorable. A few days after, at Lavoisier's country-house, electrical symptoms became manifest, though no change had been made in the method of observation. Volta was not present at this last trial.

This circumstance was the origin of all the difficulties. Some physicists, as a general rule, without a thorough examination, regard as discoverers those who are the first, by experiment, to establish the existence of a fact. Others again regard the work of experiment as a secondary matter, reserving their admiration for those who have planned the investigation.

These principles are both too exclusive. Pascal assigned to his brother-in-law, Perrier, the duty of ascending the Puy-de-Dome to observe the barometer, and yet Pascal's name alone is connected with that of Toricelli, when referring to the proofs of the pressure of the air. Michell and Cavendish, on the contrary, in the eyes of physicists, share with no one the credit of their celebrated experiment on the attraction of terrestrial bodies, although it had often occurred to others to attempt it; and, in this case, execution was everything. The work of Volta, Lavoisier, and Laplace belongs to neither of these two categories. I will grant, if desired, that a man of genius alone could conceive the idea that electricity assists in the generation of vapor; but to place this idea beyond the pale of hypothesis, special means of observation and new instruments must be invented. Those used by Lavoisier and Laplace were the inventions of Volta; they were constructed in Paris, under his own eyes; and he was present when they were first tested. Multiplied proofs of direct co-operation unquestionably connect Volta's name with every theory relating to the electricity of vapor. Who, however, would dare affirm, in the absence of a positive declaration of this great physicist to the contrary, that the experiment was not undertaken at the suggestion of the French savant? While there is doubt, would it not be natural, on this, as well as on the other side of the Alps, in referring to these phenomena, not to separate again the names of Volta, Lavoisier, and Laplace; to cease to see in it, here a question of misunderstood nationality, and there a subject of virulent accusation, scarcely excusable, if even no cloud obscured the truth?

These reflections will, I hope, put an end to a disgraceful dispute, which malicious passions have endeavored to perpetuate. They will, at all events, prove, by an additional example, how delicate a matter is the proprietorship of the productions of the mind. When three of the most brilliant geniuses of the eighteenth century, in the zenith of their glory, could not agree as to what part of the invention belonged to each, in an experiment made by all, need we be astonished to see such conflicts arise among beginners?

In spite of the length of this digression, I must not dismiss the experiment which suggested it without dwelling upon its great importance, and proving it to be the basis of a very curious branch of meteorology. A few words will suffice for this.

When the insulated metallic vessel in which the water evaporates* becomes electric, this water derives, from the bodies it touches, not only heat but also electricity, in order, Volta says, to pass from a liquid to an aeriform state. The electric fluid is, then, an integral part of the large masses of vapors which are daily forming at the expense of the seas, lakes, and rivers. These vapors, as they rise, find in the high regions of the atmosphere a degree of cold which condenses them. The constituent electric fluid is then liberated and accumulated, and the feeble conductibility of the air prevents its returning to the earth, whence it came, except in the form of rain, snow, hail, or some violent discharge.

Thus, on a stormy day, according to this theory, the electricity whose dazzling effulgence darts from east to west, from north to south, whose deep thunderings echo far and near, and which, hurled to the earth, leaves in its course destruction and death, is but the result of the daily evaporation of water, the inevitable consequence of a phenomenon developed by shades so insensible as to be imperceptible to our senses. When effects are compared to causes, nature, we must acknowledge, presents most wonderful contrasts.

THE VOLTAIC PILE.

I have now reached one of those rare epochs in which an important and unexpected fact, so often the result of some auspicious accident, in the hands of genius becomes the source of a scientific revolution.

A detailed description of the wonderful effects produced by insignificant causes, would, perhaps, be as interesting in the history of the sciences as in that of nations. If some savant should ever undertake to sketch it, that branch of physics properly called galvanism would occupy one of the first places in it. In fact, it can be proved that the immortal discovery of the pile, springs, in a very direct manner, from a slight cold with which a lady of Bologna was attacked in 1790, who was ordered by her physician a dish of frog-soup.

Several of these animals, prepared for the purpose by Madame Galvani's cook, were lying on a table at the time of an accidental discharge of an electrical machine at some distance. The muscles, although not touched by the sparks, evinced, at the moment of the discharge, the most decided contractions. The experiment, repeated with all kinds of animals, succeeded equally well, whether the electricity were artificial or natural, positive or negative.

This phenomenon was very easily explained on the well-known principle of induction, the electricity of the discharge disturbing by repulsion at a distance the natural electricity of the frog. Had it happened to some experienced physicist, familiar with the properties of electricity,

---

* It is now known that this experiment does not succeed when distilled water is used.

it would scarcely have attracted his attention; if remarked at all, the extent of the observation would have been that the extreme sensibility of the frog would render it a very good electroscope. Here was a case, however, though a rare one, where ignorance was great gain, for Galvani, though a skillful anatomist, knew very little of electricity. The muscular movements witnessed by him appeared inexplicable; a new world seemed opening before him. He applied himself to the task of varying the experiments in a thousand ways.

It was in doing this that he discovered an entirely new fact, the fact that a frog, even though killed for a long time, manifests very intense contractions, without the intervention of any foreign electricity, by merely placing a metallic plate, or, better still, two plates of dissimilar metals, between a muscle and a nerve. The astonishment of the professor of Bologna was then quite justifiable, and that of all Europe with him.

An experiment, in which the legs, thighs, and trunks of animals dismembered for hours manifested the strongest convulsions, darting about and appearing to return to life, could not long remain uninvestigated. After analyzing it in all its details, Galvani supposed the effect to be produced on the principle of the Leyden jar. According to him, the animals were merely reservoirs of electricity; positive electricity having its seat in the nerves, and negative in the muscles, the metallic plate interposed between these organs being simply the conductor by means of which the discharge is effected.

These views captivated the public; physiologists seized hold upon them; electricity usurped the place of the nervous fluid then occupying so large a space in the explanation of the phenomena of the principle of life, though, by a strange oversight, no one had attempted to prove its existence. In a word, all flattered themselves that they had found the physical agent which conveys external impressions to the *sensorium*, which makes, among animals, nearly all of the organs subservient to their intelligence, and the movements of the arms, legs, and head obedient to the will. But, alas! these delusions were not of long duration. The whole beautiful romance was dispelled by Volta's critically severe experiments.

This ingenious physicist first created convulsions, not merely as Galvani did, by interposing two dissimilar metals between a nerve and muscle, but by simply bringing them in contact with a muscle.

From this moment the principle of the Leyden jar was acknowledged to have no connection with the phenomenon; there was no longer any possible comparison between them. The negative electricity of the muscles and the positive electricity of the nerves were pure hypotheses, without any solid foundation; the phenomena seemed to have no connection with anything known, but were obscured, by an impenetrable veil.

Volta, nevertheless, was not discouraged. He claimed that, in his own experiment, electricity was the cause of the convulsions; that the muscle played but a passive part, and was to be simply regarded as a conductor by means of which the discharge was effected. Electricity, Volta had the independence to conjecture, was the inevitable result of the contact of the *two metals* between which the muscle was placed. I say the two metals, and not the two plates, since, according to Volta, with no difference in *the nature* of the two metals in contact, no electrical development could take place.

The physicists of all Europe, and Volta himself, adopted at the beginning of galvanism the views of the discoverer. They were unanimous in regarding the spasmodic convulsions of the dead animals as one of the greatest discoveries of modern times. But, however little one may know of the human heart, it is not difficult to divine that a theory, designed to connect these curious phenomena with the ordinary laws of electricity, would not be admitted by Galvani and his followers without extreme reluctance. In fact, the Bolognese school defended every foot of the immense ground attacked, which had been abandoned without opposition, by the supporters of animal electricity.

Among the numerous facts presented by this celebrated school to the physicist of Como was one which, by its singularity, for a moment, held all minds in suspense. I allude to the convulsions that Galvani himself created by bringing the muscles of the frog in contact with two plates, not dissimilar as Volta supposed necessary, but both from one and the same slab of metal. This effect, although not continuous, presented apparently an insurmountable objection to the new theory.

Volta replied that the plates used by his adversaries might be identical in name and chemical nature, and yet differ in other respects, so as to possess entirely distinct properties. In his hands, in fact, inactive couples, composed of two contiguous parts of the same metallic plate, acquired a certain power from the moment the temperature, the degree of annealing, or the polish of only one of the elements was changed.

Thus, this contest did not shake the theory of the celebrated professor. It only proved that the word *dissimilar*, applied to superposed metallic bodies, had been understood in altogether too restricted a sense.

Volta had to endure a last and very formidable assault. This time his very friends thought him vanquished forevermore. Doctor Valli, his antagonist, produced contortions by the simple contact of two portions of the frog, without the intervention of the metallic armatures, which, in all similar experiments, had been, according to our fellow-member, the principal generator of electricity.

It was evident from more than one passage in Volta's letters how deeply he was wounded by the tone of assurance with which (I give his own words) the galvanists, *old and young*, boasted of having reduced him to silence. This silence, however, was not of long duration. An attentive examination of Valli's experiments soon proved to Volta that to insure their success this double condition was necessary: as much heterogeneity as possible between the parts of the animal brought in

contact and the interposition between these same parts of a third substance. The fundamental principle of the Voltaic theory, far from being
shaken, only acquired a much greater generality. Metals no longer
formed an exclusive class. Analogy led to the fact that two dissimilar
substances, whatever their nature, give rise by mere contact to a
development of electricity.

There was nothing henceforth serious in the attack of the galvanists.
Their experiments were no longer confined to very small animals.
They produced strange nervous movements in the nostrils, tongue, and
eyes of an ox killed for several days, thus strengthening more or less
the hopes of those to whom galvanism had seemed a means of resusci-
tating the dead; but they threw no new light on the theory. By
borrowing arguments, not from nature, but the grandeur of the effects,
the adepts of the Bolognese school strongly resembled that savant,
who, to prove that the atmosphere is not the cause of the rise of the
mercury in the barometer, conceived the idea of substituting a large
cylinder for the narrow tube of this instrument, and then cited, as a
formidable difficulty, the exact number of quintals of liquid raised.

Volta gave a death-blow to animal electricity. His conceptions were
constantly verified by experiments, but these were not well understood,
and by means of them it was hoped to undermine him. His conclusions
had not, and we may add that they could not have, as yet the entire and
unprejudiced approval of physicists. The contact of two metals, of two
dissimilar substances, gave rise to a certain agent which, like electricity,
produced spasmodic movements. About this fact there was no doubt;
but was the agent in question really electrical? Were the proofs
given sufficiently satisfactory?

When two dissimilar metals are placed on the tongue in a certain
order, at the moment of contact an acid taste is produced. If the
order of these metals be reversed, the taste becomes alkaline. Now,
by simply applying the tongue to the conductor of an ordinary electrical machine, the taste is acid or alkaline, as the conductor is charged
plus or minus. In this case, the phenomenon is undoubtedly due to
electricity. "Is it not natural," said Volta, "to infer an identity of
causes from a resemblance of the effects; to assimilate the first experiment with the second; to find but one difference between them, namely,
the mode of producing the principle which excites the organ of taste?"
No one questioned the importance of this comparison. Volta's penetrating genius saw in it the basis of a thorough conviction. Most physicists required more explicit proofs. These proofs, these incontestable
demonstrations, before which all opposition must vanish, Volta found
in a capital experiment which can be explained in a few words.

Two polished disks of copper and zinc, with insulated handles, are
brought exactly in contact, with nothing intervening; by means of
these same handles, the disks are then suddenly separated; and, finally,
each in turn is presented to the ordinary *condenser*, armed with an elec-

trometer, when *the straws instantly diverge.* It was proved, too, by the same means, that the two metals are in opposite states of electricity; that the zinc is positive and the copper negative. By repeating several times the contact of the two disks, their separation from, and contact with, the condenser in turns, Volta succeeded, as with an ordinary machine, in producing bright sparks. After these experiments, the theory of galvanic phenomena was fully established.

The production of electricity by the mere contact of dissimilar metals was ranked among the most important and best-established facts of the physical sciences. If, after this, there was anything left to be desired, it was an easy means of increasing this kind of electricity. Such means are now known to all experimentalists, and it is to Volta's genius that they are indebted for them.

At the beginning of the year 1800, (the date of so wonderful a discovery could not be passed over in silence,) in consequence of some theoretical views, the illustrious professor contrived a high column, consisting of pairs of copper and zinc, each pair being separated from the adjoining ones by pieces of moist cloth, scrupulous care being taken not to invert this order. But, *à priori*, what was to be expected from such a combination? Well, I do not hesitate to say that this apparently inert mass, this singular assemblage, this pile of so many pairs of dissimilar metals separated by a small quantity of liquid, is, with respect to the singularity of its effects, the most marvelous instrument ever invented by man, without even excepting the telescope and steam-engine.

I am quite sure I shall escape all reproach of exaggeration if, in the enumeration I am about to make of the properties of Volta's apparatus, I shall be allowed to cite both those properties discovered by this scientist and those whose discoveries are due to his successors.

Every one will remark in the short description I have given of the composition of the pile, that its two extremities are necessarily dissimilar; that if zinc be at the base copper must be at the top, and conversely. These two extremities are called the *poles.*

Let us now suppose two wires attached to the opposite poles, copper and zinc, of a voltaic pile; the apparatus, so arranged, being ready for the different experiments I wish to describe.

If one of the wires alone be grasped no sensation is felt; but the moment both are touched a violent shock is experienced. This, as is evident, is nothing more than the phenomenon of the famous Leyden jar, which, in 1746, excited in so high a degree the wonder of all Europe. But the jar could only be used once; after each shock it being necessary to recharge it to repeat the experiment; the pile, on the contrary, supplying a thousand successive shocks. It may be compared consequently with regard to the nature of its effects to the Leyden jar, with this additional proviso, that after each discharge it immediately returns itself to its original condition.

If the wire from the zinc pole is placed on the end of the tongue, and that from the copper on some other part of the body, a very decided acid taste is the result.   To vary the nature of this taste, or to make it alkaline, it is only necessary to reverse the order of the wires.

The sense of sight does not escape the action of this protean instrument.   Here the phenomenon will appear the more interesting from the fact that the luminous sensation is excited without the necessity of touching the eye.   If the end of one of the wires be applied to the forehead, cheeks, nose, chin, or even the throat, the very moment the observer seizes the other wire with his hand he perceives, with his eyes closed, a flash of light whose intensity and form vary according to the part of the face in contact with the conductor.   Similar combinations create in the ear sounds, or, rather, peculiar noises.

It is not alone on healthy organs that the pile acts.   It excites or appears to revive those in which life seemed altogether extinct.   In one instance, by the combination of the two wires, the muscles of a head, severed from the body, evinced contortions so frightful that the spectators fled terrified.   In another the body of the victim half arose, its hands shaking, and striking the nearest objects, and raising weights of several pounds.   The pectoral muscles imitated the respiratory movements ; and, in a word, every life-like motion was so accurately reproduced that the question was involuntarily asked whether the experimentalist was not guilty of a culpable act, whether he was not adding cruel sufferings to those just inflicted on the criminal by the hand of the executioner.

Insects, also, subjected to these experiments, gave interesting results. The wires of the pole, for example, greatly increased the brilliancy of the glow-worm, restored motion to a dead grasshopper, and made it sing.

The marvelous effects of the pile each day acquire a more extended field of action.   But I must decline an invitation made me to treat the subject with regard to its medicinal properties and the power it possesses, it is said, of curing certain affections of the stomach and paralysis, for the lack of sufficiently accurate information.   I will add, however, that M. Marianini, of Venice, one of the most celebrated physicists of the century, has recently obtained, in eight cases of severe paralysis, results so completely favorable, by a skillful application of electro-motors, that it would be the grossest negligence on the part of the medical faculty not to give their attention to this means of alleviating human suffering.

If, laying aside the physiological properties of the pile, we consider it merely as an electrical machine, we shall find ourselves in that department of science which has been brought to a high degree of perfection by Nickolson and Carlisle, Hisinger and Berzelius, Orested and Ampère, and Davy.

At first each wire, taken separately, will indicate the ordinary temperature, that of the surrounding air; but the moment these wires are brought into contact they will acquire an intense heat.   When sufficiently attenuated they become incandescent; still more attenuated, they melt altogether, to the consistency of a liquid, even if they be of platina, the least fusible of all known metals. We may add that, with a powerful battery, two slender wires of gold or platinum exhibit, at the moment of contact, a disintegration so complete that they vanish in the form of a light vapor.

Charcoal, applied to the two extremities of these same wires, takes fire as soon as the wires are brought into contact. The light diffused by them is so pure, so dazzling, so remarkable for its whiteness, that it is not transcending the limits of truth to compare it to that of the sun. Who knows, even, whether this analogy may not be carried still further, whether this experiment may not solve one of the greatest problems of natural philosophy, and give the clew to that peculiar kind of combustion displayed by the sun for so many ages, with no sensible loss of matter or brilliancy? The carbon attached to the two wires of the pile in fact becomes incandescent, even in the most perfect vacuum. Nothing, then, is taken from, or added to, their substance. After an experiment of this kind, whatever may have been its duration, the carbons are found, as to their inner nature and weight, in their original condition.*

Every one knows that platinum, gold, copper, &c., do not act sensibly on a magnetic needle. Wires of these different metals attached to the two poles of the pile follow the same law, if taken separately. But, on the contrary, from the moment they come in contact, a very intense magnetic action is developed. Besides, during the whole period of contact, these wires are themselves genuine magnets, they attract iron-filings and communicate a permanent magnetism to steel bars placed transversely to them. When the pile is very powerful, and the wires, instead of touching, are at some distance, a bright light unites their extremities. In fact, this light is magnetic; a magnet can attract or repel it. If, to-day, without being prepared for it, I mean with only the knowledge of their day, Franklin and Coulomb should hear me speak of a flame being attracted by a magnet, the most flattering sentiment I could expect would undoubtedly be one of decided incredulity. Let us suppose the same wires slightly separated and immersed in a liquid, pure water, for example. The water will be instantly decomposed; the two gaseous elements forming it will be disunited; the oxygen will be liberated from the surface of the end of the wire from the zinc pole; and the hydrogen quite distant from that, at the point of the wire from the copper pole. The bubbles rise separately through the liquid, and the two constituent gases may therefore be collected in two separate vessels. If we substitute for the pure water a liquid holding in solution saline matter, the pile will then analyze this matter. The acids will pass to the zinc pole and the alkalies to the copper.

This is the most powerful method of analysis known. It has recently enriched science with a multitude of important results. It is, for in-

---

*This is not correct; there is a transfer of the particles of carbon from one pole to the other.—J. H.

stance, to the pile we are indebted for the first decomposition of a great number of alkalies and earths which were before considered as simple substances; it is by it that all those bodies have become oxides; that chemistry now possesses metals, such as potassium, which can be kneaded by the fingers like wax, and will float on the surface of the water, because lighter than it; and are spontaneously kindled, diffusing the brightest light.

This would be the place to introduce all that is mysterious, I should say almost incomprehensible, in the decompositions effected by the voltaic pile; to dwell upon the separate disengagements, completely distinct, of the two disunited gaseous elements of a liquid, on the precipitations of the constituent solid principles of the same saline molecule, which are affected by the particles of the fluid dissolving at great distances from each other; on the strange, wild commotions that these different phenomena seemed to involve; but time fails me. However, before finishing this picture, I will remark that the pile is not merely a means of analysis; that if, by considerably changing the electrical affinities of the elements of bodies, it often leads to their complete separation, its power, delicately managed, has become, on the contrary, in the hands of one of our fellow-members, the regenerative principle of a large number of combinations almost endless in nature and which art, up to this time, knew not how to imitate.

I will add a few more words still, to point out the different modifications undergone by the pile since passing from the hands of its illustrious inventor.

The characteristic feature of the pile consists of a large number of pairs, or, binary combinations, of dissimilar metals. These metals are usually copper and zinc; and these elements, the copper and zinc of each pair, can be soldered together.

The pairs follow in the same order. Thus when zinc is below in the first, it is indispensably necessary it should be below in all the others. Finally the pairs must be separated by a liquid conductor of electricity. Now, who cannot see how easy it is to fulfill these conditions without *superposing* the elements, without forming them into a *pile?* This first arrangement, which, by the way, was the origin of the name of the apparatus, has been changed. The pairs are not now vertical, but succeed each other so as to form as a whole a horizontal parallelopiped. Each of them is immersed in a trough containing a liquid, which is a decided improvement over the merely moist pieces of pasteboard or cloth used in the beginning.

Apparatus have been constructed by several physicists under the denomination of *dry pile*, which only comparatively may be so called, as strictly speaking they do not deserve the name. The best known, those of Professor Zamboni, are composed of several thousands of disks of paper, tinned on one side and covered on the other by a thin layer of pulverized oxide of manganese, which is rendered adhesive by means of a paste of flour and milk. The disks, of course, being piled up in the same order, their dissimilar surfaces, or, I should say, the tin and manganese surfaces of two contiguous pairs, are in contact. Here, then, we have the two metallic elements, of different kinds, which constitute what were called *pairs* in the description of Volta's first pile. With regard to the intermediary conducting liquid, those who object to apply the name of *dry piles* to those of Zamboni will discover the cause of the humidity in the hygrometrical property always preserved by the paper placed between each plate of tin and layer of powdered manganese.

The wonderful results obtained by physicists by means of voltaic piles are owing undoubtedly, in a measure, to the remarkable improvements introduced by them in the construction of these apparatus; but the chief cause is the enormous dimensions they have succeeded in giving them. The metallic pairs in Volta's first piles were scarcely larger than a five-franc piece. In M. Children's pile each element had a surface of thirty-two English square feet. Volta, as well as can be discovered from the analysis I have just given of his views, accounted for the development of electricity by the mere contact of the two metals of different natures constituting each pair. The liquid between them simply performed the office of conductor. This theory, called the theory of contact, was attacked at an early date by Fabroni, one of Volta's countrymen. He supposed that the oxidation of the metallic surfaces of the pairs, induced by the liquid touching them, was the principal cause of the phenomena of the pile. Wollaston, some time after, developed this same idea with his usual sagacity. Davy supported it, in his turn, by ingenious experiments; and finally, to-day, this chemical theory of the pile prevails almost unanimously among physicists.

I hazarded the opinion, just now, with some timidity, that the pile was the most marvellous instrument ever invented by the human mind. If, in the enumeration you have just heard of its different properties, my voice has not been altogether without power, I might now repeat my first assertion and consider it thoroughly established.

According to some biographers, Volta's brain, exhausted by long-continued work, and especially by the production of the pile, refused to furnish anything more. Others saw, in an obstinate silence of nearly thirty years, only the effects of a puerile fear, which the illustrious physicist had not the courage to overcome. He feared, it is said, that on comparing his more recent researches with those on electricity by contact, the public would immediately conclude that his mind was weakened. These two explanations are doubtless very ingenious, but they labor under the signal defect of being entirely superfluous. For the pile was invented in 1800, and two ingenious essays, one on the "Phenomenon of Hail," (Le phénomène de la grêle,) and the other on the "Periodicity of storms and the cold accompanying them," (La periodicité des orages et le froid qui les accompagne,) were not published until six and seventeen years after.

LIFE OF VOLTA—OFFICES FILLED BY HIM—HIS CHARACTER—HIS
DEATH.

GENTLEMEN : I have just displayed to your view a picture of Volta's
brilliant career. I have tried to specify, in detail, the grand discoveries
with which this wonderful genius has enriched the physical sciences.
Nothing now remains, to carry out the usual form, but to relate briefly
the principal events of his public and private life.

The painful duties which devolved upon Volta, almost from earliest
youth, detained him in his native city till 1777. This year, for the first
time, he left the picturesque banks of Lake Como and traveled through
Switzerland. His absence lasted several weeks, but was not marked
by any important event. At Berne, Volta visited the celebrated
Haller, who was fast bringing his life to a close by an immoderate use
of opium. Thence he went to Fernay, where every description of talent
was secure of a kind welcome. Our immortal countryman, in the long
conversation with which he honored the young professor, glanced at the
very numerous, rich, and varied departments of Italian literature, passed
in review the savants, poets, sculptors, and painters which adorn this
literature, with a superiority of views, a delicacy of taste, and a nicety
of judgment which left on Volta's mind an indelible impression.

At Geneva, Volta formed a close friendship with the celebrated historian of the Alps, a man most capable of appreciating his discoveries.
That was a great century, gentlemen, in which a traveler, in a day's
journey, without losing sight of the Jura, could render homage to a
Saussure, a Haller, Jean-Jacques, and Voltaire.

Volta returned to Italy by way of Aigne-Belle, taking with him to his
countrymen that precious root, the potato, which, by proper cultivation,
would render a complete famine impossible. In Lombardy, where
frightful storms destroy in a few moments cereals distributed over a
vast region of country, an article of food, which develops, grows, and
matures under the ground, sheltered from the ravages of hail, was an
inestimable gift to the whole population.

Volta had himself written a circumstantial account of his travels in
Switzerland; but it was hidden in the archives of Lombardy. Its recent
publication is due to a custom which, in all probability, will not soon
be adopted in a certain country, where a writer has dared to designate
marriage as the most serious of comic things, without being torn to
pieces for it. In Italy, where this act of our life is undoubtedly regarded
with more seriousness, each one, in his sphere of life, endeavors to sig-
nalize it by some act for the general good of his fellow-citizens. It was
the marriage of M. Antoine Reina, of Milan, in 1827, which brought to
light Volta's small work from the official portfolios of the government,
veritable catacombs, where, in all countries, heaps of treasures lie buried
forever.

Human institutions are so strange that the fortunes, the well-being,
the whole future of one of the greatest geniuses of whom Italy can

boast, were at the mercy of the administrator-general of Lombardy. I suppose that the ruling powers, in selecting this functionary, were led by their fastidiousness to require that a certain knowledge of finance should be superadded to the quarterings of nobility imperiously prescribed by etiquette ; and, notwithstanding, here was the man called on to decide, decide, too, without appeal [from his judgment] whether Volta deserved to be transferred to a wider theater, or, indeed, left a martyr at the small school of Como, he should be deprived during his whole life of costly accessories that certainly cannot supply the place of genius, but invest it with great power. Let us be quick to acknowledge that so far as Volta was concerned chance remedied the folly incident to such a state of dependence. Comte de Firmian, the administrator, was a friend to literature. The school of Pavia became the object of his assiduous care. He founded there a professorship of physics, and in 1779 Volta was elected to fill it. For many years crowds of young men from all countries thronged the lectures of the illustrious professor; there they learned, I will not say the details of science, for nearly all works on the subject give these, but the philosophical history of the principal discoveries; the subtile correlations which escape ordinary intelligence, and a matter which very few individuals have the privilege of divulging, the progress of discovery.

Volta's style was lucid, unaffected, and sometimes monotonous, but always characterized by modesty and refinement ; qualities which, when united to talents of the first order, are always attractive to youth. In Italy, where the imagination is so easily excited, they produced a genuine enthusiasm. The desire to boast before the world of the honor of being a disciple of Volta, contributed vastly for more than the third of a century to the wonderful success of the University of the Tessin.

The proverbial *far niente* of the Italians is strictly true as to physical exertion. They travel little, and among the very opulent families, some are found so thoroughly Roman that not even the sublime eruptions of Vesuvius can tempt them from the fresh shades of their villas. There are cultivated Florentines who have never seen Saint Peter's and the Coliseum except in engravings; Milanese who all their lives know only from hearsay that, at some leagues distant, there is an immense city and hundreds of magnificent palaces built in the sea. Volta himself only left the banks of his native Lario for the purpose of scientific researches. I do not think his travels in Italy extended as far as Naples and Rome. If, in 1780, he crossed the Apennines to go from Bologna to Florence, it was with the hope of finding an opportunity in the fires of *Pietra Mala, en route,* of submitting his views on the origin of natural inflammable gas to a decisive proof. If, in 1782, accompanied by the celebrated Scarpa, he visited the capitals of Germany, Holland, England, and France, it was to make the acquaintance of Lichtenberg, Van Marum, Priestley, Laplace, and Lavoisier, and to enrich the laboratory of Pavia with certain instruments for investigation and demonstration, of which descriptions and drawings, even those best executed, could give but an imperfect idea.

Accepting an invitation from General Bonaparte, the conqueror of Italy, Volta returned to Paris in 1801. He there repeated his experiments on electricity by contact, before a large committee of the Institute. The First Consul wished to be present at the meeting where the committee were to give a detailed account of these wonderful phenomena. Their conclusions were scarcely reached when he proposed to confer upon Volta a gold medal to commemorate the gratitude of the French scientists. Custom, or, we may add, academic regulations, scarcely sanctioned such a request, but rules are made for ordinary occasions, and the professor of Pavia had just placed himself outside of this line The medal was therefore voted by acclamation, and as Bonaparte did nothing by halves, the learned traveler received the same day, from the public fund, the sum of 2,000 crowns to defray his traveling expenses. The creation of a prize of 60,000 francs to be awarded to him who would give to the sciences of electricity and magnetism an impulse comparable to that received by the first of these sciences from Franklin and Volta, is not a less characteristic evidence of the enthusiasm of the great captain. This impression was lasting. The professor of Pavia became Napoleon's type of genius. Thus, step by step, we see him decorated with the crosses of the legion of honor and the iron crown, elected member of the Italian consulate, and elevated to the dignity of count and senator of the kingdom of Lombardy. When the Italian Institute appeared at the palace, if Volta, accidentally, was not in the front ranks, the abrupt questions, where is Volta; can he be sick; why did he not come? proved, only too evidently, perhaps, that, in the eyes of the sovereign, notwithstanding all their learning, the other members were but mere satellites of the inventor of the pile. "I cannot consent," said Napoleon in 1804, "to Volta's withdrawal. If his duties as professor are too fatiguing, they must be lessened. Let him deliver but one lecture during the year, if desired; but the University of Pavia would receive its death-blow the moment I allowed so illustrious a name to disappear from the list of its members; besides," added he, "a good general should die on the field of honor." The good general found the argument unanswerable, and the youth of Italy, whose idol he was, were thus enabled to enjoy a few more years of his delightful lectures.

Newton, during his parliamentary career, it is said, never spoke but once, and that was to ask the doorkeeper of the House of Commons to close a window to prevent a current of air giving cold to an orator when speaking. If the doorkeepers of Lyons, during the Italian consulate, and those of the senate at Milan, had been less careful, Volta, perhaps, from mere goodness of heart, if but for a moment, might have overcome his extreme reserve; but the opportunity not offering, the distinguished physicist will be inevitably classed with those personages who, whether from timidity or indifference, during long revolutions, are members of the most animated popular assemblies without giving an opinion or uttering a single word.

It has been said that happiness, like matter, is composed of imperceptible elements. If this idea of Franklin be correct, Volta was happy. Entirely devoted, in spite of high political dignities, to his studies, nothing disturbed his tranquillity. According to Solon's law he would have been exiled, for not one of the parties, for nearly a quarter of a century agitating Lombardy, could boast of numbering him in its ranks. The illustrious professor's name only re-appeared after the storm as an ornament to the existing authorities. Even in his most private intimacies Volta had the greatest aversion to any conversation relating to public matters. He did not hesitate, as soon as there was an opening, to cut it short by one of those witticisms or puns, called in Italy *freddure* and in France *calembour*. But, it must be confessed, practice here did not make perfect, as several of the *freddure* of the great physicist, not considered unworthy of being quoted, are far from being as irreproachable as his experiments.

Volta was married in 1794, at the age of forty-nine, to Mademoiselle Thérèse Peregrini. He had three sons, two surviving him and the other dying at the age of eighteen, just when he had given promise of the most brilliant talents. This was the only sorrow, I believe, our philosopher ever experienced during the whole of his long career. His discoveries were too brilliant, without any doubt, not to have aroused envy, but it never dared attack them, even under its most usual disguise, as it never questioned their novelty.

Contentions with regard to priority have been the torments of inventors in all ages. Spite, the sentiment to which it usually gives rise, it is not fastidious in the choice of its means of attack. When evidence is wanting, sarcasm becomes its favorite weapon, and it but too often possesses the cruel power of rendering it most cutting. It is related that Harvey, who had manfully resisted the numerous criticisms of which his discoveries had been the object, totally lost courage when certain adversaries, under pretense of concession, declared that they would concede to him the merit of having *circulated the circulation of the blood.* Let us congratulate ourselves, gentlemen, that Volta was never exposed to such contentions; let us congratulate his countrymen on having guarded him from them. The Bolognese school, for a long time, undoubtedly upheld the doctrine of animal electricity. Honorable sentiments of nationality induced them to desire that Galvani's discovery should remain entire; that it should not form a part of the grand phenomena of voltaic electricity as a peculiar clause; and yet they never alluded to the voltaic phenomena but with admiration. Never did an Italian mouth pronounce the name of the inventor of the pile without coupling it with the most unequivocal terms of esteem and profound respect, and without prefixing a word most expressive in its simplicity and especially sweet to the ears of a fellow-citizen; from Rovérédo to

Messina, educated people always spoke of the physicist of Pavia as *nostro* Volta.

I have mentioned the honors conferred upon him by Napoleon. All the great universities of Europe had invited him to join them. Of the eight foreign members of the Institute, he belonged to the first rank. So many honors never once excited in Volta's soul a sensation of pride. The small village of Como was always his favorite place of residence. The tempting and often repeated offers from Russia could not induce him to exchange the beautiful skies of Lombardy for the fogs of the Neva.

The predominant traits of the illustrious professor were strength and quickness of mind, comprehensiveness and justness of views, and truth and warmth of nature. No act of his life was ever prompted by ambition, love of money, or a spirit of rivalry. The love of study, his ruling and only passion, remained through life pure and unspotted by the world.

Volta was tall, with features as noble and regular as those of an antique statue; his broad brow was deeply furrowed by profound meditation and his countenance expressed both tranquillity of soul and penetration of mind. His manners always retained traces of the rusticity contracted in his youth. Many persons remember having seen him in Paris every day enter the baker's, and afterward, while walking the streets, eat the large rolls which he had just bought, without seeming to suspect that any one would remark it. I will be pardoned, I hope, so many minute particulars. Has not Fontenelle related that Newton had a thick suit of hair, never wore spectacles, and never lost but one tooth? Names so great justify and ennoble the most minute details. When, in 1819, Volta finally resigned the trust with which he had been invested at the University of the Tessin, he retired to Como. From this time all his relations with the scientific world ceased. He rarely received any of the numerous travelers who, attracted by his great reputation, came to pay him homage.

In 1823 a slight attack of apoplexy developed very serious symptoms; but prompt remedies soon succeeded in relieving him. Four years after, in 1827, in the beginning of March, the venerable old man was attacked by a fever, which, in the course of a few days, deprived him of his remaining strength. On the 5th of the same month he expired without suffering, at the age of eighty-two years and fifteen days.

Como celebrated Volta's obsequies with great pomp. The professors and students of the college, and all the friends of science, and the educated inhabitants of the village and its environs, hastened to accompany to their last resting-place the mortal remains of the illustrious scientist, the charitable citizen, and the man exemplary in all his domestic relations. The beautiful monument erected to his memory, near the picturesque village of *Camnago*, the native place of Volta's family, is a striking testimony of the sincerity of their regrets, and finally all Italy participated in the mourning of the Milanese.

On this side of the Alps the feeling excited was much less intense. Those who may think this strange, must remember that on the same day, almost at the same hour, France lost the author of " La Mécanique Céleste." Volta, for six years, had lived solely in his family. His active mind was almost gone. The names electrophorus and condenser, and even that of the pile, no longer possessed the power of making his heart beat. Laplace, on the contrary, retained up to his last hour that energy and activity of mind, that passionate love of scientific discoveries, which for more than half a century rendered him the soul of your reunions. When death surprised him, at the age of seventy-eight, he was publishing a sequel to the fifth volume of his great work. On reflecting on the immensity of such a loss, all will acknowledge, I doubt not, that there is great injustice in reproaching the academy for having at the first moment concentrated all its thoughts on the fatal blow it had just received. As for myself, gentlemen, I have never misunderstood your sentiments, and my only fear now is my inability to do all the justice you desire to the immeasurable services rendered to science by the illustrious professor of Pavia. I flatter myself, however, it will not be imputed to a want of conviction. In moments of pleasing revery, when passing in review all contemporary productions, any one can select, according to his habits, tastes, and bent of mind, without much discrimination, which one of these productions he would prefer to be the author of, " La Mécanique Céleste " or the voltaic pile; at the same time and always on the same level, they have presented themselves to my mind. An academician devoted to the study of the stars could not possibly give a more striking proof of the profound admiration which the immortal discoveries of Volta always inspired.

The place of foreign member, made vacant by Volta's death, was filled by Dr. Thomas Young. The academic corps is happy, gentlemen, when forced to recruit its ranks, to be able to succeed genius to genius.

THE PROBABLE FUTURE OF THE HUMAN RACE.

[From the History of Science and of Savants, by Alphonse de Candolle.—Translated for the Smithsonian Institution.]

It is not difficult to point out certain probabilities concerning the future destiny of the human race. This is, in some respects, determined naturally, but is wanting neither in importance nor interest.

In order to examine the question properly, it is necessary to bear in mind three principles: 1st, organized beings endowed with will and the faculty of locomotion always seek to adapt themselves to the circumstances in which they are placed, and none do so more effectually than man, on account of his superior intelligence; 2d, the individuals of the human species that are the least able to accommodate themselves to their circumstances are most liable to perish, or at least to leave a small number of descendants, so that populations are principally recruited by the individuals that possess the qualities best adapted to the circumstances of the country and the age in which they live; 3d, the violent contests between nations and individuals accelerate modifications and adaptations to new circumstances. The application of these laws compels us first to consider, as far as we are able, the circumstances, more or less immediate, in which our successors will probably find themselves.

If we take into consideration a near future, of a few centuries for example, or of a thousand years, we may anticipate a certain degree of stability in the physical conditions, general and even local, which affect the human species; at least, judging from the past, this seems to be highly probable. Climates have not changed since the time of the oldest historic documents. The configurations of the surface of the earth have been very little altered. Undoubtedly, geology shows us that there have been great changes, but ordinarily these took place very slowly. The supposition of a continuation of the present physical conditions during several generations of man is then presumable. Now, with the present conditions very nearly the same, it is easy to foresee two phenomena: 1st, the land will be more thickly inhabited, since certain very active and robust nations have sufficient intelligence to cross the seas, and, above all, because in every country the population constantly tends to increase; in other words, the men of our time will adapt themselves more and more to the conditions of existence offered them in their own country and elsewhere, these conditions involving an immense aug-

142

mentation of the general population of the globe; 2d, the continual transportation and passage of men from one part of the world to another will produce more and more frequent mingling of the races. Here, also, certain probabilities may be foreseen.

The races inferior in number, strength, physical condition, or intelligence must either disappear or be mingled with the races which are superior to them in all these qualities. Like the Australians, many of the races which inhabit the islands of the Pacific Ocean, the Hottentots, the natives of some parts of America, must disappear, in view of the impossibility of their struggling successfully against other nations, either in war or peace. The races less inferior, but not very active, of Mexico, Peru, and some parts of Asia, have already mingled with their conquerors, so as to constitute intermediate populations. But there are three principal races, endowed with admirable qualities for invasion, which will mix with the inferior races more or less according to local circumstances. These three principal races are: the white race, represented particularly by the Europeans and their American descendants; the yellow race, represented chiefly by the Chinese and the Japanese; and the negro race. The first has the advantage in intelligence, but it does not so well endure warm climates as the other two. The emigration of the whites to the equatorial countries will undoubtedly continue, but their offspring will be decimated in these warm regions, while those of the negroes and the Chinese will generally survive. Even the adults of the white race with difficulty endure the heat of southern countries. The mixed races will be at less disadvantage in the torrid zone than the white; but if the natural selection takes place in favor of the more colored individuals, the latter will at last prevail, in spite of all mingling. On the other hand, the negro race will not prosper in cold countries, and even the half-breeds do not bear a rigorous climate as well as the whites. In spite, then, of the mingling of the races, we may predict a continual predominance of the negroes in the equatorial, and of the whites in the colder regions. The Chinese alone seem at once sufficiently intelligent and robust to struggle in all latitudes with both these races. They are already numerous, and have commenced to emigrate. On account of their psychical and physiological qualities, and also their ingenuity and inquisitiveness, they ought to supplant the other races; but they lack courage, and are not trustworthy. The whites of Europe and of the United States will sustain the struggle, thanks to their habitual bravery, their facility of comprehension, and the confidence they can place in each other. The negroes also will prevail on account of their physical vigor. The mingling of the three principal races will not, however, be complete. There will be many and every degree of hybrid or mixed races; but in Africa, in China, and in the north of our hemisphere, the primitive races will probably continue to predominate for many centuries.

Let us now consider a future more remote, for example of fifty thousand, one hundred thousand, or even of several hundred thousands of years. It is still possible to foresee for these distant times certain tendencies and certain conditions of the human species. We should, however, bear in mind that which renders doubtful even the most plausible suppositions. For a lapse of time so prolonged, we cannot tell whether some great terrestrial or cosmical event may not change absolutely external conditions. Our globe may experience depressions and elevations which may alter entirely the nature of the habitable surface. New diseases may be manifested among men of which we have now no idea. These maladies may destroy a whole race or even affect the entire human species. Astronomers have shown us that the variations of the plane of the ecliptic and of the eccentricity of the earth's orbit are not of a nature to produce any sensible change in climates. In stating this fact, however, Mr. Croll [*] is compelled to admit that the accumulation of ice, the effect of the latter cause acting alternately upon the north and upon the south pole, must produce changes in the currents and in the dominant winds, which must be followed by changes in climate in all parts of the world. There must have been several glacial periods in each hemisphere. The least ancient in the northern hemisphere must have commenced about two hundred and forty thousand and ended about eighty thousand years ago. Sir Charles Lyell [†] has disputed the opinions of Mr. Croll, and according to him the periodicity of the glacial periods must be very uncertain. Still we cannot overlook the possibility of such events, the effect of which would be to drive all organized beings from each polar region toward the temperate zones, and those of the temperate regions to the equatorial, producing naturally the extinction of many species, and as regards man of many races.

Finally, who can foresee what may happen to our entire solar system? It is moving with great rapidity in a certain direction. Perhaps some time it may come into some part of the universe much warmer or colder than the space it has passed through for several millions of years. The sun, also, may change. Events such as these may destroy not only man but all the organized beings of our globe.

Setting aside these hypothetical cases, which are beyond the power of science to foresee, let us pass to facts which are, on the contrary, absolutely certain.

The effect of the oxygen of the air, and the incessant action of human labor, is diminishing the quantity of metals and of coal, accessible without too much effort, on the surface of the earth. Undoubtedly, the genius of *savants* will discover processes for working mines to greater depths, and for profiting by the metallic oxides distributed through the soil. New combustibles also may be discovered, but they can never be as advantageous as those we now enjoy, and the metallic dust, as for

---

[*] Croll, in Edinburgh Philosophical Magazine, 1867 and 1868.
[†] Sir Charles Lyell, Principles of Geology, latest edition.

example that of worn iron, which is everywhere scattered on the earth, will be much more difficult to obtain than the primitive accumulations of to-day.   There must be necessarily a diminution of population as these essential resources become rare and more and more inaccessible, until finally they are quite exhausted.   The people will then be in a most unhappy condition.   There will be no railroads, no steamboats, nothing which requires coal or metal.   Their industries will gradually be reduced as copper and iron become scarce.   Certain populations at once sedentary and agricultural, living in the warm countries and able to content themselves with little, will then be the best adapted to the general circumstances of the globe.   At the tropics, therefore, and in the vicinity of the great accumulations of coal in the United States, populations will remain longest collected in masses.   The rarity of the metals, however, will be a cause of decadence, even in these privileged localities.

Another change, slower but equally sure, is the diminution of terrestrial surfaces, and particularly the lowering of elevated regions, by the incessant action of water, of ice, and of air.   For thousands of years, every stream, every river, has carried toward the ocean solid particles detached from these heights, and this slow process must continue.   The mean lowering of continents has been calculated from the ooze of the principal rivers, supposing proportions to be constant.   Such calculations, however, rest upon conditions too variable to merit much confidence; but the tendency of the change is certain.   Upon high mountains and in the polar regions, glaciers corrode the hardest rocks and carry solid substances to the rivers.   Less elevated surfaces are in like manner depressed by the action of water.   The ooze is finally transferred to the bottom of the seas; and as the latter have already an extent much greater than the land and a depth surpassing the elevation of the highest mountains, it is clear that the solid land habitable by man will diminish relatively to the liquid surface.   In other words, the bottom of the seas is filling up in part and the surface must rise more or less, if we suppose the liquid mass constant.   At the same time, for several centuries the additions to certain coasts may be considered equal to the erosions of others, and partial elevations counteracted by equal depressions.

Thus, independent of abnormal events, which it is impossible to foresee, all existing phenomena indicate that the islands and continents must first diminish in elevation, then in extent, and we may predict that in some far distant future a very nearly complete submersion of terrestrial surfaces will take place, and consequently a destruction more or less complete of all organized beings, vegetable and animal, which live upon these surfaces, or even in fresh waters.   The human species, on account of superior intelligence, may survive longer than the others; but they also will then be near their end, since they will be able to live only upon boats, and there will be neither wood nor metal of which these can be constructed.   The submersion of continents will probably not be general, and volcanic or coral islands forming, there will remain a few points inhabited by man ; but of the isolation of their condition it is difficult to form an idea.

Before this extreme period, that events impossible to predict may still further remove, we should imagine the human species deprived gradually of the treasures of coal and the metals to-day within reach, and obliged to concentrate themselves upon terrestrial surfaces less in extent and insulated, as they apparently have already existed in very ancient geological times. The scarcity of the combustibles and of the metals would render communication difficult. The depression of the mountain-chains would diminish the condensation of aqueous vapors, and increase the extent of sterile regions, and countries now fertile would become like those in the interior of Australia. During this period, the populations would greatly diminish, but intelligence and morality, perhaps, having increased, this reduction would not be produced, as now, by a frightful mortality among the improvident, and still more horrible accessories, such as infanticide and war. Man may be, for example, in such a condition as to be able to control the proportion of masculine and feminine births, which is not at all improbable, according to the example of other organized species. The result would be an increasing rarity of females, and a considerable diminution of births.

In proportion as the continents, deprived of mountains, become dry in the interior, or divided into archipelagoes, the people will become more and more maritime. From the sea they will be obliged to draw the greater part of the means of subsistence ; but they will have to struggle against the encroachments of its waves. The intelligent and persevering will then be the best adapted to the circumstances ; and, in spite of their isolation, and the difficulties of navigation, they may still prosper. They may even enjoy the well-being which results from a peaceable existence ; for at this time, without metals or combustibles, it would be difficult to form squadrons to dominate the seas, and grand armies to ravage the land.

The mingling of the old races will be arrested by the separation of the terrestrial surfaces into small portions, and by the increasing difficulty of communication. What remains of the at present three principal races will probably be greatly dispersed. The islands of the northern and southern regions being exposed to the more or less periodical invasion of ice, and having no contiguity with lands better situated, the white race, which will have continued longer here than in the equatorial regions, will be that which will suffer the most. In the central archipelagoes, the colored races, remaining as pure as at present, on account of natural selection during their long isolation, will fare better.

To recapitulate, our period and that which will follow for the next thousand years will be characterized by a great increase in population, a mingling of races, and a prosperity more or less marked. Then will probably follow a long period of diminution of population, of separation of the people, and of decadence. Is not this what generally happens when there is a struggle between different influences ? Fixed, certain causes increase or diminish slowly. We find to-day that many animal species have become extinct. They at first became rare. Often driven from their habitations, from place to place, they were at last reduced to a single district, where some cause, perhaps a very unimportant one, ended their existence. In former times, if we can judge sufficiently from geological data, the living species have had a period of abundance and extension followed by one of rarity and limitation. The human species will describe in the same way a sort of curve, the extremes of which escape our powers of observation, while the mean part powerfully excites our attention. We know that one of these extremes has already existed; we foresee the time when man will occupy all the habitable surface of the earth, and will have consumed that which is now found accumulated by a long series of geological events. Without much imagination, we can then foresee the other part of the curve, tending to some final point in the far future. Such are the probabilities according to the existing state of things ; but the longer the time considered, the more it is necessary to admit the possibility of events unknown, unforeseen, impossible even to be foreseen, which may introduce entirely different conditions.

In these suppositions or reflections I am at variance with Messrs. Spencer and Galton in their writings upon this subject. Mr. Spencer* speaks very little of the physical conditions to which man will be subject. He mentions only the alternation of ice at the two poles as necessarily in time displacing man. Notwithstanding the calculations and the hypothesis of Mr. Croll, this is perhaps the least certain and the least important of the material modifications which the human species will encounter. The increasing rarity of coal and the metals is much more evident, much nearer at hand, especially the rarity of such deposits of coal as are easily attained. As to the modifications of man himself, produced through variability, competition, and the selection which results, Mr. Spencer analyzes the question with skill, but, in my opinion, not completely. The struggle, he says, becomes from century to century more active on account of the increase of the population, and the progress of science, industry, and commerce, which compels individuals to seek more knowledge and to exert greater effort. There will be, on this account, probably a more and more marked development of the intellectual faculties, (vol. ii, pp. 496, 499,) and also those of morality, (p. 497.) From these new intellectual and moral conditions, he says, there will result a less degree of fecundity, which will become another source of moral and intellectual progress.

Mr. Galton† reasons very nearly the same as Mr. Spencer in what concerns the probable intellectual development ; only he fears that the

---

* Herbert Spencer's Principles of Biology, vol. ii, book 6, ch. 13.
† Galton, Hereditary Genius, pp. 336-362.

amelioration of the faculties in the races already advanced will not be effected with sufficient rapidity to keep pace with the growing needs of a civilization which increases enormously. After having proved the extinction of several savage races through the simple effect of a struggle they could not sustain against the white race, he adds:* "We also, the promoters of an advanced civilization, we begin to show that we are incapable of progressing intellectually with the same rapidity as the demands which are made upon us. The needs of centralization, of communication, and of culture demand more brain and more mental energy than our race possess. There is loud demand for greater capacity in every social position. Neither statesmen, savants, artisans, nor laborers are entirely equal to the present complications of their different professions. .... Our race is overburdened; it seems about to degenerate, because its requirements are greater than its means. When the struggle for existence is not too great for the strength of a race, it is beneficial and conservative, otherwise it is mortal."

We may doubt some of these assertions. For example, centralization does not complicate ; it simplifies. There is, in fact, as much prevision required, as many difficulties to surmount, as much energy employed in the management of a number of small workshops, a number of small independent populations, as in the control, by a single order, of thousands of workmen and thousands of inhabitants. The division of labor also simplifies, and this always augments with civilization. It has been said, however, in regard to this, that the powers of the mind are weakened when each individual thinks only of a single thing. In this point of view, such division in highly-civilized populations is a hinderance to intellectual development.

In general, the two authors I have just quoted, while making remarks very just, sometimes very original and worthy of attention, appear to me to have somewhat forgotten the inequality of development of different classes and people, as well as the numerous causes which lead to a selection, in the bad sense of the term, or to the arrest of a selection. History, moreover, is in accord with theory in showing to what degree the advance of intelligence and morality is irregular and doubtful, even during the lapse of several thousands of years. From the time of Socrates to that of Lavoisier, how many eminent men have died a miserable death, victims of the force and ignorance of the many! How many cultivated populations have disappeared! How many savage invasions have occurred! I do not refer only to those which destroyed the Roman empire, but also to the despicable Chinese and other invasions in the civilized countries of to-day. Mr. Spencer admits with reason† that a development of the nervous system has the effect of diminishing the additions to population, and, as he considers such a development probable, sees in it a double cause of satisfaction for the future. Populations will thus tend to become stationary as to number just as they have

---

covered the terrestrial surface with very intelligent individuals. But from this happy period, and even, I suppose, during this period, there will be some families less intelligent and less provident than others. These will make the greatest additions to the population, and their numbers constantly renewed will greatly affect the supposed progression of intelligence, to say nothing of other causes of arrest.

In order to comprehend the probable facts in all their significance, and to connect them with the laws of selection, it is absolutely necessary, 1st, to attribute a major importance to the material circumstances, which must be manifested from the present time during several thousands of years; 2d, to apply the principle of the theory of Mr. Darwin to the human species. I call the principle of the theory the forced adaptation of organized beings to surrounding circumstances of every kind, the result of which is that the modifications preserved are sometimes good, sometimes bad—that is, according to our human conception of what is good or bad. We may form an idea in regard to goodness and perfection, but the course of events may not be in accordance with this idea, since many obstacles may intervene during a series of several thousands of years. The world to-day is occupied by an infinite number of vegetable and animal species, partially developed and imperfect, if the complication of organs and the division of functions can be considered imperfections. These inferior beings are adapted to the circumstances which now exist. They are better adapted to these circumstances than others we call superior, and it will be so perhaps for an immense series of centuries. We may say the same of human races and families. The rudest are sometimes the best adapted to certain conditions. Thus, the negroes perfectly resist equatorial climates, and in our civilized countries there are debased populations which accommodate themselves to miserable conditions of life such as others could not at all endure.

If men content with little did not exist, they would be formed by variability and selection. We do not know to what extent frugality and indifference to comfort might be carried in the human race, if it were not for the intervention of police-regulations and public opinion. According to what has been related of Hindoo and Egyptian agriculturists, long-continued hardship produces a granivorous or frugivorous race, singularly economical and very fruitful. In our great cities of Europe, notwithstanding the severity of climate, we should find families established in damp, subterranean abodes, under bridges, even in sewers, and adapting themselves to the conditions of existence by the premature death of the most feeble, if the will of other men did not interfere. Furthermore, coarse and immoral individuals are unfortunately adapted to certain conditions of civilized countries, such as revolutions, robbery, unjust appropriation of property by needy legislators, wars without sufficient grounds, aggressive, &c., while other individuals are adapted to conditions moral, wise, just, &c., which at the same time exist. If at

any time there should be more intelligent, and consequently more provident, men than now, there would also be among them, or in association
with them, others less intelligent and less provident, who would appropriate their goods and disregard their rights. Optimism is very seductive,
since it has power to mislead even the most practical of men,* but it is not
in conformity with the facts of the past nor the probable facts of the future.
If we judge only from known and credible conditions, selection in a good
sense affects the human race in a very doubtful, temporary, and slow
way.   It would then be a fallacy to construct, upon the basis of the
modern ideas of naturalists, the theory of indefinite improvement,
adopted by certain French philosophers of the last century.   An attentive study of the works of Mr. Darwin allows no conclusion in this direction, and the opinion of certain writers should be guarded against,† that
the often-to-be-regretted tendency of the human species is an objection
to the law of selection.

---

* See the Utopia with which Mr. Büchner ends his fourth lecture, (trad. pauc., p. 178.)
† In Fraser's Magazine for September, 1868, there is an article, not signed, but the
author of which has been indicated by Mr. Darwin, (Descent of Man, I, p. 167,) entitled
"Failure of natural selection in the case of man."   The facts given by the author are,
on the contrary, an exact and extended application of the law of selection.   Mr. Darwin has never believed that moral progress must be the necessary result of selection.
(See Descent of Man, I, pp. 166, 177, and elsewhere.)

REPORT ON THE TRANSACTIONS OF THE SOCIETY OF PHYSICS AND NATURAL HISTORY OF GENEVA FROM JULY, 1873, TO JULY, 1874.

By Prof. M. A. de Candolle, President.

[Translated for the Smithsonian Institution by M. A. Henry.]

Gentlemen: It is customary to divide this report into two parts, one appropriated to personal matters, and especially to the notice of the members deceased during the year, the other to the labors of the society. In this case the first part must unhappily be long, but in view of the serious losses sustained, you will find, I am sure, that I have not entered too much in detail.

I.—NECROLOGICAL NOTICES.

We have this year lost three of our ordinary members, Messrs. Alexandre Prevost, Gosse, and de la Rive, and four of our honorary members, Agassiz, Ramon de la Sagra, Fée, and Quetelet.

Alexandre-Pierre Prevost, doctor of sciences, was grandson of the professor of philosophy and physicist, Pierre Prevost. He made good progress in his studies at Geneva, and completed them by a sojourn at Berlin. The branch with which he was principally occupied in the latter city was animal physiology. Certain circumstances, easy to comprehend, induced him to enter into a banking-house of considerable note in London, which had for a long time been under the direction of his father and his uncles, but his health was affected by the climate of England, and after a few years he returned to Geneva. His scientific tastes then revived and were stimulated by the encouragement of his near relatives, and by his father-in-law, M. Auguste de la Rive. He published in the quarto *Mémoires* of our society (vol. xi) researches upon the nervous system of the head of the conger; in 1843 in the *Bibliothèque Universelle*, and in 1859 in the *Archives*, which supplemented the scientific part of the same journal, two memoirs upon binocular vision; in the *Archives* of the same year, 1859, an essay upon the mathematical theory of music, not to speak of numerous articles, such as reviews or criticisms in this journal, of which he was one of the editors. Alexandre Prevost served our society for a long time as secretary, and was always explicit and exact in the conscientious discharge of the duties of the office. He died on the 21st of July, 1873, in England, after a long illness, at the age of only fifty-two years.

Dr. Andre-Louis Gosse was son of Henry-Albert Gosse, that savant, so full of enthusiasm and originality, who, with the founders of the Helvetic

151

Society of Natural Sciences, in 1815 conceived first the idea of forming a scientific society which should meet, like the British Association, in a different place every year.*   Andre-Louis Gosse inherited many of the good qualities of his father.   He, like him, displayed throughout his life an extraordinary zeal for the good of his fellow-men.   His studies, his travels, his medical practice, his conversation, his writings, were inspired by this feeling; and no one could converse with him and not be affected by the influence of his generous sentiments.   While he was still a student at Paris, and soon after, in 1816, a young practitioner, his courage was put to the test in the hospital at Geneva, where several physicians had died of a severe typhus fever introduced by the armies.   On the return of peace, wishing to obtain a knowledge of the clinics of Italy, Germany, and England, and also to gain more experience of life, he traveled for three years always in a private carriage, on horseback, or on foot.   In these expeditions he carried his observations into all classes of society, and even submitted to serious privations in order to gain the confidence of the miserable peasants of some of the countries he visited.   While in Edinburgh he made known to the medical corps of that city a double-current catheter of his invention, which since, through mistake, has been attributed to Jules Cloquet.   On his return home, and having acquired a satisfactory practice, Gosse was seized with the enthusiasm then manifested in Geneva in favor of the independence of Greece.   He offered his services gratuitously to the committee of arrangements, and started at the most critical moment in the history of the contest to lend his aid and assistance in the organization for the supply of ambulances and military hospitals.   The energy he displayed was of great value to this unfortunate country—the seat of war, of pestilence, and moral disorder.

This work completed, he had entered again, not without difficulty, into the practice of medicine, when another occasion of self-devotion was presented to him.   The Swiss federal authorities were alarmed by the invasion of the north of Europe by cholera.   This was in 1831, the time of the first prevalence of the epidemic, and very little was known of this mysterious and frightful disease.   Gosse volunteered to study it from actual observation, and completed the undertaking "*sans peur et sans reproche.*"   His knowledge thus acquired was not, however, practically applied, for Switzerland never became a prey to the true cholera epidemic.   After such examples of courage and self-abnegation it is hardly necessary to add that Gosse never recoiled from any duty, either as citizen or physician.   He also manifested great zeal in the gratuitous care of the poor, in diminishing drunkenness, in ameliorating the condition of prisons, as well as in acting as mediator, although without success, in the unhappy political divisions of the country.

* The German Society of Naturalists and Physicians was instituted in imitation of the Swiss society.   The British Association, the Society of the *Scienzati*, of Italy, and others of a similar character, were formed later.

Dr. Gosse published a volume upon the diseases he called, in a general way, "*Rhumatöides;*" another entitled "Medical and Philosophical Examination of the Penitentiary System;" an account of the pestilence which reigned in Greece in 1827 and 1828; a monograph of the valuable shrub called *Erythroxylon Coca,* and a number of articles or pamphlets upon the *régime* of prisons, quarantines, economical fermented drinks, Turkish baths, various questions of hygiene, the deformations of the skull practiced among certain nations, ancient and modern, and other subjects of anthropology. His activity expended itself upon a great number of subjects, either of immediate practical utility or of theory. Any ill effects of this discursiveness were obviated by a peculiar power he had of being completely absorbed, for a time, by each subject. The various questions which engaged his attention were not mingled in his mind; they succeeded each other, and, when pre-occupied with an idea, he pursued it with indefatigable ardor. This is not the system of the constant application of specialists to a single branch, nor is it that of the diffusion of force upon several simultaneous studies which so rarely produces good effects. The activity of our honorable colleague was continued until the age of eighty-two years. He died in the full possession of his faculties on the 24th of October, 1873.

In a scientific point of view the greatest loss we have experienced this year has been that of our illustrious president, Auguste de la Rive. His place cannot be supplied among us, for his influence was due to many very varied conditions which are seldom found united : superior intelligence, a decisive and controlling will, a benevolent disposition, an ardent desire to enlighten and direct, and a peculiarly advantageous social position and relations, both within and without the country. Such a combination explains why in our re-unions he was so frequently what the English call a *leader.*

Born at Geneva, on the 4th of October, 1801, De la Rive pursued his studies in the old academy. Before the law of 1825, the instruction in that institution was very incomplete. The young men desirous to learn were themselves obliged to supply deficiencies; but does not a man, if he wishes to do so, find in himself a good master? De la Rive had, moreover, in his family an inappreciable advantage. His father,* a man of intelligence and originality, had a great love for chemistry. He taught it voluntarily, although a member of the higher administration of the country. In his laboratory or in his parlor were constantly found distinguished savans whose conversation was well calculated to excite the zeal of a young man : Berzelius, Davy, Faraday, Ampère, Arago, without mentioning the illustrious men of Geneva, spoken of by our colleague in so interesting a manner in his notice of Augustus Pyramus de Candolle. To learn the results of their labors, to hear their discus-

---

* Gaspard de la Rive, syndic, doctor and professor. See his biography by Vaucher, *Bibliothèque Universelle,* March, 1834.

sions, and realize early that a man devoted to science is not an exceptional being, but that any one may enter into the pursuit of knowledge without necessarily considering himself a genius, was the highest kind of teaching, was a stimulus both intellectual and moral.

Auguste de la Rive profited so well by his advantages that at the age of twenty-three years he was able to present himself as a candidate for a situation as professor of physics, which had just been created, and obtained it, after passing through the preliminary competition for it with distinction. This was a fortunate circumstance for him. Without this nomination, which attached him definitely to one branch of science, he might perhaps have allowed himself to be diverted into many directions. He was much interested in politics, local and general. He would have been solicited to enter the administration, and would probably have consented. Thanks to his election he concentrated his activity upon the teaching and the development of a particular science. He occupied himself very actively with the organization and direction of public instruction. As rector of the academy, and professor, he exercised over his colleagues and the youth under his care a very important influence. Politics, properly so called, became in his life only a secondary interest. Once only his tastes in this direction attained ascendency over him, when, on account of extreme distress, in my opinion legitimate, caused by a revolution, he resigned his office of professor in order to tender his services to his country, although all his colleagues, as well as the ecclesiastics and judges, less influenced by political ideas, considered themselves quite independent of all vicissitudes of public order. De la Rive then accepted a temporary mission for Switzerland to the English government, and the charge, also temporary, of deputy to a constituent assembly. This was, however, but an episode. We may say that above all else his time and heart were consecrated to science, his friends, and his family. Working during the morning in his laboratory, he afterward exercised a liberal hospitality either at his country-residence, Presinge, or at his house in Geneva. Notwithstanding the interest these details must have for those who knew De la Rive, I must return to what constituted his claim to renown, his scientific labors. These were already worthy of attention during the years 1824 to 1828, before he had especially directed his researches to the subject of electricity.

We all know how deep and unalterable was the friendship which existed between Auguste de la Rive and our colleague, François Marcet. These two friends made in company during the years I have mentioned several journeys to Paris and London, and in the intervals occupied themselves with scientific labors. Their investigations in regard to the specific heat of gases were important, since the subsequent experiments of Regnault

---

* Mémoires de la Société de physique et d'histoire naturelle de Genève, vol. vi, p. 503.

†Mémoires de la Soc. de phys. et d'hist. nat (1, p. 70,) et Bibl. univ Sc. et Arts, vol. xxxix, p. 206.

have confirmed them, only rendering them somewhat more exact. Then followed their work upon the increase of temperature in the artesian wells of Pregny. It was known that heat increased with depth in the excavations of mines, but the observations of Auguste de la Rive and Marcet gave the progression of temperature to 650 feet, in a determined locality. I had the satisfaction at this time to make a series of experiments with De la Rive upon the conductibility of heat in different woods. We established a fact which finds application in vegetable physiology, namely, that heat passes less easily in the transversal than in the longitudinal direction of the fibers. While mentioning this investigation I cannot resist the pleasure of dwelling upon the extreme modesty and amiability of De la Rive as a collaborator. Notwithstanding his great talent, he announced his opinions and accepted those of others with a charming simplicity and absence of self-assertion. As he appeared to me in his youth, so he continued even to the close of his life, when, weary and ill, he made with our young secretary, M. Edouard Sarasin, some original researches upon electricity in rarefied gases.

Ampère and Faraday did much to excite De la Rive to the study of electrical phenomena; but from the constitution of his mind I am induced to believe that the desire to establish firmly an important law, namely, that chemical phenomena are the source of electricity, was the principal motive which led him in this direction. How he succeeded in establishing this law, what ingenious contrivances he invented to prove it, and the multiplied consequences he deduced from his experiments, I cannot as a naturalist, and unacquainted with the details of physics, adequately describe. One of our colleagues, much better qualified, will refer to them particularly in an article upon De la Rive, which will be inserted in the *Archives des Sciences*. I have read a few pages of this article, and although the publication of it may not be entire, the following paragraphs will undoubtedly be retained, at least in their general import :

" In a long series of memoirs, De la Rive has passed in review most of the properties of the pile, and the effects produced by currents, contributing thus in a great degree to determine the laws and to throw light upon these complex phenomena, which were still very little understood at the beginning of the century.

" In the course of these great researches, the subject which most attracted his interest and efforts was the chemical theory of the pile. The cause of the disengagement of electricity in this apparatus had been attributed by its illustrious inventor to the contact of the two different metals which form an essential part of it. The chemical action exercised by the liquids upon the metals, was considered by Volta and his partisans as an accessory phenomenon, hardly as an effect of the current. But in proportion as the numerous relations of electricity and chemical actions were more and more exposed, the opposite theory commenced to gain ground. De la Rive for many years was one of its most ardent champions, denying that the contact of two different substances could alone produce a disengagement of electricity without chemical calorific or mechanical action.   To-day, when the dynamic theory of heat is universally adopted, this question in all its important points may be considered as resolved in favor of the view De la Rive sought to maintain.   The motive force in the galvanic pile is incontestably the chemical action, and the sum of the work produced under various forms in the circuit is equivalent to the total amount of heat which this chemical action can disengage.   If the contact of the metals, or of the metals and the liquids, has some influence—a fact still disputed—this acts as a mechanism for transformation of the force, but is incapable of creating the force itself."

" De la Rive reviewed his investigations and views in regard to this branch of science in the *Traité d'Electricité, théorique et appliquée*, which he published both in English and French from 1853 to 1858.   This admirable work did not end his productive labors in this direction, and among the researches undertaken since that time we may mention his experiments upon the sounds produced by the combined action of currents and magnets, his investigations in regard to the magnetic-rotatory polarization, and his works upon the passage of currents through rarefied gas.   The latter led to his theory of the aurora borealis, which, when he announced it, was coolly received; but every day gains new partisans."

The researches upon electricity of our learned member seemed rather theoretical than practical; but we know that the most varied applications, and often the most important, may unexpectedly proceed from the most abstract scientific principle.   De la Rive invented incidentally, while engaged in his investigations, the application of the galvanic pile to electrical gilding.   He received for this the sum of 3,000 francs from the Academy of Sciences of Paris, and with the revenue of this amount, which he gave to the Society of Arts of Geneva, a prize is offered every five years for the scientific discovery most useful to Genevese industry.

For some years the memoirs of Auguste de la Rive upon electricity, and those sent him upon the same subject, were so numerous as to necessitate the appropriation of an entire journal to them alone.   The *Archives des sciences physiques et naturelles* supplied this need.   This publication, which constituted the scientific part of the *Bibliothèque universelle*, was for a time, as well as the latter journal, immediately dependent upon De la Rive, but he always endeavored to include the assistance of his friends in its preparation.   It is evident from the number of articles upon all branches of science, that he never interfered with the freedom or direction of thought.   On the contrary, he was glad to collect good observations upon all subjects.   His great intellectual capacity, as broad as it was deep, readily accepted ideas the most varied in character, in the moral and political, as well as in the physical and natural sciences, while he still retained unimpaired interest in the especial object of his labors. Although he exercised the full powers of his mind in the preparation of his memoirs, yet the most complex questions were apparently to him very simple. He seemed to treat the varied and complicated matters of government and science which engaged his thoughts very much as an accomplished chess-player carries on several games at once without seeming to regard any one of them with especial attention.

Even the most powerful organization of the nervous system must in time give way, and with De la Rive the physical force was not equal to the intellectual requirement. Great energy is exhausting when old age prevents the regular renovation of the faculties. De la Rive experienced a slight attack of paralysis in the spring of last year, and in the autumn when he intended to go to the south of France for the improvement of his health he was seized with a second attack, much more severe, of which he died at Marseilles, on the 27th of November, 1873, aged seventy-two years. To-day, then, remains to us only the memory of this beautiful life, and an example well worthy of regard.

After De la Rive to mention Agassiz, his associate in all the scientific societies, and in the list of the eight foreign associates of the Academy of Sciences of Paris, seems but a natural transition. The life of this savant is full of interest, but in speaking of it as I should I encounter a peculiar difficulty. For thirty years the journals of every country have never lost sight of Agassiz. When in the midst of his career an excellent notice was published of him, and hardly had he closed his eyes when innumerable journals, American and European, contained detailed necrological articles concerning him. To extract from these, comment upon them, and complete them would require a volume. I will confine myself, then, to a few general observations, adding only some authentic details upon a point forgotten or generally unknown, but which is of considerable importance, both as regards Agassiz and the history of the scientific development of Switzerland. I speak of the causes which determined the learned naturalist to fix his abode in the city of Neuchâtel rather than in Germany or at Paris.

Louis-Jean-Rudolphe Agassiz was born on the 28th of May, 1807. His father was a Protestant clergyman who resided then at Mottier, canton of Friburg, and afterward established himself at Concise, not far from Neuchâtel. He manifested, it is said, from his infancy, an enthusiasm for natural history, and especially for the study of the habits of the fish of our lakes, an indication of his future tastes. He passed through the gymnasium of Bienne, and afterward the academic course of Lausanne. Having a great desire to engage in the pursuit of science, he obtained from his father permission to study surgery, which he did successfully at Zurich, Heidelberg, and Munich. It was in the latter city he received his diploma of doctor. As he had prepared an article upon fresh-water fishes, M. de Martius then proposed to him to undertake the description of the fishes of Brazil, which his traveling companion Spix, prematurely deceased, had hardly commenced. This was a great honor for a young man of twenty-one years.   Soon Agassiz turned his attention to fossil fishes, the field of his principal discoveries.   For his studies in this direction he felt the need of examining larger collections than had yet come in his way, and for this end, and also to perfect his medical education, he visited Vienna and Paris.

In the latter capital he made the acquaintance of Cuvier, and also of Humboldt, who was always ready to countenance and encourage young students, and was, at the same time, much interested in Neuchâtel, of which the King of Prussia was prince and in some sort suzerain.   I have had the pleasure of reading several letters addressed by Agassiz and Humboldt to M. Louis Coulon, of Neuchâtel.   With the permission of this honorable gentleman I will give a few extracts.   We will see from these that Switzerland was indebted to him for the establishment of Agassiz within her borders for fourteen years, a circumstance which had an important influence, not only upon his own labors, but also those of his compatriots.   M. Louis Coulon was assisted in attaining this end by his father, a merchant of long standing, a generous friend of science, who has given important collections to the city of Neuchâtel.

Agassiz to M. Louis Coulon.

"COPEAU STREET No. 4, PARIS, *March* 27, 1832.

*   *   *   "I have had the good fortune, I will not say to merit, but to win the good-will of M. Cuvier, who has placed at my disposal all the objects I wished to examine.   He has extended to me a generosity far beyond what a young man of my age ought to expect, who has as yet done but little for science.   You have seen the materials I have collected for the history of fossil fishes; you know also that on my departure for Paris I was afraid I would not be able to examine the specimens in the museum with all the freedom I desired, and I felt all the more sure of such restriction because M. Cuvier had announced a work upon this important subject, which he proposed to publish as soon as he had finished his great history of fishes.   M. Cuvier, however, not only allowed me to describe, compare, and draw from all the skeletons of existing fishes and all the fossils which are disposed in the galleries, but placed in my hands all the material he had himself collected for his own work, and even all the drawings he had ordered to be made at the British Museum and elsewhere ; and, having other important matters to occupy his attention after the completion of his work on the living fishes, and considering that I would acquit myself sufficiently well in the task I had undertaken with the fossils, left me to fill up this gap alone.   You may imagine how such encouragement inspires my zeal, and with what ardor I pursue my work.   This is one of the reasons why I refuse to see any one here, in order that my mind may not be distracted.

*   *   *   "When in the course of last summer I had the pleasure of seeing you I several times expressed to you my great desire to be settled near you, and my intention to endeavor to obtain the chair of natural history

you are about to establish in your lyceum. Your affairs must be in a more advanced state now than last year, and I would be greatly obliged if you would give me some information concerning them. I have communicated my projects to M. de Humboldt, whom I see frequently, who shows great interest in me, and aids me with his good counsel.

* * * "In my different journeys, through my relations and through exchanges I have made a very pretty collection of natural history, especially rich in the classes with which your museum is the least furnished, and which can fill the gaps in the collections in the city of Neuchâtel and render them more than sufficient for a complete course of natural history. I have also thought you might include in the plan you propose to adopt for the lyceum the increase of your zoölogical collections, and, if so, I dare to think mine would amply fulfill the end you wish to attain. If this should be the case I offer it to you. The expense of arranging it, of providing a place for it, and of its support is beyond my means, and I must endeavor to dispose of it, although it will cost me much to part from these companions of study, with which I have made almost all my researches. I have also spoken of this project to M. de Humboldt, who is much interested in the matter, and will, if this transfer takes place, make all the necessary arrangements with the government. You will do me a great service, then, if you will give me your opinion in the matter, and tell me, 1st, upon whom depends the nomination for the chair of natural history ; 2d, upon whom will depend the purchase of my collection; 3d, what you think I will have to do to accomplish these two objects. You may imagine I do not wish to give up my collections unless I have the prospect of being so situated as to be able to consult them freely."

At this time M. de Humboldt delicately remitted to his young friend the sum necessary to continue his sojourn at Paris, and M. Louis Coulon, on his part, obtained the creation of a chair of natural history for the college of Neuchâtel. In the meanwhile a very sad event occurred. Cuvier died of an attack of cholera, on the 13th of May, 1832.

Here is a second letter from Agassiz to M. L. Coulon :

"PARIS, *June* 4, 1832.

"SIR: I have received with much pleasure your interesting letter, and hasten to reply to it. What you have written gives me the more pleasure, that I see in it the immediate prospect of establishing myself near you, and of being able to consecrate to my country the fruit of my labors. It is true, as you suppose, that the death of M. Cuvier has sensibly changed my prospects ; for example, that I can, for the continuation of my work upon fishes, associate myself with M. Valenciennes, who made me a proposal to that effect, the day after the arrival of your letter, when I confided to him my projects ; the conditions offered me are very tempting, but I am too little French in character, and I am too desirous to establish myself in Switzerland, not to prefer the place you can give me, and to be as little as possible influenced by the salary which would be attached to it. I cannot refuse, without consideration, offers as brilliant as those made me, but I know how in many ways to defend myself from their attractions.   You must know me well enough from past experience to be persuaded that I would not hold a lucrative position through personal interests ; that far from this I would always sacrifice to the advancement of the establishment which would be confided to me, all the means at my disposal."

M. Coulon succeeded in guaranteeing 80 louis ($300) annually, for three years, to the future professor.   The larger part of this sum came from voluntary subscriptions, the rest from the city.   Soon after the collections of Agassiz were purchased for 500 louis, ($1,900,) of which the city paid one third, the Prince a second third, and M. Louis de Pourtalés completed the amount.   This sum allowed Agassiz to commence the publication of his history of fossil fishes.   He employed draughtsmen, and as he at the same time commenced or continued several other works, he associated himself for some of them with M. Desor, and afterward with M. Charles Vogt.   The discoveries of Venetz and of Charpentier upon the ancient extension of the glaciers then attracted his attention.   The group of scientists engaged in these interesting investigations, of which Agassiz was the center, made frequent excursions to the glacier of the Aar, where their encampment, called the *hôtel des Neuchâtelois*, is still celebrated.   This was the occupation of the summer. During the winter drawings and publications advanced rapidly, thanks, we ought to say, in good part, to the gifts of several distinguished citizens and of the government of Neuchâtel.   The latter were promoted by King Frederick William, at the suggestion of Humboldt.   This illustrious savant wrote to M. L. Coulon, at the time of the nomination of Agassiz, the following letter, which has never been published :

M. de Humbolt to M. Louis Coulon.

"It is not a request that I address to you, sir, but the expression of my sincere gratitude for your noble and generous conduct in regard to a young savant, M. Agassiz, well worthy of your encouragement and the protection of your enlightened government, on account of his talent, the variety and solidity of his attainments, and what adds to the value of these, especially in the agitated times in which we live, the amiable gentleness of his character.   I have known for many years, particularly through our common friend M. de Buch, that you pursue the study of natural history with a success equaled only by your zeal; that you have formed fine collections, which you allow others to enjoy with the most generous freedom.   It is pleasant to me to see your benevolence directed toward a young man who is dear to me, whose loss from among us we shall always regret, and whom the illustrious Cuvier would have recommended to you with like affectionate ardor on account of the excellent works he has nearly completed.   It is a great and noble thought, that of calming minds too exclusively occupied with political ideas or utopian dreams by offering them in the study of nature, and of the sciences which most immediately affect the industrial resources of the people, a salutary diversion. The respectable gentlemen who honor your council of state in this way acquire new right to public esteem. Gentle and industrious habits, great sagacity, and naturally happy dispositions, even in the lower classes, have up to this time eminently contributed to the prosperity of your beautiful country. Education adds to labor, but education in harmony with the needs of a century which does not retrograde, must lead to that union of order and public liberty which for centuries has characterized your community. I earnestly advised M. Agassiz not to accept the offers which after the death of M. Cuvier were made to him at Paris, and his resolution anticipated my counsel. What a happy thing it would be for him and for the completion of the two excellent works in which he is engaged, if he could at once, this year even, be installed upon the borders of your lake. I have no doubt of the protection that would be accorded to him by your worthy governor,* to whom I shall repeat this suggestion, and who has honored both myself and my brother with a friendship I highly prize. M. Leopold de Buch, who is interested almost as much as myself in the destiny of M. Agassiz, and in his work upon fossil fishes, (the most important yet undertaken, and equally exact in regard to the zoölogical characteristics and those of the formations,) promised me, on leaving Berlin for Bonn and Vienna, to mention the matter to him.

"Accept the expression of the distinguished consideration with which I have the honor to be your very humble and obedient servant,

"AL. DE HUMBOLDT.

" POTSDAM, *July* 25, 1832."

Agassiz took part in 1833 in the foundation of the Society of Natural Sciences of Neuchâtel, of which he was the first secretary. We remember his participation in the operations of the Swiss Society of Natural Sciences, and his famous discourse at the opening in 1837, when he announced his theory of the glacial period, to the great indignation of Leopold de Buch. In 1840 Agassiz visited Great Britain, where he pointed out to the geologists of that country evident traces of ancient glaciers. It was from England he sailed in 1846 for the United States, at the expense of King Frederick William, with the intention merely of making a visit. The interest of his first explorations. the repugnance he felt for the political revolutions of the old world, and, finally, the generous and warm reception of the Americans, induced him to prolong his stay. He accepted a place as professor, and saw develop, little by little, that brilliant career of scientific propagandism, of the creation of museums, of expeditions along the coasts of America to the region of the river of the Amazon, and to California, which attracted to him public attention, and which won for him enormous donations from wealthy Americans to the profit of his labors and of the establishments he

---

* Referring to M. de Pfühl.

directed. If at the time when Agassiz was a poor student he dreamed
of an Eldorado suited to his desires, his dream was realized more than
once toward the end of his life.

Agassiz could teach in three languages with equal grace and facility.
He was the partisan of no particular school. Science was to him neither
German, French, nor English, but of all countries. He excelled in the
examination of details, and in the comparison of forms. I cannot say
that he was equally superior in the principles of natural classification
and in theoretic deductions. It may be considered at the least singular
that the author of the immense discovery of a parallelism between the
successive forms of the embryo of a fish, and the successive forms of
the class of fishes in general in geological times should persistently deny
all evolution in the two kingdoms. However, other naturalists of great
distinction, formed as Agassiz by practical investigations, have adopted
debatable theories, and I doubt, for example, whether it would be possible
to reduce several of the hypotheses of Linnæus to the rigorous form of
the syllogism.

One peculiar circumstance in the life of Agassiz is, that he never accepted any position or desired to live in a great city. We have seen
that he preferred Neuchâtel to Paris. He had no greater inclination
for Berlin and London, where friends and even powerful patrons would
have drawn him. He probably felt within him an inward activity which
did not require the excitement of great cities, and we know that he
absolutely avoided going out of his specialty. He died in a modest
habitation, near Harvard University, on the 18th of December,
1873, from a rapid prostration of the nervous system. His obsequies
were attended by an immense assembly. The feeling caused by the
death of this man was so general among the people of Boston, that,
although he had never taken part in politics, the flags of all the public
edifices of the city were lowered in token of grief.

Donations by thousands of dollars as a testimonial still continue in
favor of the Museum of Comparative Zoölogy, the favorite work of
Agassiz. On the 26th of June the subscription amounted to $120,000.
The learned American, to whom I owe this information, thought that
this sum was not sufficient. In Europe we would consider it munificent.
Already during the year 1873 the establishment had received from
various donors $156,000. Among these contributors, Agassiz had the
pleasure of counting one of his best pupils, his only son, whom fortune
had favored, and who, making a good use of the wealth he had acquired,
gave $46,000. It is he, Alexander Agassiz, the author of the remark-
able work upon Echinoids, who has now the direction of the museum,
and we have no doubt that he will acquit himself of the charge with
great advantage to science.

Don Ramon de la Sagra, a Spaniard by birth,* was established in his
youth at Havana, where he gave much attention and labor to the develop-

---

* Born at Corunna on the 7th of December, 1801.

ment of agriculture, public instruction, and all the institutions which characterize civilized countries. While director in that city of a botanical and agricultural establishment, he caused large collections to be made of the plants of the island of Cuba, and generously distributed them among the botanists who could describe them. Augustin Pyramus de Candolle was one of the most favored in this respect, and the name of Ramon de la Sagra is frequently cited in the *Prodromus*. Notwithstanding the uncertainty of everything in Spain and its colonies, Ramon de la Sagra succeeded in collecting very valuable and varied materials, which he has introduced into divers works upon the statistics of the island, and particularly in his principal publication, which consists of several volumes in folio, *L'Historia fisica, politica y natural de la isla de Cuba*. His tables of statistics are not altogether satisfactory in regard to the nature of the population, and the administrative authorities of the country, but the volumes on natural history, which have been prepared by competent authorities, are highly esteemed. They testify throughout to the scientific zeal of the savant who collected the material for them, and the liberality of the Spanish government, which paid the cost of publication.

Ramon de la Sagra traveled in the United States, Holland, and other countries where scholastic institutions and public utility in general were the objects of his attention. He published several articles upon these subjects, as well as upon political economy. The Academy of Sciences nominated him correspondent.

Unhappily, the favorable disposition of the court of Madrid toward Ramon de la Sagra did not continue. It seems that an article by him, in a very obscure French journal, in which he declared that the Spanish government would do well to emancipate the slaves of the island of Cuba, was the cause of a disgrace carried to such an extent that Queen Isabella withdrew the pension which was the only resource of the author. He petitioned for its renewal, in view of his advanced age, but in vain. This was in 1867. From that time his condition was deserving of pity. He ended his days at Cortaillod, near Neuchâtel, on the 25th of May, 1871. Some of his friends in that city have placed a simple monument upon his grave.

The senior of our honorary members, Antoine-Laurent-Apollinaire Fée, died in his eighty-fifth year, at Paris, on the 21st of May, 1874.

In botany, he was known principally by his memoirs, in folio and in quarto, on the family of Ferns; by his essay upon Cryptogams, with exotic medicinal barks, (one volume in 4°;) and by some ingenious researches in regard to the plants that Theocritus, Virgil, and Pliny speak of in their writings. For many years he was stationed at Strasburg, as professor and director of the botanic garden, but the terrible events of the war of 1870 obliged him to leave the beseiged city after several weeks of great suffering. A bombshell entered his library; his garden, the object of his especial attention, was converted into a temporary cemetery; so that when the Swiss federal government gave permission to the old men, the women, and children to leave, he gladly availed himself of it, and he arrived in Geneva, greatly impaired in health in spite of a remarkably robust constitution. He was, moreover, much distressed in mind, for he belonged to an old French family, in whom sentiments of patriotism were very strongly implanted. In regard to his personal interests, which were much compromised, he manifested much more resignation than for the disasters of his country. We had the pleasure of seeing him sometimes at our sessions. Afterward when he had secured his pension as professor and military pharmaceutist of the first class, he went to Paris, and settled near a portion of his family. The botanical society of France nominated him president, but death found him in the midst of his books of botany and literature.

Fée commenced his career as pharmaceutist, attached to the French army in Spain during the great war. We may imagine that he was subjected to great hardships; but he was young, vigorous, well instructed, and, amid all the distractions of war, of marches and counter-marches, he never neglected an opportunity of botanising, and also of making himself master of the beautiful language of Spain, which he cultivated to the end of his days. A small volume published by him gives an agreeable account of this campaign, and was completed by another containing the description of a journey, taken fifty years later over the grounds of his former adventures.

Several of the articles of M. Fée upon literary or moral subjects or upon popular botany are remarkably correct in style, and we have always been impressed with the purity of his diction.

Jacques-Adolphe-Lambert Quetelet, director of the Royal Observatory of Brussels, perpetual secretary of the Academy of Science, Letters, and Art of Belgium, has furnished an example of a scientific career remarkably long, active, and varied. Born at Ghent, on the 22d of February, 1796, he taught mathematics in the college of that city, at the early age of eighteen years. Becoming, five years later, professor at the Athenæum of Brussels, he continued to labor and publish the results of his efforts in the domain of mathematical and physical science or of statistics, until he was seventy-eight years of age. He died on the 17th of February, 1874. Never was there a correspondent more scrupulous in replying to the communications made to him, and his liberality in the exchange of publications has been often noticed, both in our society and elsewhere.

Quetelet published the *Eléments d'astronomie* (2 vol. in 18mo, second edition, 1848,) a volume, *Sur la physique du globe*, (in 4°, 1861,) several articles upon probabilities, and the journal entitled *Correspondence mathematique et physique*, (11 vols. in 8°, 1825–'39.) He made at the observatory at Brussels a series of very important observations upon the temperature of the ground at different depths, and has given us the results of meteorological observations made with great care. He was one of the first to study atmospheric waves, the knowledge of which is necessary to fore-tell the weather. He inaugurated a series of uniform observations in numerous localities upon the times of foliation, flowering, and matur-ing of a great number of vegetables, and in general upon the periodi-cal phenomena of vegetable or animal life. The study of mathematics led him to introduce the statistical method into many branches of knowledge, and also to perfect this method. He diffused just ideas in regard to averages, and insisted more than had yet been done upon their ordinary constancy, even in social phenomena, a constancy the origin of which is easy to comprehend if we reflect upon the diversity of the causes which are almost always in action, and the slight proba-bility that they will change from one year to another. If Belgium has published statistical documents more extended and better co-ordinated than those of other states, she owes this principally to the fact of hav-ing had M. Quetelet for president of the commission of statistics. Until the close of his life, he collected and published data upon the physical and moral conditions of man, under the head of *social physics*. These were highly appreciated by the Academy of Moral and Political Science of the Institute of France, which made him first correspondent and then foreign associate. M. Quetelet, furthermore, was a member of all the scientific academies and societies of any importance, and, without having traveled much, was known everywhere as the friend of science.

During the year 1873-'74 the society received, as resident member, Dr. Adolphe d'Espine, and at the same time elected, as honorary mem-bers, Dr. Francis Forel, of Morges, professor at the Academy of Lau-sanne, (who has made some interesting communications,) and M. Poggendorff. In nominating this latter well-known physicist, of an advanced age, we wished to associate ourselves with the manifestation made at Berlin by a great number of savans and of societies, upon the occasion of the fiftieth year of the doctorate of the editor of the *Annalen der Physik und Chemie.*

Prof. Emile Plantamour was appointed president for the year 1874-'75, and the other officers of the society were continued, with thanks for the services they had rendered.

II.—LABORS OF THE SOCIETY.

Astronomy.—Colonel Gautier communicated to us the result of 227 observations made by him upon the contour of the solar disk, by means of a direct-vision spectroscope, by Hoffman, similar to that of M. Respighi at Rome. M. Gautier classes the phenomena into eruptions, exhalations, and detached formations. The details he gives, and the deductions he draws in regard to the probable nature of the phenomena, deserve to be studied in the memoir itself, which, accompanied by two plates, is published in the Archives of Physical and Natural Science, for March, 1874.

Physics.—Mr. Fol submitted to the society the plan of a manometer, designed especially for sea-soundings of great depth. This instrument consists essentially of two spherical reservoirs, superposed and connected by a capillary tube. The upper reservoir should be closed and entirely filled with a compressible liquid, for example alcohol; the other, which has an opening in the upper part, must be full of mercury, which ought also to fill the capillary tube. The quantity of mercury which will pass from the second reservoir into the first when the apparatus is submitted to pressure will give the measure of this pressure, and consequently of the height of the column of water, or, in other words, of its depth.

M. Archard described a manometer of precision, of his invention, consisting of two liquids, water and petroleum. His memoir, accompanied with a plate, was published in the Archives of Physical and Natural Science, for April, 1874.

M. Achille Cazin, honorary member of our society, on a visit to Geneva, entertained us with some recent researches on the thermal phenomena which take place in a magnetic circuit, an extract of which appeared in the *Comptes Rendus* of the Academy of Sciences.

The last work of our illustrious colleague, Auguste de la Rive, was accomplished in association with M. Edouard Sarasin, who gave the results in the session of the 20th of November last. He investigated the action of magnetism upon the electric discharge in rarefied gas, when this discharge takes place in the prolongation of the axis of the magnet. In this case the magnet produces a considerable augmentation of the current, when it acts directly upon the negative electrode. It seems, from these experiments, that there is a special and very strong resistance proceeding from the negative electrode, which the action of the magnet serves to overcome. (*Archives des Sciences physiques et naturelles*, April number, 1874.)

M. Raoul Pictet communicated to us several series of observations which he had an opportunity of making, during a long sojourn in Cairo, as director of the physical cabinet of that city. To speak first of those which treat more particularly of physics, he found, by means of a large actinometer, the measure of the intensity of the calorific radiation at Cairo. His apparatus consisted of a kind of caldron or boiler, formed of two thin parallel plates of iron, which was filled with water, and placed in a case full of cotton. This case was blackened, and closed at the side turned toward the sun by a variable number of glass plates. It results from these observations that in Egypt a surface of a square meter, exposed normally to the rays of the sun, in the middle of the day, absorbs nearly twelve calories a minute. Other observers in Europe find under like circumstances that the absorption amounts to about six calories. The diurnal evaporation produced under the action of the sun is about one-sixth of an inch of water; that which results from dry air and from wind is about three-sixths of an inch.

M. Soret made several communications upon the phenomena of polarization by diffusion of light. He has observed a trace of illumination upon a cone of solar light concentrated not only in transparent liquid or solid bodies, water-crystals, &c., but even in brilliant flames. The particles of incandescent charcoal, which these contain, therefore, still exert their reflective power contrary to the idea given by M. Hirn. This luminous trace is always completely polarized for an angle of vision of 90°.

Professor Forel, of Morges, has given us the pleasure of listening to an account of the beautiful researches he has undertaken on Lake Leman, for several years, on the transmission of light in water; and has shown us impressions obtained upon photographic paper immersed at different depths. He found that 130 to 160 feet of depth in summer was the limit, beyond which the transmitted light is too feeble to exercise any action upon the chloride of silver. In winter the water of the lake is much more transparent, and the limit extends to 200 feet.

General Dufour described the effects of a thunderbolt on a poplar tree upon his estate near Geneva; a large furrow was made in it from the top of the trunk, 80 feet in height, to the bottom. On this occasion M. de la Harpe cited a fact which he had witnessed. A bolt fell upon a group of poplars, leaped from one tree to another, passed through several, and made cylindrical holes in them of from 3 to 4 inches in diameter.

Terrestrial physics, meteorology.—Professor Plantamour presented a memoir upon the observations of latitude, of azimuth, and of the pendulum, made on the Righi, the Weissenstein, and at Berne, in 1867, 1868, and 1869. In a comparison of the observations of the pendulum on the Gebris and the Weissenstein, the weight was found to be $\frac{1}{50000}$ less than in the first of these localities. M. Plantamour attributed, this to the nature of the rocks, which are of cone-in-cone at Gebris, and calcareous at the Weissenstein. The same member announced to us the conclusion of the great work of the leveling of the polygon, traversing twice the Alps, at the St. Gothard, and at the Simplon retarded by an error, which, for a time, could not be accounted for, but which was finally found to be due to a false figure in the record of one of the sides of the polygon.

The variations, extreme this year, of the waters of the Lake of Geneva, attracted the attention both of the public and of the engineers. General Dufour proved that the high waters of 1873, however, remained below those of 1792 and of 1817, and M. Plantamour added below those of 1846. A remarkably low level followed during the winter of 1873–1874, but the public were mistaken in believing an assertion in a certain journal that the lake had never been lower.

These questions in regard to the level of the lake, which are frequently renewed, have formed the object of a special work by Professor Plantamour, founded upon thirty-six years of observations, from 1838 to 1873. The author first proceeds to the verification, at several points, of the marks successively employed, and the level of the lake having been reduced to the uniform 0 of 10 feet below the mark of the stone of Niton, the calculations for the thirty-six years have given the following results:

The lake attains its minimum (3 feet) on the 11th of February, and its maximum (7 feet) on the 7th of August. There is a first mean level from the 28th to the 29th of May, and a second from the 22d to the 23d of October. The level is then during 218 days above, and during 147 days below the mean. The level rises more quickly than it sinks. The rising is most rapid toward the 19th of June; it rises then 6 inches a day.

To show the annual variations, M. Plantamour has traced the curves of the highest levels of the means and of the lowest waters. These three curves have some analogy between them, but are far from concording. The level of the highest water varies the most from year to year, and it influences the mean more than the low water. *The mean of the high waters has not sensibly varied during the lapse of thirty-six years.* The highest maximum (9 feet) was attained on the 17th of July, 1846. The level of the low water in winter is, on the contrary, raised progressively. The lowest minimum (1 foot 3 inches) is shown on the 5th of April, 1840. That of 1873–1874, which astonished the public, remained 16 inches above the level of 1840. As to the elevation of the low water during recent years, one of our colleagues, a former member of the administrative council of the city of Geneva, calls attention to the fact that the position of the suction-pipe of the hydraulic machine has not been altered for twelve years. Professor Plantamour, in this work, which has required long calculations, has limited himself to the exposition of the figures, but any one aware of the discussions which have arisen at various times upon the supposed effects of the different levels of the lake, cannot abstain from one satisfactory reflection. The high water is frequently complained of, but never the low water, unless it sinks to such a point as to interfere with navigation, and, in some cases, with the approach to the ports. It is pleasant, then, to know that the high water has not risen for thirty-six years, and that the mean of the low water is rather higher than lower.*

The investigations in regard to Lake Leman have been continued in a most satisfactory manner since our society and the Vaudois society of the natural sciences have united in encouraging them. Prof. François Forel, who had been previously engaged with the subject, and continues to pursue it, has communicated to us a series of observations of great interest. I have already mentioned those relative to the absorption of light by the waters of the lake. He also made some upon the *seiches,* or sudden variations of level, very perceptible in the narrow part of the lake near Geneva. We know that Professor Vaucher attributed the phenomenon to the variations in the weight of the atmosphere.† M. Forel, while confirming the observations and the opinions of this savan, has

---

* Our *Mémoires* already contain numerous documents upon the level of the lake. See v, p. 63; vol. viii, p. 119; vol. x, p. 327.

† *Mémoires* of the society, vol. vi, p. 35.

made a more complete examination of the facts. He observed the sudden variations at the two extremities of the lake, and in the intermediate station of Morges, where they are less sensible. The duration of one of these sudden changes varies little in each locality, but differs much from place to place. At Geneva it is 1,590 seconds; at Veytaux, near the eastern extremity, 1,783 seconds; and in the middle, at Morges, 264. This latter locality presents a rhythmic movement of 22 seconds. M. Forel compares these movements of the lake to those of water in a basin, in which the height and duration of the waves of oscillation depend upon the form of the vase and the depth of the liquid.*

The soundings of M. Forel at different depths proved to him the existence of three strata at the bottom of the lake : 1st. An upper stratum of yellowish silt, containing a large number of animals, living and dead. 2d. A stratum of about 4 inches of black clay. 3d. A lower stratum of blue clay, very fine and very homogeneous, except near the mouth of the Rhone, where it contains some mica.

M. Raoul Pictet profited by his sojourn in Egypt to study more accurately than had yet been done the water of the Nile.   His principal operations of gauging took place near Cairo, at the bridge of Kasr-el-Nil. He sounded the river from shore to shore at 38 points, 33 feet distance from each other. The velocity was measured by means of the apparatus of Woltmann. The lowest water occurs about the 15th of May; the amount of water there is 24,000 cubic feet a second. The highest water is on the 15th of September, the amount then being 372,000 cubic feet. The mean is 168,000 cubic feet a second. The greatest velocity 3 feet below the surface is 6 feet 9 inches; the least, 7 inches.

M. Pictet has frequently observed the sand spouts, which are a daily phenomenon on the plains of Egypt. About 10 o'clock in the morning, the sun having heated the surface of the ground, there results in the adjoining stratum of air an ascensional and gyratory motion, which carries up sandy particles to a height of 5,000 to 6,500 feet. The central part of the column has a temperature of from 45° to 60°, that of the atmosphere in the shade being from 25° to 35°, centigrade.

Prof. A. Gautier presented an article upon the thermometric observations made at Labrador by some Moravian missionaries. They form a continuation of those presented in 1870.

Geology.—Prof. Alph. Favre has regularly informed the society of the condition of the labors of the Swiss Geological Commission, of which he is a member. The geological chart of $\frac{1}{100000}$ is published in eleven sheets, with five sheets of especial charts, concerning the canton of Bâle, the environs of Brugg, Mount Pilatus, the St. Gothard, and the Sentis, (in two sheets.) The commission moreover has been especially occupied on the St. Gothard, where the great work of forming a tunnel

---

* Forel upon the *seiches* in the Bulletin of the *Soc. Vaudoise des sc. nat.*, 1873, p. 213 and *Archives* of the sc. phys. and nat., January, 1874.

is in progress. An engineer, M. Stapff, has been engaged to make a careful section, indicating the strata, and to form 60 collections of the rocks extracted, of which twenty-five will remain in Switzerland and be distributed to the different museums of the country. M. Ernest Favre has given us an account of the researches M. Stapff has already made in the field of his commission.

M. Alph. Favre has shown that upon the flank of the Jura, in the region of Gex, above Farges, erratic blocks are not found higher than from 2,760 to 2,790 feet above the sea, while more to the east upon the Jura and at the Salève they are seen at a much greater elevation. He thinks this may be accounted for by the small height of the Sion Mountain over which the neighboring glacier could flow. The declivity of Divonne, on the contrary, would interrupt its expansion in the direction to the east of Gex.

Chemistry.—Professor Marignac read a memoir upon the solubility of the sulphate of lime, and upon the state of higher saturation of its solutions, which was published in the Archives of Physical and Natural Science for October, 1873.

In another series of experiments, M. Marignac examined the diffusion of two salts in the same liquid. He used salts not susceptible of reciprocal decomposition. In comparing salts capable of forming double salts with those not thus capable, he found no difference. He perceived no relation between the simultaneous diffusibility of two salts and their relative co-efficients of diffusion. The mingling of two salts diminishes always the diffusibility of the least diffusible of the two. The various acids and the various bases preserve their order of diffusibility throughout all their combinations. M. Marignac perceived no separation of the acids and of the bases in the diffusion of the salts.

A so-called kaolin was found at Colonges, near to the fort of the Écluse. M. Émile Ador made an analysis of it. He found 38 per cent. of silica, 35 of aluminum, and 27 of water; consequently, it was not a kaolin, but a mineral, analogous to the Halloyite.

Zoölogy, physical, animal, and medical.—The presence of eels in the Lake of Geneva has been sometimes denied, but also as often asserted. M. Lunel was assured that this year several of them had been taken. He attributed this fact to the elevation of the waters, which allowed the eels to mount to the mouth of the Rhone more easily than usual.

The disappearance of a species is generally slow, and more or less difficult to prove; but, as an entirely exceptional instance, M. de Candolle cited the complete absence since 1873 of the *Galericula calmariensis,* a small coleoptera, which for several years devoured the leaves of the elms in the suburbs of Geneva to such a degree as to cause the death of a large number of the trees. The proprietors in vain endeavored to exterminate the insects, when suddenly they disappeared. As this disappearance was general as well as sudden, it could not be attributed to the increase of an enemy, but must have been due to an irregularity at an important moment of some condition of its existence.

In his researches upon the bottom of Lake Leman, Professor Forel extracted from the superficial stratum of the ooze, at depths of from 82 to 100 feet, and even to the maximum of 980 feet, different crustaceans and other animals which are at present the object of special study with certain naturalists. To his great surprise he found some living limnæans (a family of mollusks) at so great a depth that they could breathe but very little oxygen, and that only in the manner of aquatic animals. These same limnæans, when placed in an aquarium, developed organs for aerial respiration.[1]

M. Henri de Saussure communicated to us the results of his study of the *Orthoptera*, just published in the second part of volume vi of the French Expedition to Mexico. In connection with Gryllides he mentions the genus *Tridactylus*, in which each individual may have three modes of living—subterranean, aerial, and aquatic. A species of the south of France is found also in the sands, sometimes submerged, of the islands of the Rhone near Colonges, where M. de Saussure has seen them alive. The two anterior claws serve for burrowing, the middle pair for walking, and the posterior pair for leaping, even when resting upon the water. The animal can rise in leaping to two hundred times its own length. It can also swim.

Dr. Fol presented a memoir in French, which he has just published in German in the Jenaische Zeitschrift, upon the evolution of *Cœlenterates*, in particular upon the egg of the species called *Geryonia fungiformis*. This work recalled to us by its nature, and by the beautiful plates which accompanied it, those of our eminent and regretted colleague, Edouard Claparéde. The egg of the *Geryonia* passes by a regular segmentation to the state of the morula, then by means of a doubling of the single cellular stratum it produces two spheres, one fitting into the other, which become the ectoderm and endoderm. This formation, of which the author observed the course, appeared to him to differ much from that of the other cases, in which the double stratum results from the invagination of the primitive sphere. The conception of Leuckart and Hæckel, of two subkingdoms having their common origin in the Protozoaires, finds support in these facts. M. Fol also examined the question whether there exist animals which in the adult condition are constructed like the egg of the superior animals in the first phases of its evolution. He pointed out, in this connection, the *Protomoyxa*, which was mentioned by M. Hæckel, and the *Megasphœra planula*.

M. Gustave Rouchette has continued the curious observations made by M. Moggride at Mentone, upon various species of ants and spiders. He showed us the seeds which the ant, called *Atta Barbara*, accumulates for food, in small subterranean cavities. When one of these seeds commences to germinate, the ants cut off the root and carry the seed into the sunshine to dry the wound. The mason spiders, which live in a

---

[1] See the articles of M. Forel upon the fauna of the deep waters of the lake, in the *Bulletin de la Soc. Vaudoisé des Sc. Nat.*, xiii, No. 72.

tube closed with a sort of a stopper, can construct this apparatus only while they are young. They give to it the color which would best cause it to be confounded with the adjacent ground. M. Rouchette has given a series of examples, confirming the observations of the ingenious English naturalist.

Dr. Lombard commented before the society upon the report of the French commission, by Dr. Baillarger, in regard to the goitre and cretinism. He finds in the facts presented a verification of the theory he has given of the cause of the goitre. This cause, according to his view, consists in a plethora of carbon, produced by the rarity of the oxygen in elevated regions. A sojourn on the shores of the sea corrects this affection by the greater abundance of oxygen, and by the iodine, which absorbs the carbon. Other causes may, in certain elevated localities, diminish the inconvenient effects of the rarity of the oxygen. M. Lombard's theory has also found support in the facts observed by the military physicians at Briançon, St. Etienne, and Lyons, and recorded in the Medical Gazette. The soldiers were the more frequently attacked with goitre in proportion as the locality in which they resided was elevated.

Dr. d'Espine has given us an oral review of his thesis upon the puerperal septicémia, tending to prove experimentally that the accidents of childbirth proceed from the absorption by the uteri-vaginal lesions of septic substances, as in any wound whatever.

Botany.—The duration of the vitality of the seeds thrown into the sea is a question which concerns both physiology and botanical geography. M. Gustave has made it the object of direct study, at the request of M. de Candolle, and the latter communicated to the secretary the results, which have since been printed in the Archives of Physical and Natural Science for July, 1873.

The progress made in the knowledge of vegetable fossils induced M. Alp. de Candolle to endeavor to connect, more than had yet been done, the botanical geography of ancient and present times. For this end he deemed it necessary to propose a classification of the vegetables, founded upon their manner of comportment with regard to temperature and humidity, which determines different groups, of classes, families, species, and geographical flora. He insists upon the persistence of physiological properties, and attributes it to hereditary descent. After having characterized five groups of plants, which he calls *megathermes, xerophiles, méso-thermes, microthermes,* and *hékistothermes,* he shows their present distribution upon the terrestrial surface, and their anterior distribution, often different even in the Tertiary Period, the nearest approached to ours. The memoir appeared in the Archives of Physical and Natural Science for the month of May, 1874.

Several botanists, members of our society, have been engaged with investigations in connection with the great publication of the Brazilian flora. M. Marc Micheli, having completed his study of the onagrarieés of Brazil, has given us some interesting facts in regard to the organization of the seeds in this family, particularly in the *Jussiœa*, and also the geographical distribution of the species. He admits five genera, one of which, the Oocarpon, is new, and founded upon the number of parts of the flower. According to his observations, the disk of certain seeds of *Jussiœa* are constituted by a portion of the endocarpe adhering to the seed, and the bilocular seeds owe this appearance to an exceptional development of the raphe. He founds the division of the genus into three principal sections upon these characteristics, which he elucidates by figures. His memoir is published entire in the Archives of Physical and Natural Science for June, 1874.

Dr. J. Müller has been occupied with the determination of a singular fungus, sent to the museum of Geneva by M. Claraz, as an organic substance, found in the waters of the Rio Negro, between Patagonia and the Argentine Republic. Notwithstanding the imperfect state of preservation, he recognized it as a *Lysurus*, and has described it, with an illustration, in the Flora of the 21st of November, under the name of *L. Clarazianus*.

Communications in regard to published works or memoirs.

Besides original memoirs and verbal communications of facts observed by the members, the society allows brief information to be given in regard to works already published. This is a pleasant way of contributing to the progress of the knowledge of the members, principally in those branches with which they are not especially occupied. If we consider the number of the publications and the short time appropriated to them at the close of each session, it is clear that these communications must be very incomplete. Still, they are listened to with interest, and thanks are due to those members who have brought to notice some memoirs, very little known, but very important.

In the course of this year the clergyman, M. Duby, has drawn our attention to the opinions of Mr. Hilgard, in regard to the Algæ and Mosses, and to various articles relative to the invasion of an American cryptogam a parasite upon the *Malvacées;* M. Alph. Favre has spoken to us of the work of M. Belgrand, upon the hydrographical study of the Seine; M. Ernest Favre of the memoirs of M. Mojsisovicz, upon the geology of the oriental Alpes, and of M. Schlutter, upon the fossil crustacea of Libanus. Prof. A. Gautier has been very zealous in informing the society of the work which has been done in astronomy and meteorology, both in Europe and America. He has mentioned especially the labors of Vogel in regard to the movements of the stars, and of Poly upon the relation between the solar spots and different meteors at the surface of the earth. Prof. de la Harpe has given us an analysis of Prof. Hayden's volume upon the geology of the Territory of Montana. M. Humbert has spoken of the observations of Fritz Müller upon the thermites of Brazil; M. Marc Micheli of those of M. Prillieux, upon the movements of the chlorophyl of the Selaginella; Dr. Prevost of the recent discoveries in regard to the cerebral system; M. Soret upon the method employed by M. Becquerel for the study of the calorific spectre by the aid of phosphorescent substances, and upon various physical memoirs read before the French association at Lyons. Finally, M. Marcet has addressed a letter to us from London, in regard to the investigations of Tyndall upon the propagation of sound in the atmosphere.

Publications of the society.—Volume XXIII, part 2, in which we publish this report, shows that the series of our memoirs continue in a satisfactory manner. The society has no other resources for the maintenance of this publication than those furnished by its members and the products of the sale or exchange of its volumes. The preceding year the family of Edouard Claparède generously aided us in publishing his last and remarkable work. If this liberality were repeated we would be able to give much more extended memoirs, illustrated with many more plates, for happily scientific activity does not decrease among and around us.

THE PAST AND FUTURE OF GEOLOGY:

AN INAUGURAL LECTURE GIVEN BY JOSEPH PRESTWICH, M. A., F. R. S.,
F. G. S., &c., PROFESSOR OF GEOLOGY IN THE UNIVERSITY OF OXFORD,
ON JANUARY 29, 1875.

I cannot enter upon the subject of this address without a brief tribute
to the memory of my distinguished and lamented predecessor, Professor
Phillips. Educated in geology by his uncle, William Smith, the father
of English geology, John Phillips was thus nearly connected with the
early history of our science, and lived to give active and efficient aid to
its progress during more than half a century. His early training was
among the Oolitic hills of Gloucestershire and the Midland Counties,
but his first independent work was among the Palæozoic rocks of Yorkshire. In later life, he returned to the ground of his youth, and spent
his last years in investigating the rich and varied succession of life in
the different divisions of that Oolitic series of which his uncle was the
first to establish the stratigraphical order; and his " Geology of the
Valley of the Thames " contains the best summary we possess of the
geology and palæontology of these strata in this and the adjacent
counties.

Besides his chief and early work on the "Geology of Yorkshire,"
Phillips was also the author of an excellent "Treatise on Geology," of
works on the Malvern Hills, and on Vesuvius, of several memoirs in the
geological survey, and of above seventy papers scattered through various
scientific periodicals. He was a fellow of most of our great scientific societies, and the record of his many valuable contributions in each special
branch is to be found in their respective proceedings. I have to note
his work here.

Shortly after Phillips's arrival in Oxford, the valuable geological collections, many of which had remained hidden for want of space, were
transferred from their old quarters to the new and beautiful museum
Oxford now possesses. Valuable as these collections were in particular
sections, especially in cave remains, there was very much to be done in
completing the series of the local formations, and in the general selection, order, and grouping of the specimens. All this was admirably
carried out by Phillips, and the geology of the surrounding district is
now illustrated by a *suite* of fossils amassed and arranged with great
judgment, and forming one of the most complete local series in the kingdom. To Phillips especially is this museum indebted for the remarkable
collection of the remains of the *Cetiosaurus* and of the Great Oolite—an
extinct gigantic reptile the size of a whale and with the gait and am-

phibious habits of a crocodile. He also brought his great local knowledge of Great Britain to bear on one of the proposed additions to the new museum, viz, that of the British ornamental rocks, of which the 127 graceful columns which decorate the building each constitutes a specimen; the size and position of the shafts exhibiting to great effect, and with permanent advantage, the character and beauty of the several rocks, including numerous varieties of our granites, serpentines, and mountain limestones, with some from the more recent Permian, Oolitic, and Purbeck strata. No such collection exists elsewhere, and with it will always be associated the name of the eminent man who by his taste and ability so ably contributed to the success of the work.

But Phillips was not only a geologist; he was a man of great and varied acquirements, a meteorologist, a botanist, an astronomer, and a physicist. Further, he was a man whose amiable disposition, engaging manners, and eloquent and fluent address, made him beloved as much as he was esteemed; and while his loss to science will be long felt, his mark must remain and his memory will ever be honored.

When in 1819 Dr. Buckland, who had a few years previously succeeded Dr. Kidd as professor of mineralogy, received his appointment to the then-recently-created chair of geology, he spoke of these subjects as the "new and curious sciences of geology and mineralogy." Geology was only then beginning to assume a recognized position, and was passing from purely speculative "theories of the earth" to the more philosophical investigations of its structure and organisms. Hutton had sought in natural existing agencies the causes of past changes on the earth; Smith had solidly laid its stratigraphical foundations; and Cuvier was devoting his great talents to the restoration of old higher forms of life. Buckland then commenced his powerful and attractive teaching, and drew around him the younger men, through many of whom his influence on the progress of geology is happily yet felt. In his hands, the interesting fauna of the surrounding district was gradually unfolded, and among the most remarkable of the extinct forms then discovered and described by Buckland was the huge *Megalosaurus* and the small Marsupials, long the most ancient quadrupeds known, of Stonesfield.

But Buckland's great work was that connected with cave remains, in search of which he ransacked England and the continent, and although the conclusions then enunciated by him, and at that time very generally accepted by geologists, have not been corroborated, the facts so well recorded and the collections so largely made remain to attest the value and importance of his labors. It was in connection with these researches that the later discovery of our time, that of the association of the extinct mammalia with the remains and works of man, was dimly sighted, but with averted eyes, by my distinguished predecessor. But Buckland did not stand alone; his opinion was shared by geologists of all countries, and it was not until another generation had passed that the evidence so often brought forward, and which had in vain sought examination, respecting the antiquity of man, was confirmed and admitted by geologists.

Such was the aspect of our science at the time this chair was established; and I propose in this address briefly to notice some of the larger features, whether on questions of theory or on questions of fact, by which its progress has been marked, and which, while they may serve to show how much has been done, will yet indicate how much still remains to be accomplished.

The geologist commences where the astronomer ends. We have to adapt the large and broad generalizations of cosmical phenomena to the minuter details of terrestrial structure and constitution which it is our business to study. The common origin of the solar system has been long inferred from the spheroidal figure of the earth and the relations of the planets to one another, and explained by evolution from an original nebulous mass; and geologists have had to consider how far such a hypothesis is in accordance with geological facts. The questions connected with the earliest stages of the earth's history are on the very boundary-line of our science, but they have too important a bearing on its subsequent stages not to command our serious attention; and though obscure and theoretical, they serve to guide us to firmer ground. This nebular hypothesis has recently received from physicists corroboration of a most novel and striking character, equally interesting to geologists and astronomers.

The wonderful discoveries with respect to the solar atmosphere, made by means of the spectroscope, have now presented us with an entirely new class of evidence, which, taken in conjunction with the argument derived from figure and plan, gives irresistible weight to the theory of a common origin of the sun and its planets; and while serving to connect our earth with distant worlds, indicates as a corollary what of necessity must have been its early condition and probable constitution.

The whole number of known elements composing the crust and atmosphere of the earth amounts only to sixty-four, and their relative distribution is vastly disproportionate. It has been estimated that oxygen in combination forms by weight one-half of the earth's crust, silicon enters for a quarter, then follow aluminium, calcium, magnesium, potassium, sodium, iron, and carbon. These nine together have been estimated to constitute $\frac{977}{1000}$ of the earth's crust. The other $\frac{23}{1000}$ consist of the remaining fifty-five non-metallic and metallic elements.

The researches of Kirchhoff, Angström, Thalèn, and Lockyer have made known that of these sixty-four terrestrial elements there are twenty present in those parts of the solar atmosphere called the "chromosphere" and "reversing layer," as the stratum which surrounds the photosphere is called from certain optical properties.

They consist of * —

Aluminium.	Cerium.	Hydrogen.	Manganese.	Strontium.
Barium.	Chromium.	Iron.	Nickel.	Titanium.
Cadmium.	Cobalt.	Lead. (?)	Potassium.	Uranium.
Calcium.	Copper. (?)	Magnesium.	Sodium.	Zinc.

Nor, with possibly two exceptions, does the spectroscope give any indication of unknown elements.

While these phenomena afford such strong additional proofs of the common origin of our solar system, Mr. Norman Lockyer, basing his inquiries upon these and other facts recently acquired on the constitution of the sun, has been led to form some views of singular interest bearing on the probable structure of the crust and nucleus of the earth. With his permission, I am enabled to lay before you some of the points in the inquiry he is now pursuing.

Observation and theory have both led him to the unexpected conclusion that in the case of an atmosphere of enormous height, and consisting of gases and of metallic elements in a gaseous state, gravity overcomes diffusion, and the various vapors extend to different heights, and so practically arrange themselves in layers; and that in the sun, where owing to the fierce solar temperature the elements exist in such a state of vapor and of complete dissociation, the known elements arrange themselves in the main in the following order: †

Coronal atmosphere........................... Cooler hydrogen.

Chromosphere... .... ···· { Incandescent hydrogen. / Magnesium, calcium.

Reversing layer .... { Sodium. / Chromium. / Manganese. / Iron. / Nickel, &c.

Mr. Lockyer suggests, and has communicated some evidence to the Royal Society in support of his suggestion, that the metalloids or nonmetallic elements as a group lie outside the metallic atmosphere. He

---

* On analyzing this list we find : One permanent gas, (hydrogen;) two metals of the alkalies, (sodium, potassium;) all the metals of the alkaline earths, (calcium, strontium, barium;) three metals of the zinc class, (magnesium, zinc, cadmium;) all the metals of the iron class, (manganese, cobalt, chromium, iron, nickel, uranium; two metals of the tin class, (tin, titanium;) one metal of the lead class, probably, (lead.)

The metals of the tungsten, antimony, silver, and gold classes are entirely unrepresented, while, if we accept the metallic nature of hydrogen, there is not a single metalloid on the list, although they have been diligently searched for.

† Mr. Lockyer points out that this order is that of the old atomic or combining weights, and not that of the modern atomic weights, as the following table shows:

	Old atomic weights.	New atomic weights.		Old atomic weights.	New atomic weights.
Hydrogen	1	1	Chromium	26	52.5
Magnesium...................	12	24	Manganese	27	55
Calcium..........	20	40	Iron	28	56
Sodium	23	23	Nickel	29	58

Aluminium does not find a place in the above list, because its order in the layers has not yet been determined by observation; but the principle referred to would place it between magnesium and calcium.

also explains why under these conditions their record among the Fraunhofer lines should be a feeble one. Hence he considers that we have no argument against the presence of some quantity of the metalloids in the sun taken as a whole, although that quantity may be small.

Mr. Lockyer then takes the observed facts together with the hypothesis of the external position of the metalloids, and is considering these two questions:

1. Assuming the earth to have once been in the same condition as the sun now is, what would be the chemical constitution of its crust?

2. Assuming the solar nebula to have once existed as a nebulous star at a temperature of complete dissociation, what would be the chemical constitution of the planets thrown off as the nebulosity contracted?

It will be seen that there is a most intimate connection between these two inquiries, the localization of the various elements and the reduction of temperature acting in the same way in both cases.

Thus, to deal with the first question: as the external gaseous vapors (those of the metalloids) cooled, they condensed and fell on the underlying layer, where they entered into combination, forming one set of binary compounds and then others as the temperature was reduced, until finally all the metals and earths were precipitated.*

If, now, we turn to the earth's crust, we find it very generally assumed that the fundamental igneous rocks which underlie the sedimentary strata, and which formed originally the outer layers, may be divided into two great masses, holding a general relation one to the other, an upper one consisting of granite and other plutonic rocks, rich in silica, moderate in alumina, and poor in lime, iron, and magnesia; and of a lower mass of basaltic and volcanic rocks of greater specific gravity, with silica in smaller proportions, alumina in equal, and iron, lime, and magnesia in much larger proportions, with also a great variety of other elements as occasional constituents; while the denser metals are in larger proportion in the more central portion of the nucleus. The suggestion of Mr. Lockyer is that this order follows necessarily from the original localization of the earths and metals before referred to, by which the oxygen, silicon, and other metalloids formed, as they now do in the sun, an outer atmosphere, succeeded by an inner one consisting in greater part of the alkaline earths and alkalies, then by a lower one of iron and its associated group of metals, and finally by an inner nucleus containing the other and denser metals.

As we have before observed, above nine-tenths of the earth's crust consists of those elements which, on the assumption of the external position of the metalloids, would constitute the outer layers of the nebular mass. Thus, oxygen and silicon alone constitute, on the average, $\frac{75}{100}$

* Firstly, those binary compounds capable of existing at a high temperature, such as the vapor of water, of hydrochloric acid, of silica, carbonic acid, and others, would be formed; secondly, the precipitation of these would give rise to numerous reactions, forming a variety of silicates, chlorides, sulphates, &c.; thirdly, with the condensation of water, the constitution of minerals would be effected, double decompositions would ensue, and the consolidation of the outer shell commence.

of the mass of acid plutonic rocks of which the upper part of the first assumed shell of the earth consists. Beneath it, as a whole, are the basic rocks, into the composition of which calcium, magnesium, and iron, combined with oxygen, enter in the ratio of, say, $\frac{35}{100}$, while the silicon diminishes in proportion. Still deeper lie the denser and harder metals, which reach the surface only through veins transversing the outer layers.

We next come to the second question, dealing with the chemical constitution of the planets. It is imagined that the same consideration would hold good, and that the exterior planets may approach in their constitution that of the sun's outer atmosphere, and that the planets may become more metallic as their orbits lie nearer the central portion of the nebula. Mr. Lockyer considers that the low density and gigantic and highly-absorbing atmospheres of the outer planets accords with their being more metalloidal; and that, on the other hand, the high density and comparatively small and feebly-absorbing atmospheres of the inner planets points to a more intimate relation with the inner layers of the original nebulous mass. For the same reason, we should expect to find the metalloids scarcer in the sun than in the earth.

In the Jovian system, and in our own moon, we have a still further support of the hypothesis in the fact that the density of the satellites is less than that of their primary.

I had hoped to have brought before you some of the results of the examination of the spectra of portions of the outer igneous-rock crust of the earth, which Mr. Lockyer kindly undertook to compare with the solar spectrum; but, owing to the state of the weather, the investigation is not yet complete. It may be stated, however, that as in the spectrum of the sun so in the spectra of the lava, greenstone, and granite already tested, no trace of the metalloids is present, although oxygen and silicon enter so largely into the composition of these rocks.

We can, however, still only look on these views as hypothetical, but they commend themselves to us by their simplicity and grandeur, and their high suggestiveness for future inquiry and research. They show us also how the spectroscope may, as the microscope has done already, aid the investigations of the geologists—the one by endowing the eye with new powers of sight with respect to the infinitely minute, and the other with new powers of tangible analysis with respect to the infinitely distant in time and in space.

Quitting the early history of our globe, we leave the domain of the astronomer and enter upon one shared by the geologist, the mineralogist, the chemist, and the mathematician. The elements which we first dealt with in their gaseous and dissociated state have now entered into a multiplicity of combinations giving rise to a vast variety of compound bodies. Instead of the sixty-four simple elements, their mutual reactions have resulted in the formation of somewhere about one thousand varieties of rocks and minerals alone, with which the geologist has in future to deal. He also has to deal with all the physical problems arising from the consolidation of the crust of the earth, from pressure due to gravitation and contraction, from the action of subterranean forces, from the effects of heat, and with all the varied phenomena resulting from these complex conditions.

Passing for the present over the intermediate stages of consolidation, the continual cooling of the globe has necessarily resulted in a thickening of its crust, the exact extent of which at the present time has long been the object of geologists to determine.

The inquiry is one of extreme difficulty, and has of late years engaged and is still engaging the attention of some of the ablest physicists and mathematicians. The early belief was that the thickness of the crust of the earth does not now exceed thirty to sixty miles; but the late Mr. Hopkins, reasoning on phenomena connected with precession or nutation, concluded that on the contrary it could not be less than eight hundred miles thick, or more; a conclusion which has been supported and extended by Sir W. Thompson, who, while maintaining the igneous origin of the globe, and the greater intensity of action in past ages, has further proved, on dynamical grounds, that the earth as a whole must now be more rigid than glass, and probably even more rigid than steel.

It is difficult, however, to reconcile these views with the extent and character of recent volcanic action. This Mr. Robert Mallet endeavors to do, in a remarkable paper recently published in the Transactions of the Royal Society. The author bases his views upon Constant Prevost's theory of elevatory forces, but considers that as the secular cooling of the globe has proceeded, and the crust become thicker and more rigid, the tangential pressure, no longer equal to the elevation of mountain-ranges, is spent in local crushings of portions of the crust; and that, by transformation of the mechanical work of compression, the heat from which terrestrial volcanic agency is at present derived is produced. Mr. Mallet contends for the high probability that this "crushing of the earth's solid crust affords a supply of energy sufficient to account for terrestrial vulcanicity," comprehending in that term earthquakes and volcanic action. Thus, instead of arising from a deep-seated and common cause, Mr. Mallet would assign present volcanic ejections to the local fusion of the strata at variable but moderate depths beneath the surface; and he considers it characteristic of such action "that it is only one phase of a unique force which has always been in action, though in decreasing energy, since our planet was nebulous."

On the other hand, these views have been objected to by other competent observers, who hold with little modification to the original hypothesis of a molten central nucleus and a shell of comparatively small thickness. Such are some of the large physical problems now occupying the attention of geologists. I shall have occasion to recur to them again.

In stratigraphical geology, the great divisions originally introduced by our predecessors stand, but their number and the number of subdivisions have greatly increased. In 1822, when Phillips and Conybeare wrote their "Geology of England and Wales," twenty-three so-called for-

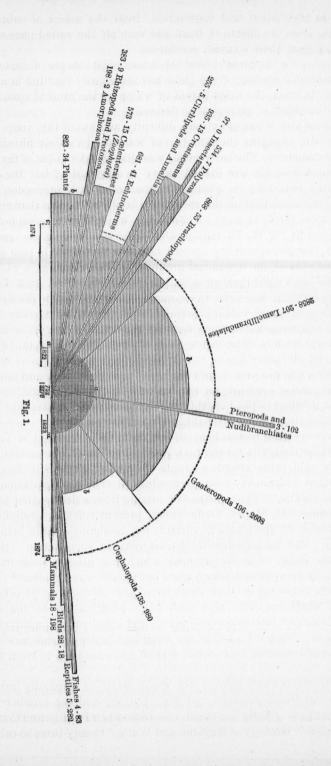

Fig. 1.

383 · 9 Rhizopods and Protozoa (*Zoophytes*)

198 · 2 Amorphozoa

573 · 15 Crelenterates

681 · 41 Echinoderms

925 · 13 Crustaceans and Annelids

97 · 0 Insects

255 · 5 Cirrhipeds and spatangoids

898 · 55 Brachiopods

833 · 34 Plants

933 · 7 Polyzoa

2858 · 207 Lamellibranchiates

Pteropods and Nudibranchiates 3 · 102

Gasteropods 196 · 2608

Cephalopods 138 · 980

Mammals 18 · 198

Birds 28 · 18

Reptiles 5 · 282

Fishes 4 · 83

1674

822

792

1276

1823

1674

mations were recognized, whereas now thirty-eight such are established, and these are divided into about one hundred and twenty subdivisions, each characterized by some peculiarity of structure or of fauna. Palæ-ontology as a separate science was not then known; structural and physical geology had chiefly occupied attention; but the study of organic remains has since advanced with such rapid and vigorous strides that the older branch of the subject was until lately in danger of being neglected and distanced.

At that time, the number of species of organic remains in Great Britain which had been described amounted only to 752, whereas now the number amounts to the large total of 13,276 species. The relative proportion between these totals and the numbers of each class is exhibited in the annexed diagram, (Fig 1*,) which shows also the vast progress made in palæontological knowledge between 1822† and 1874‡.

Some idea of the extent and variety of the past life of our globe may be formed by comparing these figures with the numbers of plants and animals now living in Great Britain. Excluding those classes and families, such as the naked mollusca and others, which, from their soft and gelatinous nature, decay rapidly and so escape fossilization, and insects, ‖ the preservation of which is exceptional, the number of living species amounts to 3,989, against 13,183 extinct species of the same classes, and the relative proportions of each class stands as in the diagram, Fig. 2.

Thus while the total number of those classes of vertebrate and invertebrate animals and plants represented in a fossil state, and now living in Great Britain, is only 3,989, there formerly lived in the same area as many as 13,276 species, so that the fossil exceed the recent by 9,287 species. It must be remembered also that plants are badly represented; for owing to their restricted preservation, the fossil species only number

---

* In these diagrams, the inner semicircle, *a a*, gives the relative proportion between each class in an area which represents the sum of the total ; and the outer semicircle, *c c*, gives the dimensions which each class would have had had the proportions between the several classes in each of the two compared periods or stocks been maintained in the same ratio as in *a a*; while the irregular segments *b b* give approximately the actual increase or excess of each class, showing how comparatively large the additions in some of them have been compared with those in others, and in the case of Fig. 2 showing how particular classes of fossils fall below or exceed in development of their living analogues. The inner numbers attached to the several classes refer to the value of each in the inner circle *a a*, and the outer numbers have reference to the values represented by the segments *b*. The sign × means that certain segments should be so many times larger.

† As there was no list of British fossils then published, I have taken the numbers given in Woodward's "Synoptical Table," published in 1830, and deducted from them those added to the stock between 1822 and 1830.

‡ I am indebted to my friend Mr. Etheridge, F. R. S., palæontologist to the Geological Survey, for the particulars of this 1874 stock. The details are given in a valuable table, which he has had the kindness to draw up for me, and which is given in full, with the details of the 1822 stock and of living species, in the appendix.

‖ The number of British species of insects amounts to between 10,000 and 11,000.

823 against 1,820 recent species. Birds are still worse represented, as only 18 fossil species occur against 354 recent species.

But the multiplicity of British fossils, however surprising as a whole,

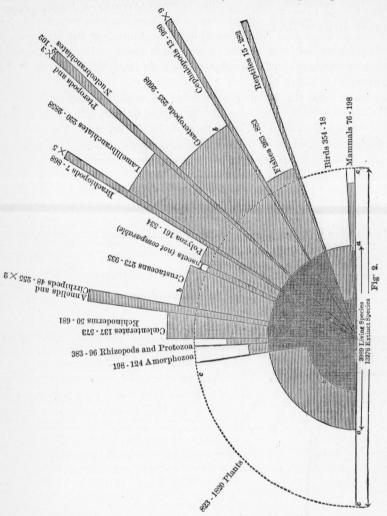

Fig. 2.

has to be viewed in another and different light. The large total represents, not as the recent species do, the life of one period, but the sum of those of all the geological periods. Geological periods, as we construct them, are necessarily arbitrary. The whole geological series consists of subdivisions, each one of which is marked by a certain number of characteristic species, but each having a large proportion of species common to the subdivisions above and below it. These various subdivisions are again massed into groups or stages, having certain features and certain species peculiar to them and common throughout, and which groups are separated from the groups above and below by greater breaks in the continuity of life and of stratification than mark the lesser divisions. As these on the whole severally exhibit a distinct fauna and flora, we may conveniently consider them as periods, each having its own distinctive life, and the number of which in Great Britain we have taken approximatively at thirty-eight.

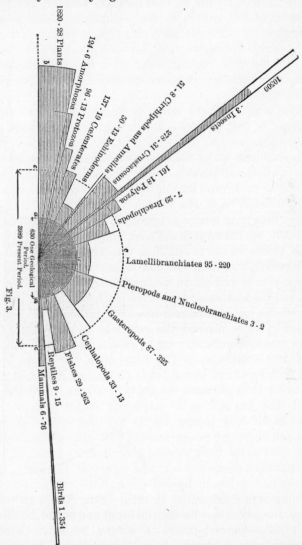

The number of species common to one period and another varies very greatly; but taking the average of the sixteen divisions of the Jurassic and Cretaceous series, of which the lists were, with a portion of those of the older series, given a few years since by Professor Ramsay,* we

---

*Anniversary addresses for 1863 and 1864, Quarterly Journal Geological Society. The tables were computed by Mr. Etheridge.

may assume that about 30 per cent. of the organic remains pass from one stage to another. Dividing the 13,276 fossil species among the thirty-eight stages, or omitting the lower stages and some others and taking only thirty, we get a rough average of 442 species for each ; and, allowing in addition for the number common to every two periods, we obtain a mean of 630 species' as the population of each of the thirty periods against the 3,989 species of the present period. On this view, the relative numbers are therefore reversed, as shown in the annexed diagram, (Fig. 3,) where the number of living British species is compared with the mean of the extinct species assumed for any one past period of the same area.

This gives a ratio for the fauna or flora of a past to that of the present period of only as $1 : 6\frac{1}{3}$. But it must be remembered that probably the actual as well as the relative numbers of the several classes *inter se* in each and all of these several formations varied greatly at the different geological periods. Still, we have no reason to suppose but that, during the greater part of them, life of one form or another was as prolific, or nearly so, in the British area then as at the present day, and we may thus form some conception of how little relatively, though so much really, we have yet discovered, and of how much yet remains to be done, before we can re-establish the old lands and seas of each successive period, with their full and significant populations. This we cannot hope ever to succeed in accomplishing fully, for decay has been too quick and the rock entombment too much out of our reach ever to yield up all the varieties of past life. But although the limits of the horizon may never be reached, the field may be vastly extended ; each segment of that semicircle may yet be prolonged we know not how far ; and it is in this extension—in the filling-up of the blanks existing in the life of each particular period—that lies one great work of the future. The field which thus embraces the study of all the varied forms of life in all past time has now, as we have just shown, attained such vast dimensions as will long require for its due and continued cultivation the active and unceasing co-operation of geologists and palæontologists.

We now come to the more especial ground of the geologist. Starting with investigations connected with the origin of the globe, he has to trace the changes it has undergone through the various phases of its history, to determine the cause of those changes, and the manner in which they were effected. Besides investigating the character and distribution of all organized things inhabiting the earth in all former periods—their order of succession, and the relation of the several and successive groups one to another—he has also to study various chemical and physical questions connected with inorganic matter.

In the infancy of the science, geologists generally sought to explain the great mechanical phenomena exhibited on the surface of the globe by energy rather than by length of action. The philosophy of Hutton, Playfair, and their successors checked this disposition, and has led to more temperate methods of explanation; but it is a question whether the license which formerly was taken with energy is not now too much taken with time. Small forces long continued, action frequently repeated, and maintained uniformity of operation, are accepted as sufficient to account for the formation of our hills and plains, of the Alps and the Andes, and for all the great general as well as special features of the earth's crust.

I am aware that in expressing other views I shall have occasion to differ from men for whose opinion I have the highest regard, and who have done infinite service to the progress of scientific geology; but I am also expressing views which I was very early led to form, and which long experience has only tended to confirm. The points at issue are, firstly, whether our experience on these questions is sufficient to enable us to reason from analogy; and, secondly, whether all former changes of the earth's surface are to be explained by the agency of forces alike in *kind* and *degree* with those now in action. It is not possible in the limits of this address to do full justice to these important questions. I may, however, briefly state my reasons for answering these questions in the negative.

The value of experience with respect to natural phenomena depends upon whether they are symmetrical and not variable, or whether they are variable and unsymmetrical. In the one case, as any one part bears a given uniform relation to the whole, if one part be known, the whole can be inferred; but in the other case, where the whole is made up of unequal and not uniform parts, the value of the evidence is merely in proportion to the number of those parts independently determined, or to the ratio between the duration of the observation and the duration of the time comprising all the phases of the particular phenomenon. Thus the path of a planet, the date of an eclipse, or the return of a comet, may be predicted with certainty by the determination of mere minute sections of their orbits, which in respect to time are infinitely small compared to the length of the cycle of revolution. On the other hand, the metamorphosis of an insect, the mean temperature of a place, or the character of a volcano, can only be accurately determined by a length of observations sufficient to embrace all the variations they respectively present in their several cycles of change. In the case of the insect, the time must be equal to the duration of the metamorphosis; in that of temperature, a succession of years is needed to obtain a mean; and, with respect to volcanoes, centuries may often pass before we become acquainted with all the irregular exhibitions of their spasmodic activity.

The necessity for a much greater extension of time becomes yet more imperative when we come to deal with geological phenomena, such as those due to the action of elevatory forces, which are extremely varied in their nature, being at one time exhibited by a raised beach, a few feet high, and at another by a mountain-chain, whose height is measured by miles; or by the small displacement produced by an earthquake, and the rectilinear fracture of a county with a displacement of thousands of feet.

In taking into consideration the weight of the evidence where the series is so variable and irregular, it is clear that the increment of value is in proportion to the increment of time. One phase of the insect life, one year's record of temperature, a century's observation of the volcano, give evidence which, although of value *pro tanto*, as one link in the chain, is entirely inconclusive when applied to the whole length. So in respect to such geological changes as those just named, the value of our experience is only in the proportion of the length thereof to the duration or cycle of the phenomenon under investigation. Thus the elevation of mountain-ranges have been events of rare and distant occurrence. Supposing, as has been estimated, that all the great chains can be referred to thirteen principal epochs; or, taking subordinate ranges, that the elevation of the mountain-chains of the Old World be limited to twenty such periods. Divide geological time (since the sufficient consolidation of the crust of the earth) by this or even by double this number, and we may form some conception of the length of the cycles involving changes of this magnitude. What that time is it is impossible to say ; we can only feel how infinitely it exceeds all our limited experience. With respect thereto, the experience of five hundred years is no doubt of value—one or two thousand years add further to it; but, after all, how insignificant that duration of time is compared to the time over which the cycle extends. It may be as 1 : 100, or it may be as 1 : 200, or more. And I shall show further on (p. 47) that there are circumstances which indefinitely extend even these proportions. I conclude, therefore, that our experience in these cases is by far too limited to furnish us with reliable data, and that any attempt to reason solely from part to the whole must prove fallacious.

Another argument adduced in support of this theory is, in my opinion, equally untenable. It is asserted that, taking the degree of elevatory force now in operation, and allowing quantity of time, the repetition of the small changes on the surface witnessed by us would produce, in time, results of any known magnitude, *i. e.*, that the force which could elevate a district 5 feet in a century would suffice in one hundred thousand years to raise it 5,000 feet. This reasoning might be conclusive, if we had cause to suppose that the force were uniform and constant, but even our limited experience shows this to be irregular and paroxysmal; and although the effects indicate the nature of the force, they in no way give us a measure of its degree.

Before I proceed further I must remove two objections which have been urged against what has been called the cataclysmic theory in opposition to the uniformitarian theory—both terms in themselves inaccurate from their exaggeration, as all such terms usually are. One is, that we require forces other than those which we see in operation ; and the other, that it is unnecessarily sought to do by violent means that which can

be equally well effected by time. It is not, however, a question raised
as to the nature of the force, but as to its energy; it is not a question of
necessity one way or the other, but of interpretation; it is a question
of dynamics and not of time, and we cannot accept the introduction of
time in explanation of problems the real difficulties of which are thereby
more often passed over than solved. Time may and must be used as
without limits; there is no reason why any attempt should be made either
to extend or to curtail it; but while there is no need for frugality, there is no
wisdom in prodigality. After all, it will be found that, whichever theory
is adopted, the need will not be very different; the mountain-range, for
the gradual elevation of which the one will ask 100,000 years, the other
may require for its more sudden elevation a force taking the same number of years to accumulate its energies.

We must, however, judge of the past by the features it has stamped
on the land,* and these we must interpret not entirely by our own experience, not alone by our estimate of force, but by our knowledge of what
amount of force the energy due to the thermal condition of the globe
can develop on known dynamical principles, and by our observation of
what those forces have effected in past times.

However we may differ in our interpretation of the present thermal
state of the globe, most geologists agree in accepting the hypothesis of
central heat as the one best in accordance with known facts relating to
subterranean temperature, the eruption of igneous rocks, the action of
metamorphism, and the crushing and contortions of rock-masses. The
radiation of heat into space has been accompanied by a gradual contraction of the central mass, and a shrinking of the crust, to which the
trough of oceans, the elevation of continents, the protrusion of mountain-chains, and the faulting of strata are to be attributed. The question is whether that contraction was accompanied by a like gradual
yielding and adaptation of the solid crust to the lessening circumference
of the globe; or whether the resistance of the rigid crust was only overcome at intervals by paroxysmal efforts. This latter was the view
held by most of our early geologists, and is still the prevailing one
abroad.

It is not necessary here to deal with the first steps of the problem.
Let us take it after, for example, the re-adjustment of the crust (when it
must have been many miles thick) which resulted in the elevation of
such a mountain-chain as that of the Alps; and here I must assume a
point in advance. The resisting strata having given way to the tension to which they had been subjected, a state of equilibrium and re-
pose would for a time ensue. As the secular refrigeration subsequently
proceeded, the tangential force due to contraction resumed action; and
while certain larger areas were depressed, chiefly by the action of gravity,

---

* The evidence of facts with respect to the glacial period has led to the admission of
a greater intensity of cold; so we contend that the evidence of the past, at times,
respecting the greater effects of heat, is equally definite.

other and smaller portions of the crust, presenting less resistance, yielded, and rose at right angles to the tangential pressure.

Now either, if the elevatory force were limited and uniform in degree, a point would be reached at which that force was balanced by the increasing resistance and weight of the strata, and the movement would cease; or else, if the energy was a constantly-generated quantity, and the rigidity such as to prevent yielding beyond a certain extent, (and no solid crust can be perfectly flexible,) then it would be a dynamical necessity that a time would come when, from the accumulation of that energy, it would overcome the resistance, and the opposing strata be suddenly rent and fractured. This primary resistance removed, the full power of the elevatory force would be brought to bear upon the disjointed mass, and the surplus energy expended in at once rapidly forcing forward and tilting up the now yielding strata along the line of fracture to that position and that height required to restore a state of equilibrium and no more. It is not possible for any number of minor forces, where the ultimate resistance exceeds each one taken separately, to accomplish in any time, however long, that which requires for its execution a major force of infinitely greater power.

Either a minor force, if sufficient to move a given weight, will go on moving, or else, if from any cause a further or secondary and independent resistance, such as in this case that dependent on the cohesion of the strata, has to be met, additional power must be brought to bear, which, if that secondary resistance be then overcome, the cumulated force, being far in excess of the residual resistance, will be immediately expended with energy in proportion to the magnitude of the resistance mastered. Thus, although a railway-engine could readily move ten carriages, it could not move one hundred. It is true that if it were allowed to proceed with ten carriages at a time it could perform the removal of the whole in ten journeys, but if that were not practicable it would require the simultaneous application, say of ten engines, to accomplish the same journey at one time, and by no other means could the inertia of the mass be overcome, although when once overcome the force employed would be largely in excess of that required for traction only.

Again, in the case of large faults traversing thick masses of strata, the conditions are nearly the same. For example, in the great Craven fault, which brings the disjointed edges of the Silurian rocks on a level with the disjointed edges of the Coal-Measures, the extent of displacement is in places as much as 4,000 feet, and the range of the fault exceeds 50 miles. If we take the thickness of the strata so fractured at 20,000 or any greater number of feet, it is not possible to conceive any small force acting through any length of time to have effected their disruption, unless it could be imagined that the fault had proceeded progressively with the gradual accumulation of the strata, which is impossible. In any way, the fracture must have occurred suddenly at the moment the tension overcame the resistance of the mass; it then necessarily follows that with the residual resistance reduced to mere gravity, a displacement, ending in a state of equilibrium of the fractured strata, would at once ensue, the amount of displacement being in proportion to the severity of the strain.

The results of the foregoing conditions are in perfect accordance with observation. The enormous crumpling and folding of the strata—the vast upthrow of their disjointed edges—indicate the energy of the forces which has been exerted, has been spent, and again accumulated. Of these forces, it is as difficult for us to realize the intensity as it is to fathom the immensity of space. These are among the questions for the future.

While thus refrigeration progressed, and the shell of the globe became thicker, other causes came into operation to give it greater rigidity, and so better fit it for the habitation of man.

In the many discussions to which this question has given rise, it has been too much assumed that the shell was of uniform or nearly uniform thickness; the irregularities of the upper surface were apparent, but those possible on the under surface have been scarcely sufficiently considered. There is, however, I think, reason to suppose, from some collateral inquiries, that the under surface of the shell is ribbed and channeled in a manner and on a scale materially to influence the operation of that fluidity of the nucleus and mobility of the crust on which so many able and elaborate calculations have been based.

Let us take, on a continental area having a mean surface-temperature of 55° Fahr., a point in the earth's crust through which any isotherm of

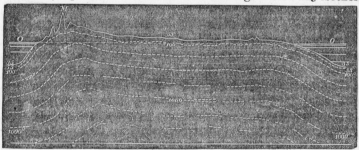

depth passes—suppose it be that of 1,000°. This earth-isotherm will possibly be found at a depth of between 50,000 and 100,000 feet.* The isothermal plane must approximatively follow the contours of the surface, and in mountain-districts, M may rise some 1,000 to 4,000 feet above its other level. But when we come to seas, such as the Mediterranean, the sea-bed has the mean temperature of the surface, (or more correctly the mean temperature of the winter-months,) and the depth of that bed being from 6,000 to 8,000 feet, the earth's thermal plane of 1,000° is thrown proportionally lower than on the adjacent land.

---

* There is reason to believe that the rate of increase of temperature of 1° Fahr. for every 50 to 60 feet of depth, which obtains near the surface, is, owing to the increased conductive power of the rocks, much less at greater depths.

With the great oceans, O, other conditions come into operation which increase the difference, for the cold Arctic waters pass in an undercurrent from the poles to the equator with so little loss of heat that near the equator a deep-sea temperature of 35° Fahr. or even lower exists. Therefore, to the depth of the ocean, we have to add a depth equivalent to the difference between the mean temperature of the adjacent land and that of the deep waters. In the Arctic zone, the temperature of the land is less than that of the sea, but as we approach the equator the former exceeds that of the latter at depths by as much as 40°, which is equal to a difference in depth of about 2,000 feet. The main channels of the great oceanic troughs in the tropics have a depth of 18,000 feet or more. If we add to this 2,000 feet for the difference of temperature between the surface and the sea-bed, and 4,000 feet for the rise under certain mountain-chains, we shall have a total of 24,000 feet as the approximate difference of level of the isotherm of 1,000° in adjacent continental and oceanic areas.*

As the position of the other earth-isotherms will in like manner occupy successive planes approximatively parallel with the surface, whether of land or sea-bed, it follows that, if a central molten nucleus exists, it will be divided into areas separated by boundary lines no less important than those formed by the continental areas between the several oceanic areas on the surface; and, as they are even more inclosed and isolated, their condition with regard to the possible existence of tidal action would approach more to that of an inland sea, such as the Mediterranean, where their influence is scarcely felt. It may be a question also whether the rigidity of the earth's crust is not influenced by this mode of structure. It must certainly have affected the permanence of continental and oceanic areas; in the one case by the convexity of the surface favoring elevation, and in the other by the concavity favoring gradual subsidence.

Notwithstanding this, it may naturally be asked, in view of the more constant slow changes and movements to which in past times the crust of the earth has been subject—and that even up to a period so geologically recent as the elevation of the Alps and the Andes—how it happens that it is now so quiescent and comparatively immovable. The hypotheses both of Mr. Hopkins and Sir W. Thompson grapple with this difficulty. The former not only considered that the crust was eight hundred to one thousand miles thick, but he also supposed that there were only local and limited bodies of molten matter, the rest of the nucleus having become solid. The latter also concludes, though on other grounds, that the secular refrigeration, combined with the excessive pressure, has led to a solidification, commencing at the center, of the whole interior of our globe;† while, as before mentioned, Mr. Mallet, admitting

---

* The numbers used are merely approximative.

† The Rev. Osmond Fisher, on the other hand, showed in 1873 (Geological Magazine, vol. x, p. 248) that on the supposition of a globe becoming solid throughout at the

the principle of a solid crust of great thickness, has proposed a theory to account for the continued ejection of molten matter from depths not far beneath the surface, and acting independently of any common source of lava supply, by the conversion of the energy resulting from crushing into heat along given lines of intense pressure.

It seems, however, to me that the uniform character appertaining to volcanic eruptions over the whole world, the traveling of earthquake movements, the flexibility yet evinced in movements of the crust, and the magnitude of the later geological changes, precludes the acceptance of the conditions suggested by these distinguished physicists, and leads me to seek for other causes to account for the present stable condition of the earth.

The cause which suggests itself to me is the intense cold of the glacial period through which the earth has so recently passed, and which has, as it were, anticipated or forestalled the refrigeration which, in ordinary course, would have taken a longer time to effect, and so would have been prolonged into some subsequent period. At present, the annual variation of temperature in these latitudes extends to a depth of about 30 feet; the maximum heat of summer being felt underground by the end of November, and the maximum cold of winter by the beginning of June, at a depth of 26 feet. But supposing the cold of winter at depths not to alternate with and be influenced by summer heat, then the abstraction of heat would continue to a depth in proportion to the length of time during which the cold at the surface was maintained; and such must have been the conditions over a large portion of the northern hemisphere (and I believe of the southern contemporaneously) during the glacial period. For as permanent ice and snow then extended down to these latitudes, the summer sun would not sensibly affect surfaces so covered, and the abstraction of heat must have proceeded uninterruptedly. To what depth the effect may have extended has not yet been investigated, but that it must have been very considerable is evident from the depth to which the annual variations are now felt. Consequently, with a uniform permanent temperature of 32° or lower at the surface, and considering the long duration of the glacial period, we may form some conception of how far beneath the surface the extreme cold must have extended; even now, in parts of Siberia, the ground is permanently frozen to a depth of 300 to 400 feet. Then the surface temperature in these latitudes, instead of commencing as now with a mean of 50°, and attaining a degree, say of 70°, at a depth of 1,000 feet, commenced with a temperature of 32° F. or less, and the isothermal of 70° must have been

---

melting temperature, and afterward cooling as a solid, the amount of crumplings and contortions of the surface which could be produced by its subsequent refrigeration would be very much smaller than sufficient to account for the existing inequalities of the earth's surface; and hence he concluded that such has not been the mode in which the earth has attained its present state, but that a crust commenced to form before the interior became solid. (See also Mr. Fisher's paper "On the Elevation of Mountain-Chains" in Trans. Cambridge Phil. Soc. for 1869, vol. xi, part iii.)

depressed below its present level to an extent in proportion to the duration of the glacial cold. On the return of the present more temperate climate, that portion of the crust of the earth, measuring certainly many hundreds, and possibly some thousands of feet in depth, which had suffered from this abnormal loss of heat, would have to recover its equilibrium with existing conditions by another change in the isothermal planes, and, until that was effected, little or no loss by radiation would take place.

Or to look at it in another way, let us suppose periods of equal temperature before and after the glacial epoch. As the radiation of heat is in proportion to the difference of temperature between the warm body and the surrounding medium, the loss of heat by the earth would, if no colder period had intervened, have been nearly equal in equal times; but with the greater cold of the glacial epoch, the same result would be effected in a shorter time, or, what is tantamount, the loss in the same time during the glacial period would be greater than in the other two periods. Thus supposing we take any given time of the glacial period to be productive of a refrigeration of the crust equal to that which would be effected in a certain longer time of the pre-glacial or post-glacial periods, then for a term of time—of length having a certain relation to the difference between the two—succeeding the glacial epoch, the earth would, with its outer crust so much below the normal, loose little or no heat by radiation, so that during that subsequent period the thermo-dynamical effects due to cooling would be reduced to a minimum or cease altogether, and a period of nearly stable equilibrium, such as now prevails, obtain.

This last great change in the long geological record is one of so exceptional a nature, that, as I have formerly elsewhere observed,[*] it deeply impresses me with the belief of great purpose and all-wise design, in staying that progressive refrigeration and contraction on which the movements of the crust of the earth depend, and which has thus had imparted to it that rigidity and stability which now render it so fit and suitable for the habitation of civilized man; for, without that immobility, the slow and constantly-recurring changes would, apart from the rarer and greater catastrophes, have rendered our rivers unnavigable, our harbors inaccessible, our edifices insecure, our springs ever-varying, and our climates ever-changing; and, while some districts would have been gradually uplifted, other whole countries must have been gradually submerged; and against this inevitable destiny no human foresight could have prevailed.

---

[*] Philosophical Transactions for 1864, p. 305.

APPENDIX.

Table showing the number and distribution of the fossil fauna and flora of Great Britain in 1874, and of the species now living and found fossil by Mr. R. Etheridge, with which is compared the number of recent species and of the fossil species known in 1822.

Period.	Plantæ.	Amorphozoa.	Protozoa and Rhizopoda.	Cœlenterata.	Echinodermata.	Annelida.	Cirrhipedia.	Crustacea.	Insecta.	Polyzoa.	Brachiopoda.	Monomyria.	Dimyaria.	Pteropoda and Nucleobranchiata.	Gasteropoda.	Cephalopoda.	Pisces.	Reptilia.	Aves.	Mammalia.	Totals.
Present	a1,820	124	96	b137	c50	d21	27	e278	f	161	7	27	193	2	g325	13	263	15	354	76	b3,989
1. Tertiary	224	2	160	66	47	37	24	123	?	150	12	93	635	1	1,180	13	123	43	16	100	3,109
2. Cretaceous	27	144	137	67	192	40	25	80	0	100	107	197	237	0	207	0	96	50	2	0	1,943
3. Purbeck and Wealden	38	0	0	0	1	1	0	11	60	0	1	9	36	0	34	0	37	43	0	30	300
4. Lias and Oolite	160	10	42	163	194	37	7	45	25	60	185	350	685	0	823	435	191	89	0	5	3,506
5. Rhætic	1	0	0	7	0	0	1	3	2	0	1	13	25	0	16	0	28	18	0	3	103
6. Trias	10	0	27	5	0	0	0	0	0	0	0	0	0	0	0	1	4	17	0	0	59
7. Permian	20	5	7	5	5	5	0	28	0	6	22	9	27	1	96	145	22	19	0	0	203
8. Carboniferous	320	9	10	125	132	23	0	195	10	64	160	143	196	30	174	52	240	0	0	0	1,989
9. Old Red Sandstone	6	0	0	53	21	1	0	17	0	13	100	22	36	10	46	0	4	0	0	0	391
10. Devonian	13	0	0	0	0	0	0	22	0	0	0	0	0	0	0	0	126	0	0	0	165
11. Silurian	4	21	0	87	90	36	2	307	0	140	263	30	102	40	102	97	12	0	0	0	1,333
12. Cambrian i	0	4	0	0	12	12	2	104	0	1	18	0	12	20	20	2	0	0	0	0	175
Total in 1874	823	198	383	573	681	194	61	935	97	534	868	866	1,992	102	2,608	980	883	282	18	198	13,276
Total in 1822	34	2	9	15	41	3	2	13	0	7	55	207	207	3	196	138	4	5	0	18	752
Living species found fossil in Britain	?10	2	56	0	5	6	10	17	0	39	4	21	160	1	306	0	0	5	?2	26	665

a Omitting 597 Mosses, 2,816 Fungi, 660 Algæ, &c.
b Excluding 175 Actinidæ, species whose remains as a rule do not admit of fossilization.
c Excluding 23 Holothuridæ, &c., species whose remains as a rule do not admit of fossilization.
d Excluding 206 soft-bodied Annelida, species whose remains as a rule do not admit of fossilization.
e Excluding 63 internal parasites, species whose remains as a rule do not admit of fossilization.
f The number of insects now known amounts to between 10,000 and 11,000 species.
g Excluding 111 Nudibranchiata, species whose remains as a rule do not admit of fossilization.
h Or excluding birds, 3,635.
i From the Longmynd to the Tremadoc rocks inclusive.

REPORT OF THE SPECIAL COMMITTEE FOR THE CONSIDERATION OF THE MEMOIR OF MR. HOFRATHES G. WEX, UPON THE DIMINUTION OF THE WATER OF RIVERS AND STREAMS.

[Presented April 23, 1874, to the Royal Academy of Vienna.—Translated from the German by M. A. Henry.]

The special committee of the Imperial Academy, called at the request of Mr. Hofrathes Wex, and which that gentleman was invited to attend, was composed of the following regular members: Fenzl, Jelinek, von Schrötter, Stefan, and Suess; and held three sessions, on the 13th of October, on the 18th of December, 1873, and the 18th of January, 1874, during which the facts contained in the memoir of Mr. Wex, and the recommendations based thereon, were thoroughly discussed.

As basis for the final conclusion attained by the commission, it seems advisable to give a short *résumé* of the observations and deductions contained in the paper of Mr. Wex.

The author first gives various data, from the second volume of Berghaus's statistics, in regard to the height of water, of the Rhine at Emmerich, of the Elbe at Magdeburg, and of the Oder at Küstrin; according to which the mean and lowest heights have sunk considerably in the course of time, while the high water is exhibited more frequently and in greater elevation.

Dr. Berghaus was led, through the examination of the heights of the water of the Elbe and the Oder, to the conclusion that in both these streams the quantity of water, when at its lowest level, had considerably decreased, and expressed the opinion that these rivers threatened to disappear from the ranks of navigable streams if this diminution continued in as great proportion as at that time, 1781.

Mr. Hofrathes Wex arrived, through long years of observations, at the same result as Berghaus, and declared that there is a continued decrease in the water of the above-named rivers, and also in those of the Vistula and the Danube. His assertion excited objections on all sides.

In opposition to it—1. The imperial Prussian private government surveyor, F. Hagen, through measurements of the high and mean heights of the Rhine at Dusseldorf, found, it is true, a slight diminution, (on an average 2.9 and 1.6 lines a day,) he explained this, however, by the recent alterations made in the stream, which promoted the removal of the ice, and the escape of the high water. 2. The imperial hydraulic inspector, Maass, found from the record of 143 years of the observations of the heights of the water of the Elbe, at Madgeburg, a considerable sinking (of 17.35½ and 34 inches) in the mean of high water and of low water, which he also attributed to changes made in the stream; the deepening of the bed, and the consequent increase in the velocity of the current. 3. The opinion was positively declared that the in recent times more abundant and rapid flowing of the high water would carry away sufficient quantities to account for the decrease in the mean and low water heights.

The author next shows—1. From the regular observations of the late Bavarian building-inspector, Grebenau, at Germersheim, of the heights of water of the Rhine from the highest to the lowest, continued during twenty-eight years, which give not only the height, but also the quantity of flowing water, that with the sinking of the mean of the levels there was also a decrease in the amount of water flowing through the rivers. 2. That according to the observations of the commission of inspection of the Elbe River, the bed of the stream was deepest when the water-marks were highest, while on the contrary, when the mean middle and lowest heights had sunken, the bed of the river had been raised by being filled in with sand, so that the sinking of the water-marks at Madgeburg cannot be attributed to the deepening of the bed of the stream. 3. That the high water cannot compensate for the decrease in the quantity of water at the low and mean heights is proved by Mr. Wex, in the first place by the before-mentioned register of the water-heights at Souder-heim, according to which it is found that the decrease in the entire amount of water is very nearly proportional to that in the water-heights; and in the second place by the measurements for thirty-two years of the water-marks of the Danube at Alt Orsova, which show a decrease, not only in the mean and low, but also in the high water recorded, which Mr. Wex correctly attributes to the circumstance that, in the large tributary streams of the Danube, the water is high at different times.

In reviewing the simple and evident facts given by our author, the commission came to the conclusion that the lowering in the mean and low water heights of the rivers mentioned, observed during the last hundred years, should be attributed to the decrease in the yearly amount of water.

Mr. Wex now stated that the diminution in the amount of water in these rivers indicated a decrease in the productive power of the springs, and further proof of this was afforded by the lessening of the water in the brooks, aqueducts, and wells or fountains.

The commission on this point were in full accord with our author, since they considered amply confirmed the conclusion that with the sinking of the mean of the low-water there was corresponding decrease in the springs and in all the water in the neighborhood of the rivers.

The cause of this decrease in the copiousness of springs may lie—1. In a diminution, owing to the advance of civilization; that is, to the uprooting of the forests, in the yearly amount of precipitation. 2. In the increased evaporation from the surface of the earth, also due to the above-mentioned cause. 3. In this change in the surface-condition of the earth, the amount of water precipitated, instead of being held in reserve and slowly percolating, rushes suddenly into the stream, and for a short time high water prevails, which is followed by a long period of dryness.

The question of the influence of forests upon the amount of precipitation has for some time engaged the attention of naturalists. Such an influence has been asserted, partly from theoretic consideration and partly on account of the entire change presented by the climatic relations of the countries in which the forests have disappeared. It was at first supposed that the woods furnished for the rain-cloud an obstacle similar to that presented by mountain-ridges to cloud-currents, and condensed the watery vapor; also, that the lower temperature and greater relative humidity of the woods promoted precipitation. In the latter view of that subject, Dr. Berger, of Frankfort, especially made some careful comparisons between the temperature and humidity of the woods and that of the open fields.

It is probable that such influence exists; but while, on the one hand, its consequence may be overestimated, on the other hand there is want of direct proof, inasmuch as the rain-measurements have been continued too short a time, both at stations situated within the woods and outside of them in the open fields. Besides, the observations of the rain-measures cannot well be compared on account of the difference in the conditions, (variations in altitude, inclination of the surface toward different points of the compass, &c.*)

On account of the great practical importance of the alleged decrease of the quantity of rain to the interests of national economy, the Meteorological Society of Edinburgh, in the year 1859, at the suggestion of its president, the Marquis of Tweedale, offered a prize for the best investigation of the question whether the amount of rain in Western Europe had undergone any alteration. The author of the article which gained the reward, Mr. T. F. Jamieson, found in the yearly measurements of rain-falls, to which he had access, no grounds for the apprehension of a progressive decrease in the quantity. There appeared to be only local oscillations, to which it was difficult to assign a cause.

---

* Möllendorf compares, in his work, The Proportion of the Rain-fall in Germany, page 95, the amount of rain for 1856–1858 of Neider-Bielau, with that of Tiefenfurt, (situated in the woods,) and found for the first 17.8 and for the last 21.8 par. inches; but he did not himself consider this result decisive. Professor Hoffman, in Giessen, found that the rain-curves of three different situations in the woods were, for the entire year, parallel with each other, which says nothing as to the alleged influence of the woods.—*Journal of Meteorology*, vol. ii, p. 231.

As to the comparative observations of rain-deposits in the department of the Loire, which it must be admitted included only twelve months, Becquerel found that the amount of rain precipitated in the neighborhood of forests was greater than at a distance from them, in the proportion of 5:4, (Comptes Rendus, t. lxiv, p. 16.)—*Journal of Meteorology*, vol. ii, p. 231.

The action of the Meteorological Society of Edinburgh in this matter led to the institution of analogous investigations, and to the establishment of a large number of rain-stations in Great Britain and Ireland, through the intervention of the British Association for the Advancement of Science, which appointed a special committee for this purpose. Mr. G. J. Symonds undertook, in London, the inspection of the stations in that city and the elaboration of the observations recorded. In most of the stations the observations examined by Mr. Symonds in the course of his investigations in regard to the question of a continual change in the amount of rain, extend back to January, 1726; and for still older measurements, going back as far as January, 1688, we are indebted to the observatory of Paris.

Mr. Symonds gives, in the Report of the British Association for 1866, page 287, a table of the rain-fall of England, taken from the registers of seventeen stations, according to dates, which are introduced to show proportions.

Periods.	Amounts.		Periods.	Amounts.	
1726—1735	94.6	86.7	1806—1815	94.6	99.3
1736—1745	78.7		1816—1825	103.9	
1746—1755	78.6	83.5	1826—1835	101.3	100.8
1756—1765	88.3		1836—1845	100.2	
1766—1775	103.6	98.4	1846—1855	100.6	98.5
1776—1785	93.2		1856—1865	96.3	
1786—1795	96.6	93.2			
1796—1805	98.7				

In the Meteorological *Annuaire* of the central physical observatory for 1873, page 254, appears the following table of the yearly amount of rain in Paris, prepared by Marié Davy :

Period.	Amount. mm.	Period.	Amount. mm.
1688—1700	517	1791—1798	414
1701—1710	481	1804—1810	518
1711—1720	465	1811—1820	496
1721—1730	378	1821—1830	514
1731—1740	411	1831—1840	507
1741—1750	420	1841—1850	529
1773—1780	540	1851—1860	520
1781—1790	507	1861—1870	493

According to the observations in England and France, there is no perceptible decrease in the yearly amount deposited, but after the lapse of ten years, oscillations in the rates of the rain-falls appear, the cause of which is at present unknown. It is rash to conclude from these facts that there is no alteration in the amount of said precipitations in Western Europe, and that in the interior of continents there is also no change. Still the rain-measurements of the continental stations do not appear to indicate such a decrease, although, to be sure, they do not extend as far back as could be desired.*

* In the Imperial Central Meteorological Establishment are the rain-measurements of about 120 stations in Europe and North America, which should be investigated with reference to this question.

A similar result was arrived at by the investigation of the Smithsonian Institution of the rain-measurements in North America, where, on account of the great extent of forest cleared away, a change in the proportion of the deposits might well be expected.

In regard to the old rain-observations, it should be remarked that they were not taken daily, but at longer intervals of time, whereby their accuracy was considerably impaired. Besides, the rain-gauges were frequently not well placed, (upon roofs, towers, &c.) Both these circumstances, taken together, might produce an appearance of decrease in the quantity of rain.*

But although nearly two hundred years of direct rain-measurement furnish no proof of a progressive decrease in the quantity of rain, in view of the facts presented by our author, (taken mostly from Milne Home's essay in the Journal of the Meteorological Society of Scotland, vol. 3, p. 35,) by Becquerel, Meteorological Atlas of the Observatory of Paris for 1867, Journal of Meteorology, vol. 4, p. 86, and by others, and which appear to indicate a deterioration in the climate after the leveling of the forests, it would not be just to consider this hypothesis of no importance.

The commission consequently concluded that an influence of the woods upon the amount of rain deposited, and especially upon the yearly contribution, is probable, although direct observation does not give sufficient evidence to determine its extent, or positively its existence.

The copiousness of the springs and the fullness of the rivers, moreover, do not entirely represent the amount of the yearly precipitation of water. On the one hand a portion is given back to the atmosphere by evaporation, and on the other a portion, determined in amount by the physical conditions of the ground, penetrates into the soil, and affords nourishment for the springs. The influence of the woods in both these tendencies cannot be overestimated.

Through direct observation in France and the forest meteorological station of Bavaria, it is evident that the oscillations of the temperature of the air are slighter in forests than upon unwooded ground. In the hours and years, particularly when the maximum of heat was attained, the sum total of the latter in the woods was much less than in the open fields.

In accordance with this the temperature of wooded surfaces in the warm years is considerably lower than that of unwooded surfaces.†

---

* The fact of the influence of height upon the results of the rain-measures has frequent confirmation; for instance, in Möllendorf's work, page 102, it appears that of several stations the lower recorded from 13 to 60 per cent. more rain than the higher.

† According to Ebermayer, the yearly oscillations of temperature in the woods (50°.0 C.) are 7° C. less than in the open fields. The yearly maximum of temperature is found to be 5°.2 lower. Likewise the daily oscillations of temperature in summer amount to 5°.9 C. less than that of the open fields. The temperature of the soil of forest-land was, in summer, 4°.0 C. less than that of the unwooded soil. (Ebermayer's Physical Influence of the Woods, Journal of Meteorology, vol. 8, pp. 209 and 232.)

In like manner the proportional humidity of the woods differs from that of the open country, and at all seasons of the year is greater in the forests.*

In consideration of these facts, it is not surprising that the evaporation in the woods is found to be far less than in the open fields.† Furthermore the evaporation does not depend only upon the temperature-but also upon the motion of the air, which in the woods is proportion, ably much less agitated.

It was now important to determine accurately the portion of the deposit lost by evaporation, a very difficult matter, since the proportion obtained by the atometer is entirely different from that of the evaporation from the surface of plants, and from the soil. Besides, the proportionate results of the atometric measurements by which the evaporation of a water-surface is obtained are influenced by the different ways of placing the instrument, sometimes exposed to the sun and rain, sometimes under shelter; by the difference in dimension of the evaporating dishes, and by the difference in the material of which the latter are composed. It ought not to be surprising, under such circumstances, if an atometer of small dimensions, made of metal and exposed to the sun, gives yearly amounts of evaporation, which far exceed (2 or 3 times) the amounts of precipitation.

On account of the difficulty of determining the amount of evaporation from the ground, and therewith the portion of the precipitation actually received by the springs and running water, this should be sought by comparing the quantities of water a stream carries away in the course of a year, and determining the corresponding amounts of rain fallen within the drainage area of the stream; also on the other hand by endeavoring to measure the amount of water absorbed by a certain portion of earth, and the amount lost from a given stratum.‡

If in the woods a considerable portion of the precipitation is received upon the twigs and leaves, the rest (according to Ebermayer, 72 per cent., Journal of Meteorology, viii, 274) on this account remains longer in the woods, and has time to sink into the soil and supply the springs. This portion, at least that part of it not dissipated by evaporation, either sinks into the ground or flows off of its surface. In the first instance it serves especially for the supply of the springs; in the second it is carried directly to the water-courses, and produces a brief, more or less considerable rising in the latter.

---

* According to Ebermayer, the difference amounts in the four seasons, calculated from the spring, to 5.7, 9.3, 5.2, and 5.2 per cent.

† According to Ebermayer the evaporation from a surface of water in the woods was 64 per cent. less than outside the same. (Journal of Meteorology, vol. viii, p. 253.)

‡ Möllendorf (The Rain-fall of Germany, p. 130–167) gives as the percentage of the deposits not evaporated and entered into the supply of the springs and rivers, for England, (4 determinations,) 31.7; for France, (2 determinations in mountainous regions,) 65.1; for Germany, (5 determinations on rivers, 7 determinations on earth-boxes and artificial drainage,) 47.3 per cent.

It must be generally acknowledged that forests, on account of their peculiar vegetation of lichens, mosses, &c., are pre-eminently qualified to absorb the precipitations, accumulate them, and give them up by degrees.

In this connection are the observations which have already been mentioned in regard to the water which penetrates the soil very slowly to a certain depth; on the one hand, upon the receptive power of different kinds of soils, upon the influence of different plants with which the soil is covered; on the other hand, upon the distribution in the soil of this penetrating moisture, as indicated by the yearly registers. It appears from the latter that the influence of the woods is greater in warm years.

According to Ebermayer, the percentage of precipitation in summer was, at the depth of—

	Without herbage.	With herbage.		
	One foot.	One foot.	Two feet.	Four feet.
In the open fields	19	19	14	11
In the woods	52	72	65	36
Difference	33	53	51	25

Older observations were undertaken by Maurice in Ghent, Gasparin in Orange, and some more recent, on a larger scale, were instituted by E. Risler at Caléve, near Nyon, (canton Wallis.) He sowed for the experiment a field containing 12,300 square meters with grain, clover, &c., determined the drainage at 0.35 meter depth, and compared the humidity of this soil with that of others cultivated under different circumstances. (Annuaire Météorologique de l'Observatoire de Paris, pour 1873, page 277.)

In reference to the portion of the precipitation which does not penetrate the soil but flows off the surface, and to which the rising of the water is especially attributed, there is no difference of opinion in regard to the influence of the woods. All admit that with the leveling of the latter, the supply of the water-courses flows in more rapidly, and that in mountainous regions the water drains off so fast from unwooded steep declivities that the streams are converted into rushing torrents.

To the cutting down of the woods and the consequent removal of the check they offered, through their interlaced roots, their mosses, lichens, &c., to the downfall of the rain, must be attributed the more frequent and destructive floods and inundations which are always to be dreaded.

The fact of the diminution of water in streams, which diminution is connected with the copiousness of the springs which supply them, being admitted, the commission find the causes of this phenomenon: 1st. In the continued cutting down of the woods, whose salutary influence in the raising of the hygrometer, the amelioration of extreme temperature, the decrease of evaporation, and the promotion of a regular escape of the precipitation is evident, while the disadvantageous results of their removal is felt in the prolonged period of dryness on the one hand, and the destructive high water on the other. 2d. In the desiccation of the lakes, ponds, and bogs, which likewise raises the hygrometric conditions, decreases evaporation, moderates extreme temperature, and, lastly, through the fissures in the soil, directly promotes the formation of springs. 3d. In the cultivation of extended tracts of land, for the irrigation of which large quantities of water are required. 4th. In the increase of the population and the domestic animals, although the diminution of the water from this cause is relatively so small as to be unimportant. 5th. Lastly, it seems to the commission that, in accordance with the opinion expressed by M. L. Saemann, that water is continually absorbed in the interior of the earth, in the formation of mineral substances into which it enters as the water of crystallization, this telluric cause of the decrease of water is worthy of consideration.

The commission concluded, in view of the data published by Mr. Wex, to support the recommendations he also gives in his report, as follows:

1st. That the Royal Academy of Science shall call the attention of the Austrian government, and of the royal commercial and agricultural administrations, to the established fact of the continual decrease in the water of springs and streams, and also to the causes of this phenomenon, and endeavor to induce these high authorities to take into serious consideration the modes of record and the preventive measures proposed by Mr. Wex to check this deterioration, which threatens with dire calamity future generations, and induce them, by the publication of suitable rules and regulations, to secure the accomplishment of the end to be desired.

A similar effort should be made by the Royal Academy of Science to bring this subject to the knowledge of the countries belonging to the Austrian crown, which have in late years been more than ever occupied in the clearing out of under-brush, the drainage of lakes, swamps, and moors, and, lastly, in the damming up of regions formerly inundated by the floods which, appearing with constantly-increasing frequency, must be accompanied by corresponding periods of drought and unfruitfulness.

2. The Royal Academy of Science should send to the scientific institutions of other countries, namely, Holland, England, France, Italy, Spain, Russia, North America, and Brazil, a copy of the memoir of Mr. Hofrathes Wex, with the request for communications of the yearly observations of the water-heights of the rivers of the different countries. In this way water-height observations might be obtained which have not been published, abstracts of which might be made and graphically represented, as in the memoir just mentioned.

3. Especially should the government of the viceroy of Egypt be advised of the wish of the Royal Academy, so that of the observations of the water-heights of the Nile above Cairo, continued for 300 years, a copy, at least of those of the last 200 years, might be obtained, with similar tables and graphical representations.

4. The Royal Academy should express to the government the wish that in more streams, and in better adapted places, regular observations, not only of the water-heights but also of the whole amount of water flowing through a stream, might be made, in order that the proportion between the latter and the water-heights may be at least approximately obtained.

The government, furthermore, should endeavor to draw the attention of the Hungarian and other foreign governments to the wish of the Royal Academy, that similar observations and inquiries might be instituted in other countries.

VIENNA, *April 23*, 1874.

THE REFRACTION OF SOUND.

By William B. Taylor.

As ordinarily received by the ear, sound may be considered as an aërial impulse or succession of impulses radiating in all directions from the origin of disturbance, and consisting *in the main* of a small to-and-fro movement generating an expanding wave of compression of determinate velocity, necessarily followed by a corresponding wave of attenuation. This vibration is a mass-movement of the air, and not a molecular movement; and the surface or surfaces of similar phase of movement are equidistant from the origin; or, in other words, the wave-fronts are essentially spherical.

The transmission of sound through liquid and solid mediums, though similar in character, and subject to similar perturbations, will not here be considered.

Sound, while differing widely from light in the character of its waves and their order of magnitude, yet thus moves like light in radial lines, and like light is diverted from its rectilinear course whenever its waves undergo an *unequal* retardation or acceleration; that is, whenever any segment of a series of advancing wave-fronts (regarded as an acoustic beam) receives from any cause an unequal velocity on its opposite sides, such beam is bent toward the side of least velocity, and from the side of greatest velocity; the line of impulse or of acoustic effect being always perpendicular to the surface of the wave-front.

By sound-beams, or sound-rays, the longitudinal direction of sound is to be understood; by sound-waves, the transverse surfaces of simultaneous movement are to be understood. The amplitude of the wave-motion is very minute, being ordinarily a barely visible magnitude. It lies in the direction of the wave-length, or of the sound-ray. In the case of light, the amplitude of vibration is transverse to the wave-length, or to the direction of the ray.

If we imagine a symmetrical boat on a perfectly still sea or lake, mechanically propelled by oars of precisely similar character and movement, it is obvious that such a boat must advance in a perfectly straight course. If placed in a uniform current, the boat, though drifting with the current, would still maintain a rectilinear path. If, however, such moving boat were to *enter* a current, or to encounter a difference of current on its opposite sides, or were it to encounter water of different density, as by passing *obliquely* from salt-water into a margin of fresh water, then, *at the moment of transition*, the oars meeting with unequal resistances, the course of the boat would be changed, or "refracted." This image may be taken as a rough illustration of the phenomenon of "refraction" generally.

There are three different methods in which sound-waves passing through a gaseous medium may suffer such unequal disturbance of velocity: first, by variations of *density* in the medium, sound moving more slowly through a dense air than a rare one, the pressure being the same; second, by variations of *elasticity* in the medium, sound moving more swiftly with increase of elasticity, the density being the same; and, third, by variations of motion or *current* in the medium, sound traveling by convection faster with the wind by a small percentage, according to its velocity, and more slowly against the wind.[*]

There is no doubt that light also would be subject to all three of these forms of refraction, as its velocity is necessarily retarded by an increase of density in the medium, by a reduction of the elasticity of the medium, and by an adverse motion of the medium.

A fourth cause of velocity disturbance in the case of sound is found in the *temperature* of the medium, sound moving more swiftly in a heated atmosphere than in a cooler one. This cause of acoustic refraction is practically a highly important one; though it may be theoretically resolved into one of the preceding conditions, since the only dynamic effect of heat on a gas is to increase its elasticity if the volume be constant by confinement, or to increase its volume if unconfined without changing its elasticity.

The relation of these atmospheric conditions to each other is exceedingly simple.

The *density* of a perfect gas (the inverse of its volume) varies directly as the pressure, the temperature being constant, or inversely as the absolute temperature, the pressure being constant.

The *elasticity* of a perfect gas varies directly as the pressure, the density being constant, or inversely as the density, the pressure being constant. It also varies directly as the absolute temperature, the volume being constant.[†]

From these relations it follows that increase of atmospheric pressure does not affect the velocity of sound; for although the *density* is directly proportional to the pressure, and this diminishes the velocity, yet as the *elasticity* is also directly proportional to the pressure, and this increases the velocity by precisely the same amount, the two effects are neutralized.

---

[*] The ratio of the velocity of the wind to that of sound (one or two per cent.) is too small to be of any account *directly*. Differentially, it becomes very important. A uniform wind has no practical effect on sound except to slightly flatten or lower the pitch in its own direction, and to sharpen or raise the pitch in the opposite direction.

[†] According to Waterston, "when air is compressed or dilated, the absolute temperature varies as the cube root of the density, and the tension as the fourth power of the absolute temperature, or cube root of the fourth power of the density," (*Rep. Brit. Assoc.*, 1853, p. 12 of Abstracts.) This would indicate a striking departure from the condition of a perfect gas.

We have as the laws of sound-motion in a perfect gas :

1st. Its velocity is directly proportional to the square root of the elasticity of the air.

2d. Its velocity is inversely proportional to the square root of the density of the air.

3d. Its velocity is directly proportional to the square root of the absolute temperature of the air.

The theoretical case of unequal elasticity of the medium, presenting no practical examples, excepting in the passage of sound from water into air obliquely, or from air into water, may be here neglected ; and the remaining actual conditions of acoustic refraction are limited to three, viz: those of density-inequality, wind-inequality, and temperature-inequality. It is important to observe that the two fundamental principles underlying the discussion of acoustic refraction of whatever origin are, first, that the directions of progressive impulse are always at right angles to the surface of the wave-front, and, secondly, that any deformation of the spherical surface of the wave-front must accordingly deflect the line of acoustic propagation from its original radial direction.

1.—REFRACTION FROM INEQUALITY OF DENSITY.

In 1852, Mr. Carl Sondhauss was the first to demonstrate acoustic refraction, and he exhibited it by means of a lens of carbonic-acid gas.

It may be here premised that, in accordance with the previous summary, *hydrogen*, having at the pressure of the atmosphere the same elasticity, should, from this circumstance alone, transmit sound with the same velocity as ordinary air; but as its rarity is fourteen times greater, the velocity of sound in this medium is increased nearly four times, so that while at ordinary temperature (65° F.) sound in air would move over 1,125 feet in a second, or one mile in 4.7 seconds, it would move over 4,250 feet per second (or one mile in $1\frac{1}{4}$ second) in an atmosphere of hydrogen. On the other hand, as *carbonic acid*, at the same pressure and with nearly the same elasticity, has a density rather more than 50 per cent. greater than air, it would retard the velocity of sound about one-fifth, or reduce it to 912 feet per second, or one mile in 5.7 seconds.

Mr. Sondhauss first employed a thin membranous balloon formed of gold-beaters' skin, but obtained more decided results by forming the envelope of a double convex lens with two spherical segments of collodion film, attached to a leaden hoop, in which were suitable openings for the introduction of the gas. The ticking of a watch placed at some distance behind such lens was heard most distinctly at a focal point in front of the lens.

" In order to arrive at a more certain decision, the experiment was arranged in such manner that while the observer sat at the other side of the lens with closed eyes and listened for the ticking of the watch, the lens was alternately removed and again brought into position, whereby it was shown that the ticking of the watch disappeared every time upon the removal of the lens and was immediately audible again when the lens was replaced between the watch and the ear."—(*Poggendorff's Annalen*, 1852, lxxxv, 381, translated and republished in the *Phil. Mag.* February, 1853, v, 75.)

The accompanying Fig. 1, representing a vertical section of the gas

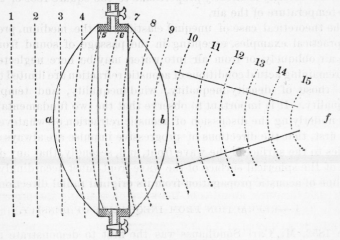

FIG. 1.—Carbonic-acid lens.

lens through its center, will serve to give a more definite idea of the action it exercises on the sound-waves passing through it. For any small area, the wave-front, at some distance from its origin, may be considered as practically a plane surface, and 1, 2, 3, &c., (Fig. 1,) may represent the successive positions of a single advancing wave-front. On entering the convex surface of the carbonic-acid lens at its central point *a*, the wave-face is at once retarded, and successive annuli of the wave passing the surface at increasing degrees of obliquity, the form of the wave-front becomes concave, as shown at 3 and 4, advancing concentrically according to the law of normal impacts, with a uniform though retarded velocity, as shown at 4, 5, 6, 7, &c. On emerging first from the outer margin of the reversed convex surface *b*, the wave-front is accelerated in passing into the common air, and meeting the boundary of the same obliquely becomes still more concave, as shown at 8, 9, 10, &c. Advancing concentrically, its impulses converge with uniform velocity, but increasing energy, toward a focal point, *f*.

It is obvious that if this convex envelope were filled with hydrogen, the action would be just reversed, as shown in Fig. 2. The wave of sound, on entering the convex surface *c*, would be accelerated (commencing at the middle) so as to acquire a continuously convex front, as shown at 5, 6, &c. Passing through the second surface, *d*, and being retarded in a reverse order, the wave-front would advance with an increased convexity, as seen at 8, 9, 10, &c., giving a general divergence of the sound-rays, the focus being negative.

It follows that to obtain a focal convergence by means of a hydrogen lens, we should have to employ a concave form, as shown in Fig. 3. In

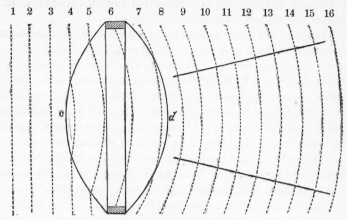

FIG. 2.—Hydrogen lens. (*a*.)

this case, the outer annulus of the wave on entering the projecting surface of the lens *g*, as at 4 and 5, would be hurried forward into a concave form, as shown at 5 and 6, having a general center of convergence at about *e*. On emerging from the second surface, *h*, (supposed here to

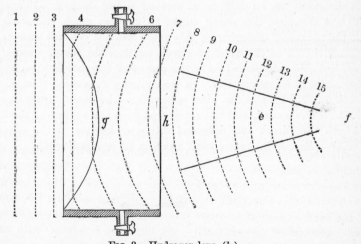

FIG. 3.—Hydrogen lens, (*b*.)

be a plane,) the wave, by oblique retardation, as shown at 7, would be somewhat flattened, as at 8, 9, 10, &c., extending the focal point of convergence to *f*. The effect of a double concave surface to the lens would be to shorten the focal distance according to the degree of concavity.

2.—REFRACTION FROM INEQUALITY OF WIND.

In 1857, Prof. G. G. Stokes showed that differences of motion in the air must exert a bending influence on the beams of sound, and that this deflection presented the only satisfactory explanation of the familiar fact of observation that sound is usually heard many times farther in the direction of a wind than in a direction opposed to its action. His explanation of this phenomenon is as follows:

"If we imagine the whole mass of air in the neighbourhood of the source of disturbance divided into horizontal strata, these strata do not all move with the same velocity. The lower strata are retarded by friction against the earth, and by various obstacles they meet with; the upper by friction against the lower, and so on. Hence the velocity increases from the ground upward, conformably with observation. This difference of velocity disturbs the spherical form of the sound-wave, tending to make it somewhat of the form of an ellipsoid, the section of which, by a vertical diametrical plane parallel to the direction of the wind, is an ellipse meeting the ground at an obtuse angle on the side toward which the wind is blowing, and an acute angle on the opposite side. Now sound tends to propagate itself in a direction perpendicular to the sound-wave; and if a portion of the wave is intercepted by an obstacle of large size, the space behind is left in a sort of sound-shadow, and the only sound there heard is what diverges from the general wave after passing the obstacle. Hence, near the earth, in a direction contrary to the wind, the sound continually tends to be propagated upward, and consequently there is a continual tendency for an observer in that direction to be left in a sort of sound-shadow. Hence, at a sufficient distance, the sound ought to be very much enfeebled; but near the source of disturbance this cause has not yet had time to operate, and therefore the wind produces no sensible effect, except what arises from the augmentation in the radius of the sound-wave, and this is too small to be perceptible. In the contrary direction—that is, in the direction toward which the wind is blowing—the sound tends to propagate itself downward, and to be reflected from the surface of the earth; and both the direct and reflected waves contribute to the effect perceived."—(*Rep. Brit. Assoc.*, 1857, xxvii, p. 23 of Abstracts.)

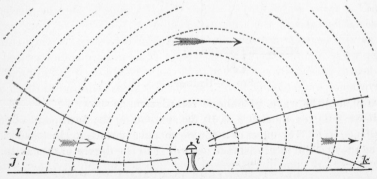

FIG. 4.—Vental refraction.

This action may be illustrated by Fig. 4, in which the larger arrow above indicates the direction and force of the wind, and the two smaller arrows below the diminished force of the wind in the same direction, by reason of the increasing resistance and retardation toward the surface of the earth. The result is a flattening of the waves at the left side and a swaying of the waves forward on the right side, thus giving the radial lines or sound-beams a curved form, (as shown by the lower lines $l\,i$ and $i\,k$,) these being always perpendicular to the wave-faces. As this curvature or refraction is necessarily upward against the unequal wind and downward in the direction of the wind, an observer at k will hear with great distinctness the sound emanating from i, while an observer on the other side at j will hear nothing, by reason of the sound-beams being tilted above his head. By rising to an elevation, as at l, the observer will hear the sound as well against the wind as with it.

It is not a little surprising that an explanation of a well-marked and puzzling phenomenon, so elegant and so conclusive as that promulgated by Professor Stokes, should have remained for fifteen years unnoticed and unthought-of by the scientific world. When in 1865 Professor Henry discovered that " a sound moving against the wind, inaudible to the ear on the deck of a schooner, was heard by ascending to the mast-head, this remarkable fact at first suggested the idea that sound was more readily conveyed by the upper current of air than the lower." And this general idea seemed confirmed by the observation that with the upper and lower currents at variance the upper wind appeared to most favor the sound. Nor was it till early in 1872 that the full significance of all this became apparent on first learning of the explanation given by Professor Stokes. And yet during the same series of observations, Professor Henry discovered that the velocity of wind in the higher regions of the air was much greater than in the lower regions.

In like manner, Professor Reynolds having, in the spring of 1874, independently arrived at the same theory, and undertaken a series of experiments and observations in this direction, remarks: " I had just reached the point of making such tests, when I discovered that the same views had been propounded by Professor Stokes so long ago as 1857."—(*Proc. R. S.*, 1874.) Professor Reynolds made the decisive observations that in the direction of the wind, the sound of a bell could be as well heard at a distance, with the head depressed as when standing; while against the wind, the sound at no great distance ceased to be heard, passing over the head, and could be regained in full force by elevation. It was found also that the elevation required to reach the lowest sound-beam increased with the distance.

If we suppose the wind near the surface of the earth (or at 6 feet above it) to be moving at the rate of six miles per hour, (one mile in 10 minutes, or 8.8 feet per second,) and at the elevation of 1,000 feet to be moving in the same direction with just double the velocity, then a vertical wave-front of sound in moving 4.7 seconds, or one mile, against such wind would be retarded 41 feet near the ground, and 82 feet at the height of 1,000 feet. This difference of 41 feet would so tilt the wave-face backward that a line perpendicular to it would have an upward direction of about 2° 21′; or, an arc described with a radius of 24.39 miles would represent approximately the upward curvature of a horizontal sound-beam, whereby at the distance of a mile it would be lifted up about 108 feet. A wave-front of sound moving in the direction of the wind would, of course, be correspondingly accelerated above, and the beam bent downward in a similar arc.

A wind blowing along the face of an extended bluff or cliff, being retarded near the same by friction, would, in a similar manner, cause a sound originating near it to be laterally refracted toward the wall in the direction of the wind, and from it in the opposite direction.

When, from any cause, the upper wind should move more sluggishly than the lower wind, as sometimes occurs, the lines of refraction above indicated would be reversed, and we should have the exceptional case of sound being favored by an opposing wind, and *vice versa.*

This very simple principle of vental refraction has thus a wide practical range, and the variety of its applications is limited only by that of the actual differences in force and direction of the winds. In short, in the case of any divergence between the upper and lower currents, in whatever direction, there will be but two lines of no refraction. In all other directions, a positive or a negative resultant must to some degree disturb the direction of the acoustic ray.

In consequence of the slight internal friction (or " viscosity ") of air, the shadow-line is not usually very sharply defined. Wave-impulses acting laterally on the adjacent air cause the sound to be feebly heard within the shadow-line ; and the sound-beam is thus practically diffracted around an obstacle to an extent which is probably some function of its intensity or energy. The effect of this, in the case of a refracted beam, is to diminish somewhat its apparent curvature, and thus to render an uplifted sound sensible to a greater distance than it would be on a merely geometrical theory, or without such marginal diffusion.

From the same cause the following practical results follow : 1st. A continuous sound, as of a horn or steam-whistle, requires at a distance a short but appreciable interval (a second or more) to be heard with its full power ; 2d. Hence, with adverse winds, sounds of single impulse, as those of bells and guns, are more refracted than continuous sounds, whose initial impulses are re-enforced by rhythmic successions, giving them greater persistence of force and direction ; 3d. It is unnecessary to add that sounds under such circumstances (with beams of convex curvature) can be heard to a greater distance when originating from an elevation, and also when observed from an elevation ; 4th. It is probable that sounds of high pitch are more refracted than medium tones and those of lower pitch.

3.—REFRACTION FROM INEQUALITY OF TEMPERATURE.

In 1874, Prof. Osborne Reynolds pointed out a third practical cause of acoustic refraction in the differences of temperature to which advancing waves of sound are frequently subjected. He remarks: "Although barometric pressure does not affect the velocity of sound, yet, as is well known, the velocity of sound depends on the temperature, and every degree of temperature between 32° and 70° adds approximately one foot per second to the velocity of sound. This velocity also increases with the quantity of moisture in the air; but the quantity is at all times too small to produce an appreciable result. This vapor nevertheless plays an important part in the phenomena under consideration; for it gives to the air a much greater power of radiating and absorbing heat, and thus renders it much more susceptible of changes in the action of the sun. . . . It is a well-known fact that the temperature of the air diminishes as we proceed upward, and that it also contains less vapor. Hence it follows that, as a rule, the waves of sound must travel faster below than they do above, and thus be refracted or turned upward."— (*Proc. R. S.*, 1874.)

Professor Reynolds cites observations showing that on a calm clear day in July, 1873, while the sun was shining with great power, loud sounds which could be heard but two or three miles were heard several times this distance toward evening after the sun had become obscured with clouds. "Here we see that the very conditions which actually diminished the range of sound were precisely those which would cause the greatest lifting of the waves."

This furnishes a satisfactory explanation of the familiar fact that sounds heard during the day-time to comparatively short distances (especially in summer and with still air) are audible many times as far in the night. "Humboldt could hear the falls of Orinoco three times as loud by night as by day at a distance of one league; and he states that the same phenomenon has been observed near every waterfall in Europe." Humboldt also remarked that the heating effect of the sun was so great that "all distant objects had wavy undulating outlines, the optical effect of the *mirage*. Not a breath of air moved the dust-like sand. The sun stood in the zenith."—(*Views of Nature*, Bohn's ed., p. 200.) Dr. Gregory, in his experiments on sound, undertaken in 1824, observed that, on January 9, in the evening, with no wind stirring, "the sound of the same charge fired from the same musket was heard much more intensely on this clear frosty night than in the day-time of January 3, at the same distance, 3,600 feet."—(*Phil. Mag.*, 1824, lxiii, 404.)

Fig. 5 illustrates this effect of heated lower strata of air in tilting up the beams of sound in all directions. If we suppose the horizontal lines to mark spaces upward, of 100 yards each, into which the air is arranged by strata of diminishing temperatures of 3 degrees each, but increasing more rapidly near the surface, (75°, 70°, 67°, 64°,) then near the ground (at 75°) the horizontal sound-beams will travel 5 feet per second (or 23.5 feet per mile) faster than at the line *n* of 70°, or the height of 300 feet; at this line, 3 feet per second (or 14 feet per mile) faster than at the line *o* of 67°, or the height of 600 feet; and at this line the same quantity faster than at the line *p* of 64°, or the height of 900 feet. The result is that a vertical wave-front 900 feet deep would, at the distance of one mile, be advanced at its lower part more than 51 feet beyond its upper part, making an angle of about $3\frac{1}{4}$°; and the corresponding upward curvature of the lower sound-beams emanating from *m* (the versed sine of this arc) would amount to about 150 feet.

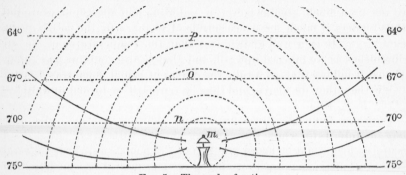

FIG. 5.—Thermal refraction.

If the temperature of the lower strata of air were found to increase only at half the rate above assumed, the lower sound-beams from *m* would be lifted one hundred and fifty feet in about two miles. If the differences of temperature were reduced to one-fourth, this amount of upward tilt would be reached in about four miles, &c.

From this it is apparent that temperature-refraction—the upward "dishing" of the lower sheet of sound by the overheating of the lower air—is not only a real phenomenon, but that in quantity it introduces a very considerable amount of disturbance in the direction of sound, and thus impairs seriously its audibility at any great distance on the surface of the earth.

In further illustration of the same principle, no less notable is the converse effect of an excess of *cooling* in the lower strata, occasionally noticed. Professor Reynolds, continuing his researches "On the refraction of sound," during the summer of 1875, found that, on the 19th of August, "after three weeks of cold and windy weather," the sea and the adjacent air being chilled considerably below the average or upper temperature, sound passing over the water reached the observers in a boat with such remarkable clearness that "guns, and on one occasion the barking of a dog, on the shore, eight miles distant, were distinctly heard, as were also the paddles of a steamer fifteen miles distant. The day was perfectly calm; there was no wind; the sky was quite clear, and the sun shining with great power." The significant circumstance is recorded that "all the time distant objects *loomed* considerably, *i. e.*, appeared lifted." In this case, "the diminution in the temperature of the air being downward, the sound instead of being lifted as it usually is, was brought down, and thus intensified at the surface of the water, which, being perfectly smooth, was thus converted into a sort of whispering-gallery."—(*Proc. R. S.*, 1876.)

This action is illustrated by Fig. 6, in which the temperature of the air below the horizontal line *q r*, being gradually less toward the earth than above the line, the sound-waves originating at *s* are shortened lat-

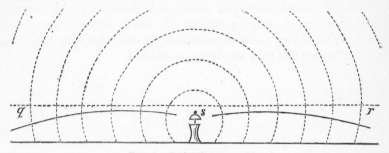

FIG. 6.—Refraction by cold.

erally (or in the direction of the lower rays) about one foot per second for each degree of refrigeration, and the sound-beams (always perpendicular to the waves) are thus gradually bent downward.

The remarkable distances to which sounds have sometimes been heard in Arctic regions receive here a satisfactory explanation. " Lieutenant Foster, in the third polar expedition of Captain Parry, found that he could hold a conversation with a man across the harbour of Port Bowen, a distance of 6,696 feet, or about a mile and a quarter."—(Sir J. Herschel, *Sound*, sect. 21.) The same author remarks of the polar regions: " In consequence of the intense cold of the icy surface, contrasted, as it sometimes is in summer, with the warmth of the air, the phenomena of atmospheric refraction are exaggerated in these regions in a most extraordinary manner; the forms of ice-bergs, rocks, etc., are seen drawn up in vertical altitude, and spread out at their apparent summits laterally, so as to present no resemblance to their real form."— (Sir J. Herschel, *Physical Geography*, sect. 98.) From which we learn that the optical deportment of the air may very often be accepted as an index of its acoustic condition.

In the play and interaction of these two great and prevalent modes of acoustic refraction—that resulting from co-existent differences of wind in varying directions and that from co-existent differences of temperature—whether re-enforcing or checking each other, or leaving a differential resultant, we have abundant opportunities to exercise the judgment and discrimination of the most diligent observers. Professor Reynolds noticed that on some clear nights in May and June, 1875, when a heavy dew indicated considerable refrigeration at the surface, " the sound could invariably be heard as far against a light wind as with it," showing that the upward refraction from wind was completely counteracted by the downward refraction from diminution of temperature. This was observed not to be the case when the cloudiness of the night prevented terrestrial radiation and the deposition of dew.—(*Proc R. S.*, 1876.)

It has thus been shown in the course of this discussion, that while the refraction of sound as illustrated by gas lenses, still retains its original interest as a striking class-experiment, the far more important examples of acoustic refraction constantly presented by the infinitely varied conditions of differing air-currents and of differing air-temperatures, have until very recently, attracted no attention, and their practical significance has been strangely overlooked.

ON THE ORGANIZATION OF LOCAL SCIENTIFIC SOCIETIES.

A letter from Professor Henry, Secretary of the Smithsonian Institution.

*   *   *   " In answer to your question, as to the plan of organization and operation of a scientific association, I submit the following:

" The object of your society being, as you inform me, to cultivate ' scientific taste and knowledge among its members,' this object should be kept constantly in view, and care be taken that it be not interfered with by a tendency to waste the time of the meetings in the discussion of irrelevant matters, especially those which relate to the government and organization of the establishment. I have been a member of several societies which failed to effect their object, by endless discussions on points of order or propositions as to the constitution and by-laws. There is in this country a tendency to express little thought in many words, to cultivate a talent for debate, or the art of making the worse appear the better cause, which is by no means favorable to either the increase or the diffusion of knowledge. The object of your society is not that of a mere debating club, but that of an establishment for the real improvement of its members in knowledge and wisdom.

" It has been from the first the policy of the Institution to encourage the establishment of such societies, on account of the great advantage they are to their members in the way of intellectual and moral improvement, as well as in the way of positive contributions to science.

" Such an association is an important organization for the advance of adult education, and the diffusion of interesting and useful knowledge throughout a neighborhood. The society must, however, be under the care of a few enthusiastic and industrious persons; it should adopt the policy of awakening and sustaining the interest of the greatest number of persons possible in its operations, and for this purpose the meetings must be rendered attractive; care should be taken to provide a series of short communications on various subjects, on which remarks should be invited after they have been read; clergymen, lawyers, physicians, farmers, mechanics, and others should all be pressed into the service, and each solicited to contribute something, the object being to make the special knowledge of *each* the knowledge of *all*. I once belonged to a society conducted on this plan, which is still in existence, and of which I had the pleasure of attending a meeting about ten years ago; and by way of illustrating what I have said, permit me to mention the proceedings on the occasion in question. First a number of mineralogical specimens were presented and described, next a short paper was given on the local geology of the vicinity, and then a brief lecture on astrology, in which the process of casting nativities was described. This last subject, which, on first thought, might appear beyond the capacity of the majority of an ordinary audience, proved to be a source of interesting remarks, in which nearly all participated. This arose from the fact that astrological ideas and usages survive in modern civilization, and each one was enabled to give an example of ideas and usages still existing in different parts of the country, as to the influence of the moon in various processes of agriculture, on disease, and even in relation to the survival of astrology in our language, and general superstitions.

" The farmer should be encouraged to bring to the meeting specimens of the various botanical productions which he meets in with agricultural operations, as well as specimens of the different soils of which his farm is composed. These should be referred to a committee, and their names and peculiarities given at a subsequent meeting. If a plant or a mineral or an animal is unknown to any member of the association a specimen of it may be sent to this Institution, where it will be examined, and, after being properly labeled, returned.

" The mechanic should be encouraged to give accounts of the processes which he employs, or of any facts which he may have observed of special interest in the course of his operations.

" In short, all the members should be induced to observe, and also be instructed as to the method of observation. It is of vast importance to an individual that he be awakened to the consciousness of living in a universe of most interesting phenomena, and that one very great difference between individuals is that of *eyes* and *no eyes*.

"What I have said relates to the uses of a local society in the improvement of its members; but the importance of an establishment of this kind should not be confined to the mere *diffusion* of knowledge. It should endeavor to *advance* science by co-operating with other societies in the institution and encouragement of original research. Thus it can make collections of the flora and fauna, of the fossils, rocks, minerals, &c., of a given region, of which the location of the society is the center, and thereby contribute essentially to the knowledge of the general natural history of the continent. It can also make explorations of ancient remains and collect and preserve the specimens of the stone-age, which still exist in many parts of our country, and to which so much interest is at present attached. Further, it can induce its members to make records of meteorological phenomena, many of which, of great interest, can be made without instruments, such as the times of the beginning and ending of storms, the direction of the wind, the first and last frost, the time of sowing and harvesting, the appearance and disappearance of birds of certain kinds, the time of the blossoming and ripening of various fruits, &c.; and, as soon as the means of the establishment will afford, a series of meteorological observation should be entered upon with a perfect set of instruments.

"In order, however, to give still greater interest to the society, it should make arrangements in due time for the publication of its proceedings, to be exchanged for the transactions of other societies at home and abroad, the foreign exchange, if desired, to be made through this Institution.

"I beg leave to assure you that the Smithsonian Institution will be happy to co-operate with your society in every way in its power."

ETHNOLOGY.

INTERNATIONAL CODE OF SYMBOLS FOR CHARTS OF PRE-HISTORIC ARCHÆOLOGY.

TRANSLATED BY OTIS T. MASON.

[From the supplement to the eleventh number of Matériaux pour l'Histoire Primitive et Naturelle de l'Homme, 1875.]

Many systems of symbols for archæological charts have been devised by those engaged in this study. They have failed to become popular, because they were understood only in the idiom wherein they were written, or they have been so mixed up with geology on the one hand and with history proper on the other, as to become far too complex for popular use.

The first attempt to invent a set of international symbols was made by the Archæological Section of the Scientific Association of Cracow, in the appointment of a commission for this object, with Count A. Przedziecki as its president. This distinguished scholar presented to the fifth session of the International Congress of Anthropology and Prehistoric Archæology, held at Boulogne, 1871, a full report of the results of the labors of this commission. It will be found in the report of that meeting.

A committee was appointed to examine and to report upon this paper. The committee was composed of MM. E. Cartailhac, C. Marinoni, J. da Silva, H. Hildebrand, Count A. Przedziecki, V. Schmidt, and Count G. Wurmbrand. The author of the scheme having died soon after the meeting at Boulogne, the committee never met, and the project was dropped.

In pursuance of the learned Pole's labors, M. Ernest Chantre prepared a chart of a portion of the Rhone basin, with a new system of symbols. This chart he presented to the next meeting of the Congress at Stockholm, 1874. At the session of August 14 the congress took into consideration M. Chantre's " Projet de légende internationale pour les cartes archéologiques préhistoriques," and charged its executive committee to nominate a commission to discuss the project and to fix upon a definite system. The commission consisted of: Capellini, Italy; Desor, Switzerland; Dupont, Belgium; Engelhardt, Denmark; John Evans, Great Britain; H. Hildebrand, Switzerland; Leemans, Holland; P. Lerch, Russia; G. De Mortillet, (although absent,) France; F. Romer, Austria; Virchow, Germany. 221

The commission met August 15, and selected M. Capellini chairman. Their first act was to add M. Ernest Chantre to their number. After a long and animated discussion at Stockholm, a subcommission was appointed, consisting of MM. Mortillet and Chantre, to prepare an international code of symbols, taking into account the discussions which had taken place. In addition to this, the commission reserved to themselves individually a period of three months in which to prepare and send in their own views.

Papers were sent by MM. Engelhardt, John Evans, Leemans, P. Lerch, F. Romer, and Edward Dupont, who also transmitted a note from M. Van der Maelen, author of the Archæological Chart of Belgium.

Aided by these excellent papers and by the learned discussion at Stockholm, the subcommission have been able to finish their honorable task.

They divide their work into three chapters :

Chapter I. The Charts.
Chapter II. The Symbols.
Chapter III. The Colors.

CHAPTER FIRST.

THE CHARTS.

§ 1. *Special charts.*

Wherever it is possible, charts prepared especially for the purpose are decidedly preferable.

Scale.—In choosing the scale for a chart we must be governed entirely by the purpose in view. The scale will vary according to the number and variety of the sites which we design to indicate. Generally, a large scale is preferable, because it enables us to multiply the marks of location, and to make them more exact and easy of identification by archæologists who wish to visit the monuments and to become acquainted with the facts. The large scale charts are inconvenient, however, in two respects. The first is scientific. They cover so little ground, and separate the places of discovery so widely, that we are unable at a single glance to observe the relations of the parts to the whole. The second is economic. In enlarging the scale the price increases rapidly in proportion. This naturally diminishes the number of purchasers, and consequently retards the progress of science. In choosing our scale we must bear in mind these two facts. If we desire to exhibit a small locality in minute detail, a large scale is preferable. If we wish to give a comprehensive view of a large district, a small scale is best. In fulfilling these conditions, other things being equal, that scale is best which is most favorable to the purchaser.

Topography.—In an archæological chart it is not necessary to make the topography as prominent as in a geographical chart. Where the topography is too marked the archæological signs are obscured, the signs and the colors not being sufficiently distinguishable. Indeed, it is possible that the dark shade of the topographical portions might render the exact location of the archæological symbols impracticable.

In remedying this inconvenience, we must not go to the other extreme and efface the topography so completely as to render it difficult to lay down the symbols. The chart is also in this way rendered so pale as to be disagreeable to the eye. But that which is still more misleading is the impossibility in such cases of appreciating certain laws of archæological distribution in relation to valleys, plateaus, plains, mountains, forests, and marshes. The best plan is to have the chart contain all the topographical data, but in feeble tints. The sheet should be printed in a legible manner, in a gray, bistre, or sepia color, rather than in black.

Routes and names of places.—In charts designed specially for prehistoric archæology, the highways, railroads, and even byways, might be laid down. These are indispensable in locating the explorations of the country, in directing to special diggings, and in guiding archæologists who wish to visit the sites. These indications of roads would be disadvantageous only in cases where we wish to trace the ancient highways, and even then this objection might be obviated by the use of different colors for different epochs. As to the names of places, it is not necessary to give any in addition to those which belong to antiquities, with the exception of a few, perhaps, which are indispensable as points of reference in guiding our study of the chart.

§ 2. *Government charts.*

The execution of a special chart is very expensive. Very often, most frequently, indeed, one does not possess the means to have them drawn and engraved. In such cases one must have recourse to charts already accessible. They are not very expensive, although they are often overcharged with other matters. Sometimes we have the good fortune to possess such a map as that of the French commission, which is not thus marked up. We have in such a case only to put the letters or the symbols where we wish them.

These chart reports may be had not only of whole districts, but of small sections. These sheets may be combined in any way, or a special district may be made up by cutting parts from two or three charts. Nearly all enlightened countries have excellent charts on a large scale, which can be easily obtained.

Such are, for example, those of the following table :

Country.	Scale.	Sheets.	Country.	Scale.	Sheets.
England	1 : 63360	110	Hungary	1 : 144000	198
Austria	1 : 144000	31	Do.	1 : 288000	17
Do.	1 : 288000	31	Do.	1 : 432000	9
Do.	1 : 432000	2	Central Italy	1 : 86400	52
Bavaria	1 : 50000	112	Ancient Sardinia	1 : 50000	91
Do.	1 : 500000	3	Do.	1 : 250000	6
Belgium	1 : 20000	450	Pays-Bas	1 : 50000	62
Do.	1 : 40000	72	Poland	1 : 126000	60
Do.	1 : 160000	4	Prussia	1 : 100000	319
Bohemia	1 : 144000	38	Russia	1 : 126000	792
Do.	1 : 288000	4	Saxe	1 : 100000	28
Do.	1 : 432000	1	Sweden	1 : 100000	233
Denmark	1 : 80000	81	Do.	1 : 200000	28
France	1 : 80000	274	Switzerland	1 : 100000	26
Do.	1 : 320000	33	Do.	1 : 250000	4
Do.	1 : 864000	4	Wurtemberg	1 : 50000	55
Hanover	1 : 100000	67	Do.	1 : 200000	4
Do.	1 : 250000	4	Do.	1 : 400000	1

CHAPTER SECOND.

THE SYMBOLS.

§ 1. *Qualities of the symbols.*

The symbols of prehistoric archæology, in order to become general and international, ought to be—

1. *Simple.*—They must be as simple as possible, so that they can be traced upon a chart by any one, even if he have no experience in drawing. Simplicity is necessary, not only for the making of the symbol, but still more for its easy reading. Complicated signs take up too much room, and are too difficult to draw with accuracy.

2. *Trenchant.*—They must be distinct, one from another, an indispensable condition to the easy and rapid reading of the chart. They ought to present the greatest diversity possible consistent with simplicity.

3. *Special.*—They should not be those already in use for other purposes, especially in general topography. For example, the small circle would be an excellent sign for prehistoric stations, but since it is in use for actual stations, cities, towns, villages, &c., according to the scale, it must be rejected. Its employment would render the distinction of prehistoric sites impossible in cases where only black color is used.

4. *Universal.*—They must be recognizable by all nations. This rejects the employment of initial letters—words, and consequently initial letters, varying in different languages.

5. *Mnemonic.*—They must call to mind the object which they represent. Count Alexander Przedziecki, in his series of symbols, proposed at Boulogne, introduced such signs as a human skull, a stag's horn, a little house on piles, &c. While the mnemonic character has been retained, the symbols have been laid aside as too difficult to draw.

6. *Multipliable.*—It is impossible to limit in an absolute manner the number of symbols. It ought to be larger or smaller, according to the scale of the chart, and the simplicity or complexity of each separate work.

The signs should form a species of alphabet, out of which new words might be created when the occasion arises. With this in view, we have distributed them into three series, sufficient for all our needs : *the radicals, the derivatives, and the complementaries.*

§ 2. *Radical symbols.*

The radicals are the simplest symbols, characterizing general facts, the salient points of prehistoric archæology. They can be modified easily, and so combined as to form new symbols, more or less numerous, as the case may demand. Nine radical symbols will suffice for the prehistoric.

◠ Cavern, souterrain, shelter.

△ Menhir, pillar, standing-stone.

⌐⌐ Dolmen, allée-couverte.

◠ Tumulus, mound.

⌣ Sepulture, human remains.

☐ Camp, entrenchment, oppidum.

ⅢⅢ Palafitte, pile-dwelling.

△ Discoveries, stations, hearths.

⊤ Mine, quarry, digging.

At the first view these symbols are recognized as simple, and they can be made universal. They are as trenchant as possible. The only ones which have any resemblance are : cavern and tumulus, but the former is a portion of an elongated ellipse, higher than wide, the other is an arc of a circle, and much wider than high ; menhir and find, both triangular, but the former is an oblong isosceles triangle, the latter is equilateral, furthermore, the base of the menhir extends beyond the sides, producing a very marked difference ; dolmen and palafitte, in the dolmen there are two supports, visibly inclined, while there are four or five beneath the palafitte, and all are perpendicular. Furthermore, the upper line or table of the dolmen passes by the support, while the upper line of the palafitte does not. They are special, having no analogues in ordinary charts. It was for the purpose of fulfilling this condition that the symbol for camp, instead of being a closed square, is partly open on one side. We have rejected the closed square, because it is often employed in ordinary charts as a sign for a castle or a tower, and the square entirely open on one side serves to designate the ruins of a castle or a tower.

S. Mis. 115——15

These signs are, on the whole, mnemonic. Of the nine radicals, eight are as much so as possible : the opening of the cavern, the pillar-stone, the dolmen, the tumulus, the sepulchral fosse, the enceinte, the pile-dwelling, and the mining-hammer. There remains only the symbol for *finds;* but it was impossible to make this mnemotechnic. We have, therefore, agreed upon the symbol most generally employed, one previously proposed by M. Chantre in the *Projet d'un Légende Internationale,* and which has received the approbation of the congress.

Finally, these signs are multipliable, as we shall proceed to show in the following section, devoted to derivatives.

§ 3. *Derivative symbols.*

The radical symbols which form the base of the system, and which indeed would suffice on maps of a small scale and for general purposes, ought to be capable of such multiplication as is demanded by a chart on a larger scale and with greater specialization. It is this more refined analysis which calls forth the derivative signs. These ought to be, as much as possible, only the evident modifications or simple combinations of the radical symbols themselves. We shall give successively the tables of derivative signs, proceeding in each from the radical which forms the starting-point.

1. *Radical cavern, souterrain.*—The caverns, grottoes, souterrains may be either natural or artificial. It is important to distinguish between these two classes. The radical symbol may be used in both cases; open for the mouth of the artificial caverns, which are generally smaller and better illuminated ; dark for the grottoes and natural caverns, which are deeper and more obscure.

Cavern, grotto, natural shelter.

Grotto or souterrain, of human construction.

Natural sepulchral grotto.

Artificial sepulchral grotto.

Subterraneous refuge.

The study of sepulture being of the highest importance in archæology, the sepulchral grotto should be distinguished, which can easily be done by combining the symbol, *natural grotto* or *artificial souterrain,* with the radical *sepulture.*

Finally, the subterraneous refuge or fortification is designated by the symbol *artificial souterrain,* combined with the radical *enceinte* or *fortification.*

2. *Radical menhir, pillar-stone, monolith.*—This radical, recalling vividly the true menhir or standard stone, should remain as a symbol of this kind of monuments.

The alignment or the avenue of stones, rude or dressed, is designated by the radical *menhir* above a line parallel to its base.

The cromlech or enceinte of standing stones is indicated by the radical *menhir*, around the base of which is a semicircle of dots.

The radical *menhir*, surmounted by a short inclined line, represents the rocking-stone; with a dot in the middle, a hollowed stone; with a broad dark base, a rock with runes, inscriptions, or sculpture.

Finally, the stones with legendary inscriptions, the origin of which is more or less obscure, are indicated by the radical colored dark.

 True menhir or worked monolith.

 Series of menhirs, alignment, avenue.

 Cromlech or enceinte of stones.

 Rocking-stone.

 Hollowed stones.

Sculptured or inscribed stones.

Monument, rune.   (Pierre à legende.)

3. *Radical dolmen.*—The radical *dolmen* is sufficient for all the series of monuments which belong to this group, embracing allées couvertes, gallery-graves, &c. By combining this radical with that of tumulus we obtain the symbols of a dolmen under a tumulus, and of a dolmen over a tumulus.

Dolmen, allée couverte.

Dolmen under a tumulus.

Dolmen over a tumulus.

4. *Radical tumulus.*—In this group the first symbols are easily comprehended. The tumulus of sepulture is composed of two radicals, *tumulus* and *grave;* the fortified tumulus, mound of observation, foundation

of a tower or castle, earthwork surrounded by a moat or an entrenchment, are all denoted by the association of the radicals *tumulus* and
enceinte.

The long barrows of Great Britain are represented by the radical *tumulus* with a circular depression in the top.

Thr tumuli of Hungary and Russia, which often inclose chambers of
wood, may be shown by a dark square in the center. A mound surmounted by a colossal statue may be represented by a tumulus symbol,
on the top of which is the sign for a sculptured menhir.

To the tumulus belong really the class of objects called mardelles.
Although this is a term rather vague in its application, it is nevertheless
the reverse of tumulus, and may be represented by the symbol inverted.

Simple tumulus.

Sepulchral mound.

Fortified tumulus.

Long barrow.

Tumulus inclosing a wooden chamber.

Tumulus surmounted by a monument.

Mardelle.

5. *Radical sepulture.*—The radical *sepulture* may likewise be combined
with other radicals. A variety of readings may also be given to it by
the use of complementary signs, thus: an inclosed line parallel to the
bottom indicates sepulture by inhumation. A small black dot, standing
for a mass of charcoal, indicates burial by incineration.

Cemeteries are denoted by the same symbols, to which are added the
sign plus to show that many graves are grouped together.

Simple sepulture, accidental burial.

Sepulture by inhumation.

Sepulture by incineration.

Cemetery by inhumation.

Cemetery by incineration.

6. *Radical camp, enceinte, fortification.*—The radical *camp*, &c., serves
for all fortified inclosures, whether they are entirely surrounded by
defensive works, ditches, or embankments, or have the earth-work on

one side only, and are protected on the rest by escarpments or water-courses.

Frequently the enceintes are accompanied by tumuli or mounds of observation; they are then indicated by the combination of the radical with that of tumulus.

Sometimes we find, especially in Hungary, defensive works which are not inclosed at all. They are long lines of entrenchment, and may be represented by the radical with a line parallel to its base.

☐ Camp, enceinte, oppidum.

◠ Enceinte with tumulus.

☐ Fosse, rampart, longitudinal defense.

7. *Radical palafitte.*—This radical suffices for all this class of monuments, lacustrian and palustrian stations, true pile-dwellings, cranoges, &c.

8. *Radical discovery.*—As we have before mentioned, the radical discovery is a purely conventional sign, which is in no wise mnemotechnic. It is reserved to mark the localities of isolated finds. Its derivates are rendered as mnemotechnic as possible.

For the localities of groups of objects, sometimes called treasures, cachettes, &c., two radicals are joined into a lozenge. When this is colored, it designates an atelier or foundery. Stations, habitations, &c., are indicated by two radicals forming a six-pointed star. It is the nearest to round, which, in ordinary topographical charts, marks places of actual habitation.

There are two kinds of stations which the palæoethnologists of Scandinavia and of Italy desire to see represented by special symbols; they are the kjökkenmöddings of the north and terramares (marl-beds) of the south. These stations, generally in the form of mamelons or mounds, are indicated by the radical *discovery*, three in a group, forming a truncated triangle; in the symbols of kjökkenmödding the middle triangle is colored and the outer two are plain, and in the terramare the outer two are colored and the inner one is plain.

△ Discovery of isolated objects.

◇ Discovery of objects in masses.

◆ Atelier, foundery.

✡ Station and habitation.

 Kjökkenmödding.

▲▲ Terramare, (marl-bed.)

9. *Radical mine, quarry.*—As in the case of palafittes, the radical *mine* or *quarry* needs no derivatives. Indeed, it seems to be necessary to justify its use at all. This symbol may be very handy in prehistoric charts to indicate the source whence materials, such as silex, sandstone, amber, jade, and other minerals and rocks are obtained. For example, a dolmen is constructed of rocks not to be found in its immediate locality; the symbol mine is placed at the nearest point where the materials in question are to be found, and a line is drawn from this spot to the dolmen, to show the connection of the two.

§ 4. *Complementary symbols.*

The complementary symbols are simple signs, which, in combination with the preceding, render archæological identification as complete as possible. In the execution of the chart, they play a part analogous to the accents and punctuation-marks in writing. These complementaries are grouped in three categories: the first relates to the state of preservation in which the monuments are found; the second to the number of ruins, &c.; the third relates to their age.

First category—The state of the monuments.—This category embraces four symbols. The circle under a symbol indicates that the site has been explored. The oblique line crossing the symbol designates a dilapidated monument, menhirs tumbling over, &c. The double-diagonal crossing upon the symbol indicates the site of monuments entirely in ruins or destroyed. Finally, a short oblique line on the right side of the symbol points out false identifications, wrong references, &c.

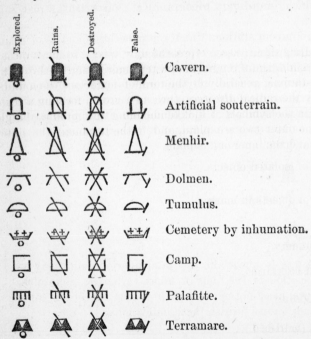

Explored.	Ruins.	Destroyed.	False.	
				Cavern.
				Artificial souterrain.
				Menhir.
				Dolmen.
				Tumulus.
				Cemetery by inhumation.
				Camp.
				Palafitte.
				Terramare.

Second category—Number of monuments.—This category embraces certain signs placed like the exponents in mathematics at the side of the principal, on the right of the upper part. If the number of objects is known, it may be expressed in figures; if not, the sign *plus* is used to denote plurality, and the double plus to mark a great number.

Several.   Many.   Definite number.

U⁺   U⁺⁺   U⁵   Artificial sepulchral grottoes.

⌣⁺   ⌣⁺⁺   ⌣⁹   Mardelles.

⌣•⁺   ⌣•⁺⁺   ⌣•/27   Burials by incineration.

Third category—Age of the monuments.—In fact, the respective ages of monuments should be denoted by different colors, as we shall see in the following chapter. Where prehistoric facts can be indicated by one color only, because labor is an item, or because the symbols are to be placed on a general chart, or because the different colors are used to indicate historic epochs, political and administrative divisions, geological strata, &c., it is necessary to add certain complementary signs, which are to determine the age.

ꟼ   Palæolithic age.

↑   Neolithic age.

⚹   Bronze age.

ꟼ   Iron age.

As may be seen, these signs proceed from the most simple to the more complex, as civilization advances. They are to be placed on the radicals or the derivatives; or two or three of them may be grouped upon a symbol belonging to two or three different ages, as a cavern wherein are found palæolithic and neolithic remains, and implements of bronze.

Palæo-
lithic.   Neolithic.   Bronze.   Iron.

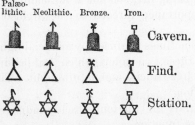

Cavern.

Find.

Station.

In case where the age is uncertain, the interrogation point may be added. As to the position of the finds in lakes, turbaries, mountains, plains, forests, &c., we need not make any provision, since the topographical signs already in use furnish these indications.

CHAPTER III.

COLORS.

The employment of complementary signs to designate age, although they are simple and easily used, has the inconvenience of complicating the definitive symbols, and consequently of overcharging the chart. The age-signs should be used, therefore, only when we can do no better. They may be replaced, as Mr. Chantre proposes in his scheme, by designating the age of the monument by means of different colors. This method has the additional advantage of being more easily read at a single glance, and of suggesting the whole truth to the mind without an effort.

The difficulty is to find four colors sufficiently distinct, trenchant, and unalterable by natural and artificial light. By distinct colors we mean those about which there would be no dispute. They are blue, green, yellow, and red. Gray, rose, mauve, and violet are less distinct, and their adoption would give rise to numerous tints which, in time, would be difficult to distinguish and characterize. For these reasons they are laid aside.

For the easy reading of the charts, it is indispensable that the colors employed should be distinct. After numerous trials we have come to the conclusion that those best adapted to our purpose, the black being left for topography, are blue, green, red, yellow, lake, and bistre or sepia.

The last-named color being often employed in topography, as we said in the chapter on charts, ought to be dismissed from the list of symbols. Lake ought also to be set aside on account of its fading out in the light. Employed on the labels of the museum of Saint-Germain it becomes lighter and lighter, until in five or six months it disappears altogether

The first four colors remain: blue, green, red, and yellow. Against the last named, a grave objection raised by the northern archæologists, who are obliged to labor a great deal by artificial light, is that they have great difficulty in distinguishing this color. But this may be remedied by using a yellow-brown. Therefore the yellow will remain devoted to the palæolithic age, which being little or not at all manifested in the north, is a study of least importance directly to the archæologists of that region.

The blue and the green are also sometimes confused by artificial light, but it is possible to find shades of these two colors which can be distinguished with sufficient ease both by artificial and natural light. The red does not present a single objection.

The colors chosen, after careful trials are the four already indicated by Mr. Chantre, with some change of function.

Palæolithic age............................Yellow-brown.
Neolithic age...... ....Green.
Bronze age............................ ......Red.
Iron age......................................Blue.

We have just given the reason why the brown-yellow was assigned to the palæolithic age. As regards the metals we have connected them as much as possible with mnemotechny. The red is assigned to the bronze, the principal element of which is red copper. The blue is relegated to the iron, which frequently reflects that color. These tints are so natural that they were always employed by the Egyptians many centuries ago.

These are the results at which we have arrived in studying the subject thoroughly, and on all sides, starting with the "Projet de Légende," and taking into account the discussion of the commission appointed by the International Congress at Stockholm, as well as the learned communications of several members. We submit with confidence, to all archæologists who are occupied with prehistoric studies, this collective work, which is sufficiently simple, distinct, and precise for all their needs.

The subcommission,

GABRIEL DE MORTILLET.
ERNEST CHANTRE.

CERTAIN CHARACTERISTICS PERTAINING TO ANCIENT MAN IN MICHIGAN.

By Henry Gillman.

In a former paper, entitled "The Moundbuilders and Platycnemism in Michigan," and which was printed in the Smithsonian Report for 1873, reference was made to the discovery by the writer of perforated humeri in the mounds on the Detroit and Rouge Rivers, Michigan. In a subsequent paper* occasion has been taken to give some further statements in regard to this peculiarity; its being a characteristic of platycnemic man, as thus absolutely established, being dwelt on as of importance.

The humeri from these mounds presenting the curious feature referred to I have calculated as being, at the least, 50 per cent. of the entire; which is of much interest taken in connection with the fact of the extraordinary development of platycnemism afforded from the same source. The perforation is considered to belong to only 31 per cent. of the humeri from the mounds in other parts of the country, and, as has been stated, is a Simian characteristic, which, significantly enough, is found to pertain in the largest degree to the lower races of man, while it is very rare or almost absent in the Caucasian.

The term "perforation" of the humerus, as applied to this form of armbone, in which the fossæ at the lower end are found to communicate, is certainly an unfortunate one, a misnomer, and, as suggestive of artificial origin, calculated to mislead, though it is not easy to propose a substitute.

In this connection I have thought it may prove of interest to figure some of these specimens found by me at the Rouge River; and in the accompanying cut (Fig. 1) I give a representation of the lower extremity of a perforated left humerus from the Great Mound there, to which I have so often had occasion to refer. It is of full size, and the posterior surface is shown.

This is a good example of the peculiarity, the opening being large and strongly defined; and though the bone is apparently of great antiquity and much decayed, the proximal end having totally disappeared, the articular surface is well preserved all along the outline of the aper-

* "The Ancient Men of the Great Lakes," by Henry Gillman. Read before the Detroit meeting of the American Association for the Advancement of Science, August 16, 1875. See note, "Perforation of the Humerus conjoined with Platycnemism," American Naturalist, vol. ix, p. 427.

234

ture, clearly defining its nature, and establishing the genuineness of the specimen as an instance of the characteristic.

In Fig. 2 is illustrated the inferior extremity of a right humerus from the same mound.   In this, the opening, though smaller, is as well developed as in the first example, and the bone, though of about the same

FIG. 1.

FIG. 2.

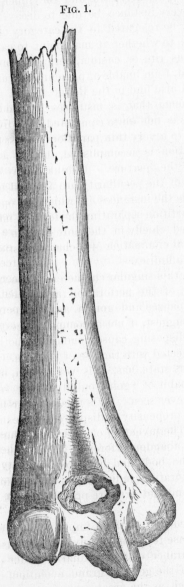
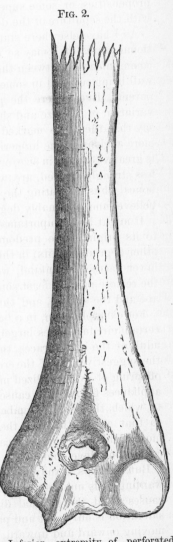

Inferior extremity of perforated left humerus, from Great Mound, Rouge River, Michigan.   Posterior surface ; full size.

Inferior extremity of perforated right humerus from Great Mound, Rouge River, Michigan. Posterior surface ; full size.

age and greatly decayed, (being equally defective as to the loss of the upper end,) from the various evidences presented by it apparently belonged to a different individual.

It is remarkable that so many of the humeri from this mound are fractured at or toward the middle of the shaft, the proximal end being wanting. An entire humerus is extremely rare, and the upper end is seldom found. This cannot in every instance be due to decay. Such cumulative testimony can hardly be relegated to the category of mere coincidence or accident. But as to whether it may point to cannibal propensities, or some superstitious rite or custom, perhaps connected with the sepulture of the deceased, I am unable at present to determine.

As I have elsewhere stated, " I also find in the Rouge Mound transitional states, if I may so call them ; that is, instances in which the communication between the fossæ is not quite completed, the dividing wall being reduced in some cases to a very thin partition, almost transparent. Even where the perforation is accomplished, there is a great variation in the size and shape of the aperture." I think I may safely say that the more marked cases of the peculiarity are afforded by the more ancient of the humeri ; while the instances in which the opening is greatly reduced in size, or the partition separating the fossæ is more or less strongly defined, are witnessed chiefly in the more modern of the bones; thus indicating the gradual elimination of a characteristic of, I believe, unquestionably degraded affinities.

It might be of importance could this singular characteristic be traced to its origin. The predominance of the perforation (associated with other degraded traits) in the chimpanzee and gorilla, as well as in the lower races of mankind, would suggest, if not a common ancestry in the remote past, at least some predisposing cause common to both the ape and the savage, and this connected with the use of the arm.

For example, man, in a barbarous state, has, as is well known, under certain circumstances largely the habit of " going on all fours." In the adult of the higher races, this is never seen. (It is needless to refer to the suggestiveness of the creeping propensity as displayed in the infant offspring of even civilized man.) The invention of various mechanical appliances forbid, and cause to be abandoned forever, the grosser uses to which this noble member of the body had been formerly applied; so that at length, with the ameliorating influences of civilization, a more highly and finely educated hand and arm are produced, with corresponding development.

But, perhaps, it may be considered that (without implying such were wanting) it is unnecessary in this case to insist on any special cause or causes; that the gradual disappearance of the peculiarity under consideration is only part and parcel of the general grand evolution, that moving onward and upward, in which, as the great poet of our day has expressed it, we

"Let the ape and tiger die."

In here presenting some illustrations of the artificially-perforated skulls, of which I gave an account in my paper on "The Ancient Men of the Great Lakes," and from which a notice was printed in the "American Naturalist" for August, 1875, I shall not scruple to avail myself of a part of the material there used, adding such further information as has since come to my knowledge.

This artificial perforation of the top of the cranium, made after death, seems to me to betoken a singular practice connected with the burial-ceremonies of the aboriginal inhabitants of this country, and of which I can find nothing on record in the books, notwithstanding the remarkable nature of the custom and the indubitable marks which would remain to testify in instances where it had been adhered to.

The circular aperture, evidently made by boring with a rude (probably stone) implement, varies in size, in some skulls having a diameter of one-third, in others one-half or three-quarters of an inch or more, and beveled or flaring at the surface. It is invariably placed in a central position at the vertex of the skull.

The first instance of its being brought to my knowledge was in the year 1869, when I took from the Great Mound on the Rouge River two fragments of crania, each of which exhibited this perforation. A skull recently presented to the museum of our scientific association by Mr. A. C. Davis, and which was exhumed from a mound on Sâble River,

FIG. 3.

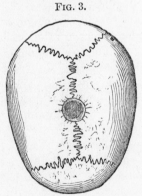

Perforated skull from mound at Sâble River, Michigan, (Lake Huron,) one-fourth size.

Lake Huron, Michigan, also has this mark. From ten to fifteen skulls were taken from this same mound, all being similarly perforated, and there being, as I am informed, no other remains interred with them.

During last summer (1874) in some further excavations made in the Great Mound at the Rouge River, Michigan, among other relics exhumed were eight crania, two of which had this aperture. Of the remaining bones pertaining to the two skulls in question, I specially noticed that many were wanting, and that those present were heaped en masse and not in the usual manner of burial, seeming to imply that they were interred subsequently to being denuded of the flesh and the other soft parts of the body.

Besides the foregoing instances of this curious custom which have been brought immediately to my knowledge, I have since been informed of a skull having been found at Saginaw, Mich., which presented the peculiarity; but in this case there were three perforations, arranged triangularly—cocoa-nut fashion.

FIG. 4.

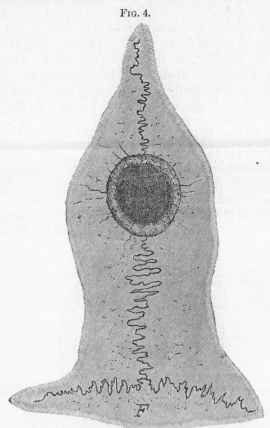

Perforation, Sâble River skull, full size. F, frontal.

All inquiry which I had made of learned societies or individuals in regard to this observance elicited an utter disclaiming of all knowledge on the subject. The two largest collections in ethnology in this country, the Smithsonian Institution and the Peabody Museum, contain no evidence of it. Prof. Joseph Henry, in replying to my queries, stated that the only information he had procured in relation to perforated skulls was the following note from Professor Mason, of Columbian College, Washington: "It is an interesting coincidence that the head-hunting Dyaks of Borneo have a house in the center of their village, in an upper story of which they keep the heads which they capture suspended by a string which passes through a perforation in the top of the skull." [This custom of the Dyaks is, I believe, no longer adhered to, having been abandoned shortly after their becoming semi-civilized.]

The late Professor Wyman, in a letter written me the day before his death, emphatically states that the fact of this perforation was new to him, adding: "There is nothing of the kind in any of our skulls in the museum, nor have I seen it mentioned as existing elsewhere."

A friend has learned for me that an educated Indian makes the statement, in reply to our inquiry, that he remembers hearing his father say that formerly the heads of distinguished men and chiefs were honored by this mark after death. I mention this for what it may be worth.

The skull from the Sâble River mound (Fig. 3) is of a dark color, and its latitudinal or cephalic index, 0.770, would place it within the orthocephalic or medium range, the altitudinal index being inferior, or exactly 0.745. The foramen magnum approaches a central position, its index being 0.445. Fig. 4 shows the perforation of the skull, full size.

The two perfect specimens from the Rouge River are decidedly brachycephalic crania, the cephalic indices being respectively 0.822 and 0.853, the altitudinal indices being inferior, or respectively 0.733 and 0.828, while the indices of the foramen magnum are, in the one case, 0.465, and, in the other, 0.397.

In Fig. 5 is given the first mentioned of these crania; Fig. 6 ex-

FIG. 5.

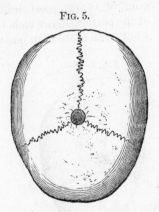

Artificially-perforated skull from Great Mound, Rouge River, Michigan, (No. 1,) one-fourth size.

hibiting its perforation of the actual size, from which it will be seen that the incision has been made at the exact junction of the sutures, which, singularly enough in this case, occupies a central vertical position, as do the perforations in every instance which has come to my knowledge.

That the position of the junction did not influence, much less control, the location of the perforation, is evident, however; for in the other Rouge River skull, (Fig. 7,) the incision is, as usual, exactly centered, though the junction of the sutures occurs but 0.2 of an inch in advance of the selected position. This constantly-recurring central location of the hole would apparently imply that the suspension of the skull was, at least,

FIG. 6.

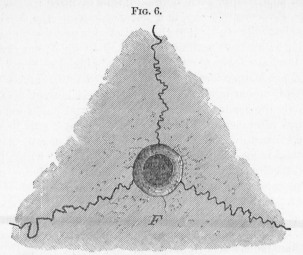

Perforation, Rouge River skull, (No. 1,) full size.   F, frontal.

one of the objects sought by this observance, the even balance of the head when thus treated being, of course, most desirable. This latter skull presents the smallest of the perforations which I have as yet seen; this as exhibited in Fig. 8 is but little more than one-third of an inch in diameter.

FIG. 7.

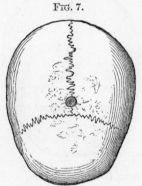

Artificially-perforated skull from Great Mound, Rouge River, Michigan, (No. 6,) one-fourth size.

The numbers (No. 1, No. 6) appended to these figures refer to the numerical order of these skulls in the "Table giving the dimensions of crania from the Great Mound at the Rouge River," and which forms a part of the paper to which I have already referred. They are used in this connection for the convenience of those who shall have access to the Report of the American Association for 1875.

And here I wish to remark that but two rejoinders were elicited by my notice on " The Artificial Perforation of the Cranium" in the American Naturalist. One of these was from Dr. Ford, who subsequently kindly forwarded for inspection a perforated skull, (Fig. 9,) the only one

FIG. 8.

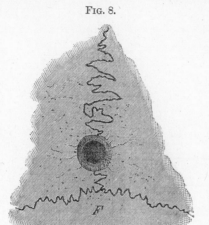

Perforation, Rouge River skull, (No. 6,) full size.   F, frontal.

in the medical museum at Ann Arbor. The specimen was taken from a mound at Devil River, Michigan, by Rev. Dr. Pilcher. This peculiar keeled cranium, of which only the upper portions of the frontal and parietals remain, presents, I find, the extraordinarily low cephalic index of 0.557. In obtaining this, I have allowed only 0.25 of an inch for the additional

FIG. 9.

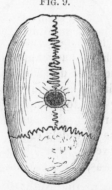

Perforated skull from mound at Devil River, Michigan, (Lake Huron,) one-fourth size.

length which the occipital (that bone being totally wanting) would have given. This probably gives the quantity rather under than over the true length. The breadth is barely 4.07 inches. The perforation, shown at full size in Fig. 10, is elliptical in form, (the diameters $0'.8 \times 0'.7$;) the major diameter running right and left, or latitudinally, as if to heighten the narrow aspect of the skull.

So far, all that I had learned directly or indirectly in regard to this singular custom confined it within the limits of the State of Michigan. But lately I have received the second rejoinder, called forth by my note in the Naturalist. This is a letter from the Rev. Stephen Bowers, dated Santa Barbara, Cal, September 6, 1875. The writer proceeds to say

FIG. 10.

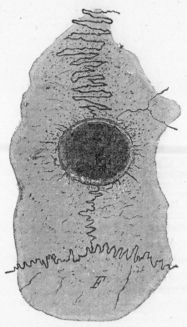

Perforation, Devil River skull, full size.   F, frontal.

that he had read my article on perforated skulls with interest; that during the past four months he had exhumed from 500 to 1,000 skeletons, and found but one such as I describe. It was that of an old man, and the hole, about one-third of an inch in diameter, was in the top of the skull. It was the only skeleton found in that place. In fact, from the description, it was clearly an additional example of the custom, and one of much importance, as so widely extending the area in which the practice was observed, if we may consider a single instance sufficient proof of this. The skull was, however, unfortunately broken by accident, and destroyed.

Since sending my notice to the Naturalist in April last, (printed August, 1875,) my attention has been called to a note in Harper's Magazine for May, 1875, and issued since my remarks were written, which states that "a communication made by Dr. Prunières (de Marvejols) before the meeting of the French Association for the Advancement of Science, at Lille, treated of the curious artificial perforations common among the Neolithic skulls of the Lozère. These perforations vary in the pieces exhibited from an inch to an inch and a quarter in diameter. Near the perforated skulls were found rings of cranial bone, which seemed to be designed as amulets. These were evidently worked with flint tools. The men of the polished stone age practiced trepanning; for if some of the skulls appear to have been perforated after death, others were treated during life, and the patients had lived for years afterward. One skull presented three perforations, made near each other on a line fore and aft. There is no distinction of age, the excisions occurring upon infants as well as upon adults. The motive of this strange custom was either medical or superstitious. They probably attributed disease to supernatural agencies; the evil spirit escaping through the opening made by the sorcerer, who wrapped the operation in a shroud of mystery by preserving the detached piece as a precious relic. From the appearance of these facts reported by the learned archæologist of Lozère, he said that a new light had been shed upon the intellectual state of man in the polished stone age. It explained his religious conceptions, and confirmed the discovery of the figure of a goddess in the caverns of Baye, (Marne.) M. Broca remarked that perforated skulls were also found at the last-named station. Among the skulls dug up by General Faidherbe were found two in the same condition. Dr. Chil, from the Canary Islands, said that perforated skulls had been found in the ancient burial-places of his country. Notice was also called to an example from the Grotto of Lorde, upon which M. Hamy and M. Chaplain-Duparc gave some interesting details. A similarly perforated or trepanned skull was found by Mr. E. G. Squier among some ancient Peruvian crania collected by him."

I have not seen the original report; but the concluding remark on the Peruvian skull removes some doubt as to the kind of perforation described. In the well-known instance discovered by Mr. Squier, the character and the meaning of the operation (trepanning, the excision having been made during the lifetime of the individual) are so evident, and the shape (rectangular) and the position (on the left side of the frontal bone) so different from that of the perforations which I have described in the crania from Michigan, that I never for a moment associated them, and therefore made no reference to the Peruvian skull. The same view, we may presume, was taken by the learned persons to whom I referred my discoveries, who could scarcely be supposed ignorant of the case in question.

I find no positive statement as to the position of the perforations mentioned at the meeting of the French association, but judge from certain remarks that (again unlike our instances from Michigan) there was no constant position observed. In certain cases of trepanning, the position, of course, must have varied with the location of the injury to be operated on.

In short, the perforation which I find in Michigan crania is exceptional, rarely present; it is simply a circular hole about half an inch, more or less, (about ⅓′ to ¾′,) in diameter, apparently rudely bored, invariably in the top of the head of adults, and made after death ; while those cases described in France, though only so recently brought to notice, are quite numerous, and appear to be what may be more correctly termed trepanning ; that is, the part of the skull operated on was removed entire, and all ages are represented.

It has suggested itself to me that the superstition of the modern North American Indian in regard to there being two souls, one of which visits the body after death, may be of illuminative tendency in this direction. We know that the roof-like coverings of their graves, made of wood or bark, always have a perforation at one extremity for the supposed entrance and egress of the soul. But the question arises, Why, then, is not the perforation of the skull constant, or at least more frequent, in our mounds ?

The accompanying table gives the dimensions of the perforated skulls which have come before me, and to which special reference has been made in this paper :

Table giving dimensions, &c., of perforated crania from mounds in Michigan.

Locality.	Capacity.*	Length.	Breadth.	Height.	Breadth of frontal.	Latitudinal index.	Altitudinal index.	Index of foramen magnum.
Rouge River, Michigan, (No. 1) ...	18.65	7.30	6.00	5.35	4.02	0.822	0.733	0.465
Rouge River, Michigan, (No. 6)	18.23	6.80	5.80	5.63	4.63	0.853	0.828	0.397
Sâble River, Michigan	18.06	7.18	5.53	5.35	4.31	0.770	0.745	0.397
Devil River, Michigan	....	7.30	4.07	......	4.52	0.557	....	0.445

Locality.	Frontal arch.	Parietal arch.	Occipital arch.	Longitudinal arch.	Length of frontal.	Length of parietal.	Length of occipital.	Zygomatic diameter.	Circumference.
Rouge River, Michigan, (No. 1)....	12.15	12.00	11.65	14.00	5.50	4.40	4.10	......	19.00
Rouge River, Michigan, (No. 6)....	11.10	13.15	11.00	14.85	5.40	4.60	4.85	5.60	24.40
Sâble River, Michigan	11.50	13.10	10.60	14.75	5.25	4.60	4.85	5.60	24.40
Devil River, Michigan	......	......	......	......	5.10	5.00	......	......	......

* Only comparative. Time did not permit to obtain the exact (absolute) capacity.

In this connection, and in concluding, I have considered worthy of being mentioned the fragment of carved bone represented in Fig. 11, a side-view of which is seen in Fig. 12. This was lately taken by me from the Great Mound at the Rouge River, and it is the only relic of the kind which I have seen exhumed from the mounds in Michigan. Though but a small fragment remains, it is sufficient to prove the workmanship to have been of no mean order and of remarkably neat finish, surprisingly so when we consider the rude implements which, in all probability, alone were available for its manufacture.   The illustration scarcely

FIG. 11.

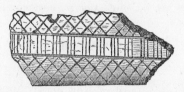

Carved bone (fragment) from Great Mound, Rouge River, Michigan, full size.

Fig. 12.   Fig. 13.

does it justice.   The front or carved surface is convex, as shown in Fig. 13, while the back is flat and perfectly plain and smooth.   In its perfect state, it was probably intended to be worn as an ornament, the remains of a finely-drilled hole at one side appearing to have been one of the means for its attachment to the person.

THE STONE AGE IN NEW JERSEY.

By Dr. C. C. Abbott, Trenton, N. J.

Chapter I.

LOCALITIES.

The aboriginal inhabitants of New Jersey appear to have had an eye
for the picturesque in landscape-scenery, although facility in procuring
food and safety from attack were the objects mainly in view in settling
at any point; still, we find that wherever the scenery is commanding,
as in the northern mountainous portion of the country at such grand
localities as the Delaware Water Gap, we discover there remains in
abundance, but as we go inland they are less numerous, as the hills
decrease and the rivers dwindle into brooks. Yet so abundant were the
Indian villages and numerous these people that almost every brook that
harbors a fish has now lying among the pebbles on its bed, or in the turf
upon its banks, flinty arrow-points or delicate fish-spears.

The abundance of the weapons and domestic implements of the
aborigines suggests that each village had at least one implement-maker;
that the various stone articles were the product of the skill of some
one of every community, who was exclusively devoted to the business of
making them. Although, when on hunting-expeditions or in battle, the
single specimens lost would have the effect to mingle all the "styles"
throughout the State; yet if we compare a *suite* of arrow-heads, spears,
lances, or even axes, from a single locality, with a similar series from a
distant section of the State, there will be found with each a peculiarity
of its own, an individuality, so to speak, that characterizes the two collections. The similarity of stone implements the world over is one that
extends to those forms that are simplest, and is not an indication that
because the same results have been wrought out by widely-separated
tribes there was necessarily a kinship.

Studying the localities in the State where relics are most numerous,
we have been surprised with the frequent exhibition of the implement-
maker's peculiar tastes, and are convinced that widely-differing shapes
of wrought stones in some cases have had an identical purpose; and
certainly it would be difficult to suggest names for each type, they being
more numerous than the occupations of a primitive people.

While weapons in the majority of localities greatly predominate over
the domestic or agricultural implements, still, in some sections of the
State, the opposite is the case, at least approximately, as evinced by the
number of the latter class of relics equaling the former in an average
day's search.

246

When we consider, in another chapter, the relics designated as "rude implements," we shall find that these are not especially characteristic of any one locality, but seem scattered uniformly over the State, while they are deeper in the soil than the majority of so-called "surface"-specimens.

Starting at Trenton, N. J., the head of tide-water, and following the river's course in a southerly direction, we find the rocky, mountainous shores of the upper river succeeded by a gravelly, bluffy bank on the New Jersey side, which varies in height from twenty to one hundred feet, and finally disappears near the town of Burlington, being replaced there and thence by almost continuous level, sandy shores, terminating at Cape May, the southern extremity of the State. Along the first five miles of the brow of this bluffy bank, and extending inland some half mile, is the tract from which has been gathered the great bulk of our collection and the most interesting specimens. This bluff does not always immediately face the river, but, receding half a mile or more between Trenton and Bordentown, forms, between these two points, a semicircular tract of meadow, of varying elevation above the river's level, and on the higher portions, or knolls, are found numerous relics; but the greater number are from the hill-top fields, although it may be that the rare occurrence of plowing in the meadows, as compared with the uplands, may in some measure account for the difference.

A glance at this limited tract of country, even in the highly artificial condition that it now presents, will plainly show why it was a favorite spot with the red men. Placing their wigwams on the brow of the hill, they had at their command an unbroken stretch of forest of white-oak, pine, and chestnut, harboring the elk, deer, and bears, while in the deep creeks traversing the meadows below them, and the broad river beyond, were fishing-facilities that in that ancient day were not to be excelled by any within a thousand miles.

CHAPTER II.

RUDE IMPLEMENTS.

So attractive to the amateur, or the more scientific student, are the finished specimens of wrought jasper and polished porphyry, that the "rude implements," sparingly scattered among them, and buried still more deeply in the soil, are either overlooked, or the passing glance given them suggests that they are unfinished specimens, or the crude results of a beginner in the art of flint-chipping. This we believe to be an error. These "rude implements" are usually formed of the mineral that characterizes the locality where they are found; those met with at Trenton, N. J., are all of the sandstone that forms the bed of the river at the rapids, and crops out here and there. This rock varies somewhat in texture, and the implements also are found to be made both of the denser and the softer strata of the stone, as though fragments were broken off and chipped into shape from any convenient point.

This class of antiquities is not abundant, considering the whole number of specimens we have gathered, about ten thousand, and embracing nearly every class of relics. The proportion is less than 2 per cent. of the whole number. Careful examination of a series shows that they cannot be merely roughly-outlined pieces intended for future more finished work, inasmuch as the present general character and dimensions of the great bulk of them renders additional chipping impracticable. The larger "rude implements" would, if further chipped away, form axes and lance-heads of much smaller dimensions than the great majority of those that we now find.

Figure 1 represents an average specimen of the flat-bottomed, peak-backed stones, known in some localities as "turtle-backs," a name that admirably describes their general appearance. Made of the ordinary Delaware River sandstone, this specimen measures four inches in length and two and one-half inches in width. The bottom is nearly a perfect plane, and shows, by the slight indentations and scratch-like markings, that it has been chipped into its present shape, and not accidentally broken. Its greatest thickness is one and one-eighth inches; the "peak," or highest point of the back, being in the middle of the specimen, measured lengthwise, but rather nearer one side than the other, or off the center; but the broader side of the back does not appear better adapted for cutting than the narrower or more abruptly descending side.

Although this stone, from long exposure, has become porous upon the surface, the edges still remain sharp, regular, and exhibit an amount of skill in "flint-chipping" about equal to that of the ordinary slate lance-heads, spear and arrow points. Close examination shows that the back has been worked into its present shape by a series of powerful blows, or by pressure, leaving large surfaces usually, several of the planes being those of a single detachment of a fragment of the rock, in some instances extending from the peak to the edge of the implement.

Had these fractures occurred in an ordinary water-worn pebble, throughout its rough-and-tumble existence, they would assuredly have happened at various periods, and, besides leaving different degrees of weathering on the fractured surfaces, would also exhibit traces of the causes that produced the breakage, as in scratches where a flinty rock had graved and cut the underlying pebble, in ground-off angles where some huge mass had been rolled upon and crushed off the weaker projecting portions left by a previous altering agency. It is needless to state no traces of occurrences like these are discoverable, but, on the contrary, every portion of the surface plainly indicates that, by a "tool" in the hand of a workman, was the "turtle-back" shaped.

It is not easy to conjecture the special use of such a stone implement. There is nothing about it to show that it was intended to be attached to a handle. It seems impossible, in fact, to use it otherwise than by holding it in the hand, and yet, if for cutting-uses only, why the peculiar and carefully-wrought peak? There is nothing to show it was ever used in connection with another implement, for such joint uses would be indicated by battered surfaces at different points; yet we have found no "turtle-back" that showed other contact than that of the "hammer stone" that pecked the level side of the implement.

Figure 2 is a smaller specimen of "turtle-back," varying principally from the preceding by the back being rudely ridged rather than pointed. It is two and seven-eighths inches in length by one and seven-eighths inches in width. The greatest thickness is nearly three-fourths of an inch. The bottom, or under surface, is even more uniform than that of the preceeding specimen, and indicates that the more prominent points of the under surface were rubbed away, although not sufficiently to give a perfectly smooth or polished surface. Viewed from above, it bears considerable resemblance to an implement for skin-dressing, to which use it was probably applied.

Figure 3 is a small ax or hatchet, that makes a step, as it were, in advance of the "turtle-backs." Two and one-quarter inches in length and two and one-eighth inches wide, it is brought to a good edge of two inches in length, from a base one inch and one-eighth long by one-half inch in width. As will be seen in the illustration, this specimen still retains one characteristic of "turtle-backs," in that it is flat upon one side and is chipped upon its upper and lower edges or side, as well as sloped to the front or cutting-edge proper. The cutting-edge has been dulled by exposure, but is still sufficiently keen to be used as a skinning-knife, an incision having previously been made. Although calling it an ax or hatchet, we believe its use was that above mentioned.

If the climate of our country during the stone age was even as temperate as it is now, warm clothing was an imperative requirement; and it is safe to infer that a prominent use of all these rude implements was in rendering fit for clothing the skins of the large mammals once numerous in this region.

Figure 4 is an interesting specimen, previously designated as a hatchet, but which is now classed and considered as a "rude implement." Three and one-quarter inches in length by two and one-half inches in breadth, it presents nothing in common with the types—if we may call them so—of these ruder forms of implements. From the base, which is the unchipped natural surface of the stone that has been selected, this implement is chipped equally on both sides, and brought to an edge along each margin, and at the same time tapered to an obtuse point, sufficiently marked, however, to indicate that it was intended to pierce as well as cut. The broad base, which is sufficiently wide to allow the specimen to stand upon it without support, upon a level surface, precludes the idea that there ever has been a long shaft attached, and so converting the specimen into a spear-head.

Held in the hand, it would seem to be an awkward instrument for most purposes, but best adapted probably for incising the skin of an animal with the point, and then, by the long cutting-margins, detaching the skin from the carcass. The point has probably been much more acute than now, and, when in its original condition, it certainly *could* have been so used; or, held in the hand by the base, it would, by a well-directed blow, split the long, hollow bones of a bison for obtaining the marrow, being, for such a purpose, an admirable combination of wedge, hammer, and hatchet; and such split bison-bones have been found in New Jersey.

Figure 5 represents a specimen most like a weapon of any of the rude implements we have as yet been able to find. Its shape at once suggests its use, and, considering the rough workmanship that has been expended upon it, it seems admirably adapted to the supposed use to which it was put. It foreshadows the tomahawk of more modern times. There appear to have been no fractures since the implement was made. The whole surface presents the same degree of weather-worn appearance, and it is doubtful if even the rude edges were more regular in design or sharper than at present. Very nearly eight inches in length, the specimen may, for purposes of description, be divided into two sections—the front or blade of the weapon, and the hammer-head or back. The blade or front portion is four inches in length, forming nearly a continuous line with the top of the back; the elevation of the outline or margin being less than half an inch at the angle of the back and edge. Below, the line of the back and that of the blade form an obtuse angle; the blade being beneath an inch and three-eighths wider than the narrower portion or hammer-head. The entire margin of this specimen has been chipped into its present shape and condition, giving it a rudely-rounded appearance at the top, edge, bottom, and extremity of the back. This chipping has not been done by an ordinary hammer stone, pecking off the small fragments and producing the peculiar dotted appearance common to the ordinary grooved cobble-stone axes; but the stone has been *flaked* off in larger pieces, although the appearance varies from the shelly fracture of jasper, having nothing in common with those minerals that have this peculiar fracture, well named conchoidal. As a large portion of the side of this specimen is smooth, it is probable that the mass, as originally detached from the rock, bore some resemblance to the weapon or implement as it now appears. The interest, as it seems to us, that attaches itself to this rude hatchet, is that it is the most primitive specimen we have met with that clearly indicates that a handle has been fastened to it. A split or forked sapling could have been as readily attached to an ax of this shape as to any of the grooved forms. The shallow notch beneath, at the junction of the back and blade, was evidently so chipped to make the attached handle more secure. Armed with such a weapon, a powerful man could do great execution in close combat.

It must be borne in mind that the specimens here figured are not isolated instances of rude stone implements bearing peculiar markings; although in a large series there will of course be some even possibly more rude, and again others that seem a partial transition from the "turtle-backs" to the ax, or the latter to the spear-head-shaped specimens. Other than the specimen last figured, (figure 5,) we have now lying on our table two specimens with about the same amount of work upon them, but varying somewhat in details. The larger of these is of the same length as figure 5; but the blade narrows gradually toward the back, which is about two-thirds of the width of the front or cutting edge. There is no defined spot to show where or how a handle has been fastened, but such must have been attached in some manner to render the stone at all available as a war-weapon or an implement of the chase. The other, smaller specimen of a rude ax is five and one-half inches in length, with a front or cutting edge of three and one-half inches in extent; and from this edge the specimen tapers to an acute point, giving it the form of an acute, nearly equilateral, triangle, with a slightly-curved base. It shows clearly that it has had a handle attached, as in case of figure 5, and, with the pointed back and curved edge in front, well represents the tomahawk of the Indians in use after the introduction of iron, and still in use among the wilder tribes of the West.

Figure 6 represents a small ax, showing that occasionally considerable labor was expended in even this class of rude implements. The general outline is good, much resembling that of the preceding figure. Unlike that specimen, however, it clearly retains the marks of the hammerstone, showing that it was slowly pecked into shape, and not formed by hard blows and large fragments broken off. One side is flatter than the other, indicating that it approaches the specimens we have figured as the types or starting-points of this series of stone relics. The cutting-edge is still well preserved, but shows no indication of having been polished or sharpened otherwise than by pecking fresh fragments off as the old edge grew dull by use. This specimen measures three and three-fourths inches in length, by two and one-half inches in width at the front or edge, and tapers then to a back about one inch in width, which has also been chipped to a moderately sharp edge.

Figure 7 represents a common form of "rude implement," that returns to the "turtle-back" variety in the characteristic of a perfectly flat bottom or under surface, which in this case appears to have been the face of a smooth fracture effected by a single blow upon the rock from which the specimen was detached. The object of the specimen is wholly different from the "axes" we have been describing; this being a spear-head apparently, as the well-defined point is unquestionably the important feature of the weapon or implement of the chase. It is not easy to comprehend why spear-heads should have been thus fashioned, that is, flat upon one side, and so ridged upon the other as to make the greatest thickness equal to half the length, as in this and many other instances. We will find, however, that this character re-appears in other specimens of a later period, of the highest degree of polish and workmanship. The specimen in question measures three inches in total length by two and one-fourth inches in greatest breadth, and is a fair representative of the "flat" spears found in localities where these rude implements are met with, as in the gravelly bank of the Delaware south of Trenton, N. J., and occasionally on the surface of the ground in the same neighborhood.

Associated with this flat-sided variety, but in far smaller numbers, is a larger implement, that may be considered as a rude spear-head. Certainly, the shape of the specimen, (figure 8,) as in the preceding case, shows the point to have been the principal object in view. This specimen was found upon the surface, but is identical with those associated with the gravel of the river-bank. Indeed, specimens of every type of "rude implements" are found upon the surface, and are plowed up every spring and autumn; but this in no way militates against the opinion that these ruder forms are far older than the well-chipped jasper and beautifully-polished porphyry stone-work.

The hatchet and the spear represent the two types from which the more modern stone weapons have proceeded, and if we look upon these as having been suggested by the use of the "turtle-backs" previously for the uses to which the hatchet and spear were afterward put, so far as that was practicable, then we have an unbroken line of development in the manufacture of tools.

Rude implements of a "domestic" type are exceedingly rare. We have met with but two such specimens, (figures 9 and 10.) Figure 9 represents a nondescript form, innumerable uses for which can be imagined, but not easily demonstrated. Sir John Lubbock, in his "Prehistoric Times," (2d ed., p. 340, figures 199–200,) figures a very similar specimen from Madras. The similarity in size and shape suggests the probability that both these specimens were put to the same use; and, curiously enough, the India specimen, like figure 9, was found at a considerable depth below the surface of the ground. Everything connected with the history of this specimen shows that it should be classed with the "turtle-backs" and the other forms that we have figured. It is just six inches in length and two and three-fourths inches in greatest breadth. Nearly four inches of its length is of this width, where it tapers to a stem-like handle a little over an inch in width. The whole surface still retains traces of the blows of the hammer, and the edges, those of the handle included, are all rudely chipped.

With one other illustration of "rude implements" we shall close our consideration of this portion of the subject. Figure 10 represents a form of this class of relics wholly unique. That it is a product of human workmanship no one can doubt; but, as in many of the preceding cases, it is difficult to say for what it was especially designed. It was found on the surface of a sandy field, where many of the ordinary shapes of Indian relics occur. If intended for an ax with a handle, "all in one," then the purpose is well carried out; but why so carefully rounded a blade? No detailed description other than some of the principal measurements are necessary. The illustration gives an accurate idea of the weapon itself. The handle and "back" straight portion of the blade measure together exactly five and one-half inches. The diameter of the circular blade is about four and one-half inches. The straight back of the implement is the only portion of the natural surface of the stone from which it was made. An examination shows that some large bowlder has been broken into laminæ, and one of these, originally about one inch in thickness, has been afterward chipped until the handled disk has been produced as we now find it. The edge apparently has never been sharper, about one-fourth of an inch in width, and the whole general appearance tends to show that it is an agricultural implement. While this impression militates against the idea of a great antiquity for these rude specimens, an antiquity that antedates agriculture even in its most primitive condition, yet there seems no other method of utilizing this unique specimen.

CHAPTER III.

GROOVED STONE AXES.

These, although having a general similarity, are not exactly alike, and we have had in our possession at various times several hundred. The universal exception that co-exists with every rule here obtains in the pattern of ax that is grooved upon each side, near the head and across one margin, but whether the top or bottom is uncertain. Such specimens are alike sometimes, even with regard to size. So far as the continuation of the groove across one margin is concerned, we find that a forked sapling can be best attached to such axes by placing the flat margin in the fork of the handle and drawing the ends together *over the groove*, thus making it the top or upper margin of the implement. We shall, therefore, in describing this pattern of ax, which is the most nearly uniform of all the styles, consider the groove as being across the *upper* margin. Careful examination also of the edges of such specimens as we have had seems to us to show also that this manner of securing the handle was that pursued by the people who made and used these axes.

Figure 11 is a very good example of the most common type of grooved stone axes; that is, such as we have described in the preceding paragraph. This ax measures eleven and one-half inches in total length, and is but four inches wide at the broadest portion, the ridge immediately in front of the groove. The groove itself is but seven-eighths of an inch in width, and the head, or that portion posterior to the groove, varies from one and one-half inches to one inch in length. The cutting-edge is but two and one-fourth inches in extent, and is still moderately sharp and well preserved. Although the specimen still shows the marks of the hammer, yet it might almost be placed under the head of polished axes, as

the weapon has been so carefully smoothed down that the slight inequalities and shallow indentations can scarcely be felt by the hand. Its
weight is seven and one-half pounds. With the handle placed where the
groove is, it must have produced a great strain upon the wrist. The
small extent of the edge suggests that it was intended to inflict *one effective blow*, and not that its main use was chipping or girdling of trees.

This specimen was found on a small gravelly island in the Delaware
River, and was presented to the author by his friend Mr. W. Dean, of
Lambertville, N. J.

Figure 12 represents the average style of ax of this particular pattern, which we believe is found throughout the United States. They
vary from two to five and seven inches in length, and occasionally, as
we have seen, reach eleven and one-half inches. The smallest specimen
we had met with for a long time was scant three inches; but, as the extreme edge was wholly broken away, it probably measured, when perfect, fully three inches. (See figure 13.) We have since collected a
still smaller and more perfect specimen, (figure 14,) which measures only
two and one-half inches in length; the perfect back being in the natural
condition of the pebble from which the little ax was made.

This variety of ax is most usually found to be of sandstone, and the
ordinary cobble-stones, or water-worn pebbles of the adjacent river-beds.
At and above Trenton, N. J., the bed of the Delaware River is wholly
composed of loose stones of various sizes, with here and there an out-
cropping of stationary rock. These loose pebbles or cobble-stones are
found on examination to frequently bear considerable general resemblance to the finished axes, and to need little work upon them other
than making the groove and rubbing one end down until a cutting-edge
is produced. So abundant, as it seems to us, are the well-adapted
stones, in shape and size, that we wonder why so frequently we meet
with stone-axes that have been carefully pecked over the whole
surface to bring them down to the proper shape. This may be explained, perhaps, by the suggestion that many axes were made where
stones at all suitable were difficult to obtain, and that the frequent wars
or wanderings of a community and bartering may have resulted in the
commingling of the axes of a multitude of localities, many of them
miles distant from each other. We know, too, that tribes came from
long distances to make autumnal visits to our sea-coast, and, of course,
on such journeys would always be provided with, and frequently lose,
as they passed through the State, many specimens of every variety of
both weapons and domestic implements.

Occasionally, this pattern is produced in porphyry, and in that case
is invariably polished. We have knowledge of some specimens of this
pattern, and of this material, of immense size and weight, but could
not, unfortunately, learn the exact numbers of inches and pounds; but
we do not suppose they really measured more than figure 11, although

the weight was probably more, inasmuch as figure 11, if of porphyry, would certainly be considerably heavier.

When made of porphyry, these axes were valued much more than those of ordinary sandstone, inasmuch as they were continually ground down to new edge, as the old one wore away or was accidentally broken off; and the original owners were so choice of them that they continued the resharpening until there was scarcely any blade left, and that little unavailable in consequence of the thickness of the ax across the back and at the groove.

Figure 15 is an admirable example of an ax made of a porphyry pebble of this pattern, worn down by continual resharpening. The specimen now measures four inches in length by three and three-eighths in width, and is two and one-half inches across the head or back. It has a well-defined groove running along its under margin, a feature common to this pattern of stone axes.

Occasionally, an ordinary sandstone or cobble-stone axe of this pattern is to be found very carefully smoothed over its whole surface. We can scarcely call it a polish, and yet it is very near it. In such specimens especially, the uniformity in the width and depth of the groove is truly remarkable. This groove varies much in depth, and a noticeable feature is that the depth of the groove is in no wise in accordance with the size and weight of the ax, as would be the natural inference. Thus, in figure 11, the groove is very shallow and narrow, being about one-quarter of an inch only in depth, while in some of the smaller specimens it is fully one-half an inch deep, and we have met with instances fully five-eighths of an inch in depth. The depth of groove may perhaps be a good index to the degree of patience in the various individuals of a community. We have before us a very fine sample of ax from Indiana, the remarkable features of which are the depth and width of the groove as compared with the general measurements of the implement itself. The ax measures six inches in length by four and one-half in width, and the groove measures one and three-quarters in width by seven-sixteenths of an inch in depth. Such a groove compared with the example in figure 11 seems the more strange when we remember that the latter, in size and weight, is about double that of the deeply-grooved Indiana specimen.

Figure 16 represents as fine a specimen of a polished ax as we have ever seen. This ax was found in Elsinborough Township, Salem County, New Jersey, by Dr. John W. Ward, of Trenton, by whom it was kindly presented to the writer. It is now preserved in the cabinet of the Peabody Academy of Science, at Salem, Mass. The illustration gives a better idea of the specimen itself than any description can. Suffice it to say that the whole surface has been beautifully polished, the edge rendered as sharp as practicable, and it is still perfect, equidistant from each side, and describing a very nearly accurate circle. It will be noticed that this specimen has two grooves, one of them shallower and much less well defined than the posterior and deeper one.

The object of this double grooving does not appear. It is a feature we have not met with in any other specimen. The preservation of the edge and the general freshness of the whole surface makes it highly probable that it is among the very latest of the stone axes made in New Jersey, or, indeed, anywhere within a reasonable distance of this State; therefore it has probably seen little if any service, perhaps being used as an ornament or badge of office.

When we consider the class of relics known as " skinning-knives," we shall find that some of them are similar in many respects to this specimen, and that possibly we have erred in calling figure 16 an ax. It has, however, some features so common to the true axes that the likelihood in the case is much in favor of classing it as we have done.

Figure 17 represents a fair average specimen of a cobble-stone ax, in which the groove extends entirely around the weapon. One feature is particularly noticeable in these axes, viz, that the groove is always nearly in the middle of the specimen. We have examined a large series of axes, and find that the following characteristic is common to all the examples that have come under our notice, viz: that when the groove extends entirely around the ax, it is in advance of the grooves that do not meet above, or on the upper margin, as in figures 11, 12, 13, 14, and 15. There was something in the method of using these rude implements that is yet to be learned before an explanation can be given of this curious feature of the varying position of the groove. Certainly, the original shape of the selected pebble had nothing, or very little, to do with determining the location. This specimen (figure 17) is about the average size of any ordinary collection of these stone axes as gathered from any one neighborhood. They range from four to eight inches in length, seldom exceeding this limit, as compared with the whole number found; and the number of instances of axes of less length than four inches is comparatively few. As a class, the completely-grooved axes do not appear to be as well finished as the preceding style; and being usually of "crooked" or irregularly-shaped stones, when a number are together, there appears to be but little in common except the features that pronounce them all " axes" or malls.

A very fine specimen of a large ax is in the cabinet of Rutgers College Museum, at New Brunswick, N. J. It was found within the limits of that town, on the banks of the Raritan River, which was probably a favorite locality with the aborigines, who perhaps were further attracted to the place on account of the native copper that was formerly found there, and which they highly prized for a variety of purposes, especially ornamental. The ax above referred to is of identical pattern with that figured by Squier and Davis in Smithsonian Contributions, vol. 1, page 216, figure 108, (Anc. Mon. Miss. Valley,) but is somewhat larger and heavier. The former measures nine inches in length by six inches in width, and weighs an ounce or two over nine pounds. The western specimen "is made of very compact greenstone, and measures eight inches in length by five inches and a half in its greatest breadth, and weighs eight pounds." S. & D. further state that this "is regarded as a genuine relic of the mound-builders. Its form is almost identical with that of the forest-ax of the present day."

Figure 18 represents the finest specimen of a large stone ax that we have ever met with. Very many that we have seen have been as large; a number have been of more finished workmanship, but no one has as many features of interest as this. The specimen measures eleven inches in length. The conical head is three inches long, the groove and ridges together two and one-quarter inches, and the blade within a small fraction of five and three-quarter inches. The conical head does not appear to have met with any very hard usage, and was probably intended for ornament. It would seem as though the ridges, at each margin of the groove, would be of great advantage in securing the handle to the ax, inasmuch as it secures greater depth to the groove without cutting too deeply into the body of the implement itself; but such plausible reasoning somewhat vanishes when we come to compare weights and find that this specimen (figure 18) weighs but six pounds, whereas figure 11, with one pound and a half greater weight, has a groove only one-half the depth and width, and as near as practicable to one end also, while in figure 18 it approaches to the middle.

A pertinent question may here be asked, By what means were these cobble-stones shaped into axes? We have frequently already spoken of "hammer-stones," but we have as yet found nothing that seems adapted to such work when it comes to a deep, narrow groove; for while some of the axes have the grooves finely polished, others present in the groove the same pitted appearance that characterizes the general surface of the specimen.

This ax (figure 18) was found on the shore of the Delaware River, close to the water's edge, and was presented to the writer by Dr. J. W. Ward, of Trenton, N. J.

Squier and Davis, in the Smithsonian Contributions to Knowledge, vol. 1, page 217, speaking of stone axes, state that "it is clear, from the weight of many of these axes, that they were designed to be wielded with both hands. Some weigh not less than *fourteen* pounds, but most range from six to ten. The average weight of the ordinary iron-ax of the present day is about six pounds." Between the weight of our heaviest ax and their maximum there is a difference of five pounds, which we have not yet been able to make up;* but, whether so or not, it is very safe, we think, with the New Jersey axes, to consider figures 11 and 18 about as heavy as they were *ordinarily made;* and, in treating of this subject in the manner that we do, the most that we hope is to convey a good *general idea* of what stone weapons, ornaments, and domestic implements were in use among the aborigines during their primitive stage of culture.

---

*Since the above was written we have found an ax weighing one ounce less than fourteen pounds.

Figure 19 represents a specimen of ax of somewhat similar outline to the preceding, having the ridges that are on the margin of the groove very well defined, but the tapering, conical head is by no means as artistically finished as in the other instance, (figure 18.) As the illustration shows, this specimen has been chipped, or, more properly, pecked, over its whole surface, and is a good instance of the perseverance and patience of the primitive folk who accounted such weapons among the chiefest of their worldly goods. Axes of this shape and pattern occur in every part of the State, associated with the pattern described in figures 11–15. So different are they in the one matter of the groove and its position, that it seems exceedingly probable that the two patterns had different uses, and yet we cannot see in what the one shape is superior to the others. On examining the hammer-heads, or "backs," of a large number of the pattern of figures 11–15, we find there indications of the hammer-head portions having been struck frequent and hard blows with another stone, as though this style of ax was largely used in splitting wood; while, in the present type (figures 16–19) there is much less indication of such battering of the head. But we have not sufficient evidence as yet to make any separation of these styles into " war" and "domestic" axes, or some such distinctive designations.

Figure 20 represents an exceedingly crude ax, that, when figured, was the very "plainest" specimen we had ever met with. Since then, however, we have had one other that is even more primitive, and yet unquestionably a " grooved stone ax." The specimen here figured (figure 20) has the groove on each side and above and below of a uniform depth, and is well defined throughout, as the illustration indicates; but, in the still plainer specimen, the groove consists of a faint roughening, that seems of little use, being scarcely uneven enough to prevent the fastening from slipping; but, like figure 20, the groove at the top and bottom is practically deepened by a projecting knob of the stone, at which points all the strain of the fastening of the handle must have come. In the specimen figured, (figure 20,) the sides of the blade of the ax have been dressed down with a hammer-stone to a pretty well defined edge; but in the still plainer ax before us we find that upon one side a few chips only have been struck off, and on the other two great portions have been artistically knocked away, and the then roughly-prepared blade has been rubbed with a polishing-stone until a small but highly-polished edge has been produced. We cannot imagine any more difficult task than *really* cutting wood or splitting bone with such a weapon as this, and would restrict its use to bruising the bark of trees; but the trees once dead, they would require something better than these rude axes to fell them. Judging from their present appearances, the edges only of these axes have been used; the back, which is very uneven in each case, does not show any trace of having ever been struck with a hammer; and we find in many of the axes, especially in the pattern of figure 11, that they were so struck, thus converting the ax for a time into a wedge. Loskiel* says: "Their hatchets were wedges, made of hard stones, six or eight inches long, sharpened at the end and fastened to a wooden handle."

Occasionally we meet with a crooked or bent ax, which has, however, more method in its irregularities than has figure 20. Such an ax we now have, which was originally an ordinary cobble-stone that was decidedly bent or bow-shaped. Such shaped stones were frequently chosen, as we have seen a number of specimens from widely distant localities. The best illustration of such bent axes is one measuring nine inches in length by three and one-half inches in width. The head alone is the natural surface of the stone, except a narrow strip immediately in front of the groove; all the rest has been dressed down, and tapers gradually to the edge, which has been moderately sharp but never polished. These so-called bent axes are attractive in appearance as seen in the cabinet, but do not seem to possess any especial advantage over any other form.

With one more illustration, that of a fantastically-shaped cobble-stone ax, we will conclude this portion of our subject. Figure 21 represents a small ax with three uncommon features : the near approach of the groove to the middle of the specimen; the almost flat surface of one side of the implement; and the *intended* double edge. We say *intended*, but it may be that the shorter end has had a cutting-edge thereon, although there is no trace of it left now; or the broken condition of this end may be the preparatory chipping, to have it ready for grinding to a cutting-edge at any time it might be desirable to do so. This specimen measures six inches in length by two and one-half inches in breadth, except at the projection immediately in front of the groove on the upper margin, which projection is about one-half an inch in length. What might be the object in having one side flat, or nearly so, does not appear; but it will be seen that this peculiarity is not confined to this ax, or to a few axes as a class by themselves, but occurs in weapons and implements of a far different nature.

It would be easy to go on for an indefinite time, and point out peculiar features in the multitudes of stone axes that are to be found in every museum, and scattered throughout the country, but it is unnecessary to give additional examples. We probably have particularized more than was necessary, and certainly have gone over the ground sufficiently to give a general idea of the common characters and average appearance of this class of relics.

Whatever may be thought of the scientific value of single specimens of these axes, or of other relics found lying upon the surface of the ground, that value is enhanced perhaps, or at least interest is attached to the specimens, when we occasionally have the good fortune to unearth a so-called "deposit" of these specimens, sometimes numbering several hundred.

In one case, in digging a cellar in Trenton, N. J., one hundred and

---

* Mission among N. A. Indians, (Delawares,) page 54.

twenty were found, " all closely huddled up together," as my informant described them. They were about three feet below the surface, and a " foot deep" in the gravel underlying the soil. They were surrounded by, and entirely covered with, a bright brick-red powder. Again, in digging the receiving-vault of the Riverview Cemetery, near Trenton, N. J., "a bushel-basketful of these axes was found, packed closely together, six feet deep in the ground." On the face of the bluff fronting the Delaware River, immediately below Trenton, N. J., several such instances have come to the notice of the writer. In the first two instances, the specimens were all grooved cobble-stone axes. In another instance, the " axes (?)," fifty in number, were of the ungrooved pattern, all of porphyry, well polished, and appeared to have been carefully deposited, and not thrown pell-mell into the hole dug to contain them.

Dr. Daniel Wilson, in " Prehistoric Man," page 412, gives an illustration and comments on an " inscribed ax" that was found in New Jersey, and so claims a notice here. We will quote the doctor in full concerning it. He says: " In 1859, Dr. John C. Evans, of Pemberton, N. J., communicated to the American Ethnological Society an account of a stone ax inscribed in similar [that is, to the ' Yarmouth Bay Stone,'] unknown characters, which had been recently plowed up on a neighboring farm. The ax, which measures about six inches long by three and a half broad, is engraved from a drawing furnished to me by Dr. Evans. Dr. E. H. Davis, after carefully examining the original, informs me that, though the graven characters have been partially retouched in the process of cleaning it, their edges present an appearance of age consistent with the idea of their genuineness, and the circumstances attending its production furnish no grounds for doubting its authenticity. Two of the characters are placed on one side in the groove for the handle; the others apparently form a continuous line, running round both sides of the ax-blade, as extended here, (figure 50.)"

We probably spoke too hastily in attributing to plow-scratches, such a case as this, of an inscribed ax;* but, nevertheless, we have no faith in an ancient *foreign* origin of these figures. If not intended as a hoax by some witless idler, then it is the meaningless fancy of some eccentric aboriginal. But one single fact has come under our own notice that in any way bears upon the subject of the age of these relics.

The instance referred to was as follows: On the 3d of July, 1869, a large white-oak, measuring twenty-seven feet in circumference at three feet from the ground, during a high gale of wind was blown down. A short time afterward the immense stump was uprooted, preparatory to leveling the ground. The hole that the extracted roots left measured seven feet in depth and thirty-three in circumference. Four feet below the bottom of this hole, or eleven feet from the surface of the ground, we found a very rude stone ax, that was entangled in a mass of fibrous roots that had been cut off from the main mass of roots of the tree. In

*Amer. Nat., vol. vi, page 160.

this case an ax must have been buried in the earth before this old tree was an acorn. Now, as to the age of the tree. There were not less than five hundred rings clearly to be traced on a section of the tree afterward made; and a large portion of the center and another portion about the circumference could not be determined accurately, but which, on comparison with so much of the tree as retained the rings sufficiently distinctly to be counted, might safely be estimated at as many more circles.

Without allowing for any time to have elapsed from the occurrence of the ax falling on the ground, or of its intentional burial, we have here with considerable certainty the long stretch of one thousand years that this ax has been quietly resting in the ground.

CHAPTER IV.

CELTS.

We propose to consider, under the name of "celts,"* the class of relics that approach most nearly to the ordinary stone axes, but which are without any groove or other indication that a handle has been attached. These celts vary more in size among themselves than in any other feature; and we have separated the specimens obtained into two classes, viz, celts and "skinning-knives," the latter being, in our judgment, too small to be used as weapons, under which heading we think the ordinary celts, or ungrooved axes, must be placed.

Considered with reference solely to size, we can be moderately sure of correct nomenclature in saying that a stone dressed down until its thickness is less than half the width, with one end sharpened to a cutting-edge, and the length not less than five inches, may be taken as a celt, or ungrooved ax. Still, it must be borne in mind that smaller *grooved* axes occur.

The use or uses to which some of the larger of these celts were put is very difficult to conjecture, inasmuch as no trace of a handle having been attached can be detected. Mr. John Evans, however, describes several methods employed by savages in hafting just such stone implements. A fact to be taken into consideration, however, with reference to our New Jersey specimens, is, that the great prevalence of grooved axes renders it probable that the ungrooved were used without handles, since grooved or ordinary axes occur, made of the same hard materials as the hand-axes, viz, porphyry and hornstone. Concerning the use of these hand-axes, or "polished celts," Mr. Evans remarks: "Among modern savages we have instances of similar tools being used in the hand without the intervention of any haft, though among the Australians the butt-end is sometimes enveloped in a mass of resinous matter, so as to form a knob which fits the hand." And again: "They were

* From the Latin *celtis*, a chisel.

also employed in times of war, as weapons of offense and defense, as a supplementary kind of tomahawk."*

The term "wedge" has been applied to this pattern of "ax," and may very possibly be a correct designation for the flattened specimens, but scarcely applicable to those that are nearly or quite cylindrical or conical in shape. The term "wedge," however, suggests the use of a hammer, and we do not usually find the back of the so-called wedge exhibiting traces of having been struck with such stone hammers as were in use when these "wedges" were made.

Figure 22 imperfectly represents a specimen of the larger ungrooved axes, that show but little trace of human workmanship, other than the finely-wrought edge, and a limited polished surface on the upper and lower margins. It measures seven and three-quarters inches in length, by three and one half inches in width, at a point a little in advance of the middle. It is of ordinary sandstone, and originally was very nearly of its present shape. One side is much flatter than the other, and appears to have been first pecked away and then somewhat polished. The margins have been polished for a short distance from the edge, and, on the lower margin, there is a very smooth surface, little over an inch in extent either way, that appears to be such "peculiar polished space, which has been produced by the friction of the wood," as described by Lubbock as exhibited in some specimens found in Europe. There does not appear to have been any hard hammering upon the head of this stone celt; but, if the handle had been attached after the manner of the grooved ax, as the polished space seems to indicate, we cannot see how a hard blow could fail to displace the implement.

While such celts are usually cobble-stones from the river-bed, materially altered only at one end in the production of the edge, many are porphyry pebbles, handsomely polished over their whole surface, and not only admirably edged, but the opposite end frequently ground to a very beautiful, tapering point. Such point-headed polished porphyry axes are among the very handsomest of all the relics found within the limits of the State. This pattern (figures 23 and 24) is found in every part of the globe where polished stone implements occur, showing it best met those common wants of all mankind, wherever they may have happened to be; and possibly, if we could determine one use to which such axes were adapted, of a strictly universal nature, it would be safe to apply a name suggested by such use to this form, now known by the objectionable term of "celt."

Sir John Lubbock† figures a celt, similar to figure 23, from Ireland; Nilsson figures‡ them from Scandinavia; and the pattern is nearly approached in axes from Accra, West Africa, figured by Sir J. Lubbock.§

Of a porphyry polished celt, similar in shape to figure 23, that the

---

*Ancient Stone Implements of Great Britain, page 153.
† Prehistoric Times, 2d ed., figures 97–98, page 88.
‡ Stone Age in Scandinavia, plate vii, figures 151 and 162.
§ Journ. Anthrop. Inst., London, vol. 1, page xcv (Proc. Eth. Soc.)

writer forwarded to Sir J. Lubbock, that archæologist writes: "The polished ax about which you inquire is very similar, as you suppose, to the one figured in Prehistoric Times, so much so, indeed, that I had placed it in a drawer with similar axes from various other parts of the world to show how much they are alike."

While this form (figure 23) is usually of porphyry and highly polished, it is sometimes met with of softer mineral, and the specimen in question is peculiarly interesting on this account; for, although of the tapering form, and accurately outlined, it is of sandstone, and pecked into shape, having a highly-polished edge only, instead of being so worked over the whole surface.

We have ventured to call figure 25 a "celt," rather than a "skin dresser," because the cutting-edge varies decidedly in its character from the general run of "skinning-knives." The edge, it will be seen, is narrow, and slopes suddenly from the thickest portion of the implement, and is not produced by a gradual slope from the back of the instrument, as in the majority of so-called skin-dressers, or skinning-knives. There may, perhaps, be no sufficient reason for calling figure 25 a celt, since its size certainly precludes the idea of its utilization for chopping, unless for very slender and tender marrow-bones; but we have a good example to follow in so doing, as we shall see.

Sir John Lubbock,[*] in some "Notes on Stone Implements from Africa and Syria," gives natural-size figures of stone axes, which certainly are identical in shape, and have been used, no doubt, in an identical manner. The author says, with reference to them: "Some of the West African axes, as will be seen by the figures, (plate ii, figures 1 and 2,) closely resemble some of the smaller axes so common in Western Europe;" and adds, as we have already observed of the preceding pattern, "Indeed, this type may be said to be cosmopolitan, and needs no description."

We find that Sir John Lubbock simply uses the term "ax" in speaking of these African relics, and if it is applicable in the one case it is in the other, but unless the term is *properly* applied to implements that cannot be made to cut in any useful manner, which is not the case, the designation is certainly a misnomer.

Figure 26 may properly be placed in the same "class" with the preceding. Although a much less finished specimen, it was unquestionably put to the same uses. It is made of a fine-grained porphyritic stone, and has been polished over its entire surface. This little "celt" measures two and one-eighth inches in length by one and three-quarters in width. The cutting (or skin-detaching) edge was originally good. The back has a ridge running obliquely across it, from which the surfaces slope at an angle of forty-five degrees. Had this specimen been used as a wedge for splitting wood, certainly the back was not favorably fashioned for receiving a hard blow; moreover, the ridge, which in that case would have

[*] Journ. Anthrop. Inst., London, vol. 1, page xcii, plate 11, figures 1 and 2, (Eth. Soc. Procs.)

been much battered, is still moderately well preserved. This double-faced condition of the backs of small axes is not unfrequent among the grooved cobble-stone specimens.

Localities known to have been the former sites of Indian villages are where these celts are now found in greatest abundance; a fact which does not hold good with reference to the grooved stone axes; although these, too, have been found in "deposits" occasionally, as described in Chapter III. In the instance referred to in the preceding chapter, of a deposit of fifty polished porphyry celts, we have possibly an indication that the use of these implements was of a domestic and not warlike character, supposing that the specimens were buried for the purpose of concealing them from an enemy, should a sudden raid be made upon the village. If such celts were weapons, they would always be in demand, but as domestic implements, there might be times of considerable duration when they would not be required. If so, what method more natural than to bury them? The fact that undoubted weapons are also found buried in considerable numbers does not, we think, militate against this supposition, since, in the burial of weapons, the deposits were made by the makers of such specimens, and were usually in subterranean arsenals; the specimens being generally in an unfinished state.

CHAPTER V.

FLINT HATCHETS.

We have seen that all the specimens as yet described under the head of axes and celts have been, without exception, pebbles or "cobble-stones," worn into shape by polishing-stones or *pecked* by a stone hammer into the required form. We have nowhere made any allusion to a chipped ax. The term "chipped" was purposely reserved, as it were, for flint-like stone-cutting implements, which we further propose to designate as hatchets, to distinguish them from "axes" proper; that is, *pecked* or polished pebble implements. The distinction between the two is, that an ax has a polished edge, and a hatchet a chipped edge.

Flint hatchets (which in New Jersey are never true flint) are found associated with other implements, as arrow-points and spear-heads, in very scanty numbers, if we consider the very hatchet-like specimens only as really the implement in question, and consider those as "implements" having no particular use in view, or as rude spear-heads that do not present the ideal outline of the hatchet in every detail. If we chance, however, upon the site of an Indian village, or if, along the river or creek bank, we come upon a mussel-shell heap or fresh-water *Kjökkenmödding*, these rough flint hatchets will be found much more abundant, and sometimes even sufficiently numerous to be quite characteristic of the particular locality.

The flint hatchets vary considerably in size and somewhat in shape, and are always of jasper or white quartz. The latter, however, are rare; at least, we have only met with some eight or ten during four years' systematic collecting. The jasper forms are of all the colors that appear in that mineral—red, yellow, brown, blue, green, chocolate, and variegated. They never exhibit the fine finish of some of the arrow-points, and appear to have been made, in a great measure, of portions of the jasper masses that could not be fashioned into those remarkably delicate shapes which, as will be seen in another chapter, are exhibited in some of the arrow-points that we have gathered. Jasper is not found in New Jersey *in situ;* fragments and an occasional pebble in the river-gravels being all that occur, except in the shape of finished "relics." The fragments, however, are abundant about sites of aboriginal villages. Sandy fields, with no stone of any kind near, are occasionally thickly dotted with the little flakes and " failures " of some ancient arrow-maker.

Figure 27 is a beautiful mass of many-colored jasper, red and yellow predominating, that has been laboriously chipped until brought to its present shape, which, we think, warrants its being designated a hatchet; but, indeed, were there not other specimens to be found that more clearly show the work of man, it might be considered merely a chance-shaped fragment of a jasper bowlder. We give it the first place in our list of hatchets because of its size, it being the largest specimen that we have met with, and as serving as a good link between this form of weapon and the axes proper; and certainly, from its size, it was fitted to perform the duties of any ax we have figured. The hatchet (figure 27) measures six inches in length by three and one quarter inches in width. It is chipped to an edge at one end and along the upper and lower margins. The amount of work expended upon it is very great, and we should judge to very little purpose, if wood-cutting was the intended use of the implement; but for mussel-shell crushing, or, better yet, bone-splitting—its most likely use—it is moderately well adapted. The illustration is very imperfect in its details, although correct in outline. It shows far too few of the innumerable surfaces caused by the forcing-off of small flakes, from every portion of the surface, to give a good idea of the specimen itself. The edge, which was apparently much sharper, has been dulled by use and long weathering. It bears no traces of a handle having ever been attached; and yet it would seem to be comparatively useless unless wielded by such an appendage.

Figure 28 represents a not uncommon form of flint hatchet, that we considered, when we found the specimen figured here, as rare. Since then we have met with a large number, all agreeing with it in size, shape, and material. It may be questioned, perhaps, if such an implement should be called a hatchet; many would look upon it as a "scraper." We shall see, however, that those specimens, so abundant in New Jersey, and which we have called "scrapers," are much smaller chipped flints as a class, and have a handle of the mineral itself; the complete implement being chipped out of one piece. We, therefore, incline to the belief that this specimen is a double-edged hatchet, if the ends were used in cutting, or a single-edged one, if a bone handle was ever attached to the lower, straighter margin. With a handle so attached, it certainly could then be used advantageously as a hatchet or chopping-knife, and, when sharper, as an instrument for detaching the tough hide of the bison or deer, both of which, from the crumbling bones that we have occasionally exhumed, we *now* know were formerly found in New Jersey. Again, such a hatchet would be useful in breaking apart the tough vertebræ of the sturgeon, once so numerous in the Delaware River. These immense fish frequent the shallow portions of the stream during the summer, and are, even now, captured by the spear when found in such localities. If the stone-age people valued the sturgeon as an article of food, which is probable, they would require the very largest and sharpest of their stone weapons to capture it and to divide the carcass. An occasional glance at the fauna of the locality from which we gather "relics" will give us many valuable hints as to the probable use of the various implements. Again, may not such a chipped flint as figure 28 have been a sort of "handy comeby," and not specially set apart for any particular use or uses? Some such shaped flint, bone-handled, as we have described, would be admirable for splitting marrow-bones, crushing large mussels, girdling trees, or cutting saplings for lance-handles; and, if put to any or all these uses, must we not call it a hatchet?

Figure 29 represents a form of flint hatchet that approaches the "lance-head" in shape, but is, of course, too short and broad to be used for such purpose. Having a well-defined edge upon each side, as well as in front, where it becomes obtusely-pointed, it appears evident that it was used to split rather than to pierce. If a handle was attached, we suppose it to have been placed at the flattened or straight base, and to have been of bone, as in figure 214 of Lubbock's Prehistoric Times, second edition, although this illustration referred to is that of a knife, and not a hatchet. We think it not improbable that just such "flints" as these were inserted in long wooden clubs as "teeth," and that clubs thus formed were used in war. The war-club was, and is, a favorite weapon, and the vast majority of such specimens as figure 29 were very possibly used in this manner.

Figure 29 bears much resemblance, except in being more pointed at one end, to modern Esquimaux scrapers, as figured by Sir John Lubbock,* but is just double the size. There is this difference, however, between either the modern or the prehistoric scrapers and such an implement as we here designate a hatchet, viz, that the former have one flat, smooth surface, the plane of a single cleavage, while the hatchets have an edge, beveled from each side, which are both equally well chipped. These more elaborate "hatchets" may have been used as "scrapers."

We would also call attention to the similarity of our specimens, as represented by figure 29, to a flint implement from Le Moustier, also

---

* Prehistoric Times, 2d ed., p. 93, figs. 105-107.

figured by Lubbock.* Although figure 29 is somewhat larger, and has not "one side left unchipped," the variation in general characteristics is very slight, and an identity of the uses of the two specimens is highly probable. We, too, have met with some specimens of this pattern of "flint hatchet," with such an unchipped surface as is particularly pointed out in the Le Moustier implement by Lubbock. Such identity of European and American specimens of flint-work, even to the details, is certainly remarkable.

Figures 30, 31, 32, and 33 represent the smaller flint hatchets, which are much more abundant than the larger examples which we have just described. They do not vary very greatly in their general outline, being usually triangular, or nearly so, in shape, and varying but little from three inches in length by two inches in greatest breadth. We have gathered several dozens of these small hachets, usually associated with arrow-points and spear-heads and the other ordinary shapes of surface-relics.

On the sites of the long-past labors of "Indian arrow-makers," and we have visited several such localities, these small hatchets are found in an unfinished state, mingled with the mass of chippings that accumulated during their manufacture, and that of arrow-points, spear-heads, &c. The unfinished specimens are almost always such as have been discarded, in consequence of some defect in the mineral which was not discovered until the specimen was well toward completion. This fact combats, we think, the assertion, often made, that the Indian arrow-maker was a good practical mineralogist. These specimens were always commenced from masses of the rock *not* a great deal larger than the intended implement, and small enough to develop to the experienced the weak points of the mineral.

As already stated, the more usual sizes of hatchets are such as we have figured, (figures 30–33.) Their size should be no objection to the proposition that they were used as cutting-tools. We have already seen that axes are equally small. Sir John Lubbock figures† one from Ireland, which is as small; and, on page 182, speaking of Swiss axes, says, " With few exceptions, they were small, especially when compared with the magnificent specimens from Denmark. In length, they varied *from six inches to one*, while the cutting-edge had generally a width of from fifteen to twenty lines;" and, again, on page 93, speaking of so-called " axes," or hatchets of the *Kjökkenmöddings*, says, " They are * * * rudely triangular or quadrangular in shape, with a cutting-edge at the broader end, and two and a half to five and a half inches in length, with a breadth of one and a half to two and a half inches." Now, the New Jersey specimens differ only in this, that both sides are chipped; otherwise they are identical. As we have abundant reasons for knowing that mussels (*Unio* and *Anodonta*) were a favorite food, these little flint

* *Id.*, p. 320, figs. 182-184.
† Prehistoric Times, fig. 93, 2d ed.

hatchets may have been used principally to crush their shells, inasmuch as very many of these implements have been found with heaps of the burned shells.

We would here call especial attention to the rude, green-jasper hatchet, (figure 30,) which has its edge derived by striking off a large chip, struck at one blow, giving it, on one side, a smooth surface, which edge meets .with the opposite more gradually-wrought surface. This specimen is of peculiar interest in agreeing so nearly with an illustration of a European *Kjökkenmödding* ax, given by Sir John Lubbock, in "Prehistoric Times," plate 1, figure 8.

In conclusion, we would direct attention particularly to the hatchet, (figure 33,) which very nearly approaches the lance or arrow head; and indeed it may properly be one of these two implements rather than a hatchet. We place it here, however, as showing how readily some of these smaller weapons run into other forms. While figure 33 would make a small spear-head, and be well adapted for that purpose, yet, as it appears to us, it is quite as well shaped for a hatchet as any of the preceding figures.

The few chipped jasper implements, which we have designated as "flint hatchets," resemble very closely the smaller specimens of "rough-hewn celts" figured by Mr. Evans in the fourth chapter of his work."[*] There are some points of difference, however, which are well worth indicating, and the principal variation is, that our jasper specimens are, as a rule, thinner, and show a much more elongated oval section; indeed, in section, the New Jersey specimens are quite irregular, the mineral not being as easy to work as the true flint. This difference, however, does not arise because the jasper will not yield to chipping and pressure; since for symmetry and accuracy of the beveled edges, some of our jasper arrow-points are not excelled in specimens of a similar character in any other part of the world.

There appears to be fully as much variation in outline in the English celts of this class as in the flint hatchets, such as we have described. In all, a well-defined cutting-edge obtains, and this feature decides the use of the implement, call it by whatever name one may. The "celts" of England and "flint hatchets" of New Jersey are so nearly similar that we doubt not that their uses were identical; which uses, however, it would be difficult to determine accurately, as our only means of learning their history is the scarcely safe plan of judging of them, as allied to similar implements of iron now in use.

Some of the flint implements figured by Lartet and Christy, in "*Reliquiæ Aquitanicæ*," bear considerable resemblance to the specimens we have figured in this chapter; but, just as in the preceding comparison with English rough-hewn celts, we find the French specimens are much thicker, and shaped by the detachment of much larger flakes, than, as a rule, fly off from jasper when it is worked. Indeed, it would appear

---

Loc. cit., pp. 60–77.

as though the jasper, agate, hornstone, and chert, of which our "flint implements" are made, is really better adapted to the purpose than true flint; for the "cutting-edges" of the implements found here in New Jersey are much sharper and more regular than the same are in the allied implements made of true flint; and this fact may explain why the true flint celts had their edges ground, to make them sharp, which grinding is wholly wanting to the "flint hatchets," such as we have described. The edges here are so finely chipped and sharp that grinding or polishing is unnecessary. We doubt if a ground-edged celt could be put to any use to which the chipped jasper hatchet would not be equally well adapted.

CHAPTER VI.

LANCE-HEADS.

Wherever we find arrow-heads, and other larger specimens, more properly designated spear-points, there also occur in varying numbers, but nowhere rare, certain leaf-shaped and irregularly triangular-worked "flints," which we will call "lance-heads." A distinction is made between the lance and the spear, inasmuch as the former is without a notched or stemmed base, or both, which features singularly or together characterize the spear-head proper, which, also, are smaller as a class than lance-heads, but too large to be of use if placed at the end of an arrow. The size, however, is not of much importance in distinguishing the various types, since all classes of weapons invariably merge into each other.

There is considerable variation in the minerals used in the production of these lance-heads, and, in localities where they are abundant, are usually of the native rocks most easily worked. About the Delaware River, and, indeed, throughout the State, the majority of these specimens are of slate, the harder, more finely grained, least shelly layers of this material having been utilized exclusively. Our collection of them, all from the neighborhood of Trenton, N. J., consists of slate, yellow jasper, milky quartz, agate, and a micaceous sandstone, seldom used for any purpose, as far as our collecting-experience extends.

While these lance-heads are, we might almost say, *never* wrought with that care which characterizes arrow and spear points, still they have had sufficient care bestowed upon them to show that they were for an important purpose. They are quite abundant in the bed of the river at Trenton; whether lost during a battle, or overboard during fishing excursions, it is impossible to state; but while, as a class, they certainly have a very warlike appearance, they would make admirable sturgeon-spears, for which purpose they were probably used, since sturgeon was once extremely numerous in the Delaware.

Figure 34 represents an average specimen of these long, slender, fine-edged slates, which we have designated lance-heads. They vary little from five to seven and one-half inches in length by from two to three and one-half inches in width; the longer specimens are usually the more slender ones, suggesting the possibility of the broader and shorter specimens having had a different use from the others; but whether for war or hunting, the larger, more slender slates appear to us to be the more effective weapon.

In no one of these lance-heads have we met with any deep notches in the sides, near the base, indicating whereby they were attached to hafts or handles, as is shown in an English specimen figured by Jewitt. Speaking of this specimen, he says,* " It will be noticed that its sides, as they begin to diminish, are deeply serrated for fastening with thongs to a haft or handle." One specimen in our collection has a single deep notch, presenting the appearance of having been purposely made, in chipping the specimen, but it is within one and three-fourths inches of the point, and the lance-head itself measures five and one-half inches in length. Many of these slate lance-heads are weather-worn, the faces produced by chipping being very nearly obliterated. Such worn specimens are associated with the less-worn and sharply-edged ones, and are supposed to be older specimens, discarded in consequence of the loss of the extreme point or the edge being dulled, and replaced by newer and better ones. The abundance of these lance-heads may be judged from the fact that in an area of not over one hundred acres in extent we have collected more than three hundred perfect specimens, besides a great number of fragments.

There is a curious fact to which attention is called with reference to these pieces of lance-heads, viz, that fully 95 per cent. of these fragments are the *pointed* halves of the specimens, their excellent state of preservation showing that they were broken off while the weapon was comparatively new. So unusual is it, in our own experience, to find the basal half of a lance-head, that we have sometimes thought it possible these so-called broken lance-heads were in reality not fragments, but purposely fashioned for war-club teeth, as was suggested with reference to one of the forms of chipped jasper under the heading of " Hatchets."

As these points of lance-heads are very abundant in some limited localities, it may be that they were broken in battle, and that the owner of the lance retained the handle with the base still attached, to be re-headed. If such were the case, of course the battle-field would have about the proportion of points to bases, *i. e.*, 95 per cent.

Figure 35 † represents the largest and finest lance-head that has ever come under our observation. It measures eleven and one-quarter inches in length by but two and seven-eighths inches in width, and is placed at the head of the list of this class of specimens on account of its size and symmetry.

Of the history of this magnificent specimen we know nothing, further than that it was presented to the East India Marine Society, at Salem,

*Grave-Mounds and their Contents, London, 1870, p. 117.
†Omitted from the illustrations.

Mass., by Jos. Story, in 1824. It is now in the museum of the Peabody Academy of Science of the same place, and is labeled as coming from New Jersey; associated with it is a specimen of another class, to be figured and described in a succeeding chapter. It is of the same mineral, also from New Jersey, and presented by Mr. Story in 1824.

Figure 35 is chipped from yellow jasper, the same in every particular with the many jasper specimens that we have procured near Trenton, N. J. A glance at the illustration will, it is thought, satisfy any one as to its intended use, however difficult it may seem to us to securely attach to it a shaft such as would be required to effectively wield so formidable a weapon. Certainly, the well-defined point, and the width of the implement, in comparison with its length, both show that its use was *for piercing.* Any manner of using other than by thrusting would certainly break a piece of stone so slender and somewhat brittle; and if an edge had been intended to be used as a knife, would not the opposite edge have been left blunt, or at least, not been as well chipped as the cutting-edge? And if a bone handle had been fastened along one side, would not some trace of such handle be visible?

As specimens of such large lance-heads are very rare in New Jersey, it is more than probable that they were the peculiar property of "chiefs," or "kings," and possibly were used on state occasions as a badge of office, rather than on the field of battle. There is too much work on such a lance-head as figure 35 to risk its being broken in a fight.

Messrs. Squier and Davis* figure a "flint" similar to figure 35 in size and mineral, but varying from it in being pointed at each end. After mentioning the use to which the stemmed examples were put, they add, "There are others, however, the manner of using which is not so obvious. No. 3 is an example. It measures eleven inches in length by two and a half in greatest breadth. It has been suggested that it was fastened at right angles to a handle and used as a sort of battle-ax." We think this latter suggestion a very plausible one, as the specimen is double-pointed, and with a handle at the center would make a good "double-headed" weapon; but, the base of figure 35 being as markedly blunt as the point is acute, such use cannot be applied to the specimen we have here described.

Flint lance-head-shaped implements, quite similar to many of our surface-specimens of jasper, but less symmetrical as a class, are characteristic of the "drift" in Europe. Tylor says, †"A set of characteristic drift-implements would consist of certain tapering instruments like huge lance-heads, shaped, edged, and pointed, by taking off a large number of facets, in a way which shows a good deal of skill and feeling for symmetry; smaller leaf-shaped instruments; flints partly shaped and edged, but with one end left unwrought, evidently for holding in the hand," &c.

While the New Jersey specimens as a class are probably smaller,

---

*Anc. Mon. Miss. Valley, p. 211, fig. 99, (No. 3.)

† Early History of Man., 2d ed., p. 197.

they were fashioned about equally as carefully as those Mr. Tylor has described.

Figure 36 is a beautiful specimen of a lance-head of bluish-gray " flint," mineralogically unlike any other specimen in our collection. It is the leaf-form of arrow-head enlarged, and is of excellent workmanship. This measures a little less than five inches in length by two and one-eighth inches in greatest width. We have met with but few specimens of this class of the size of figure 36 made of anything but slate, the jasper examples generally being considerably larger. It would be interesting to know if these lance-heads were considered by their original owners as different implements, the size determining the use. It at least seems fair to infer that these smaller examples were more used in hunting than in war, and just such a lance-head as this is adapted to the chase of such aquatic animals as are still to be found within the limits of our State, as the otter, muskrat, and, until within a few years, the beaver. These animals were hunted with spears, especially in winter, and figure 29 is still keen-edged enough to be as effective as the steel spear-point of the present day.

Figure 37 represents a good average specimen of the lance-heads of yellow jasper, that are met with about Trenton, N. J., but are comparatively rare elsewhere in the State. The majority of the specimens found are somewhat narrower, and a little longer than the one figured, which is the only specimen we possess. Figure 37 measures five and one-quarter inches in length by three and one-half inches in width. Neatly chipped from a large flake of yellow-brown jasper, its edges are well defined, as also the point and base. It is nowhere thicker than five-eighths of an inch, and is far less heavy than its large extent of surface would indicate. Whether used in war or in hunting, it would be difficult to determine, but it is of such dimensions as to combine the hatchet with the lance, and, in accordance with the mounting, would deal a telling cutting blow or thrust. This specimen is one of a number that were discovered in plowing a piece of newly-drained meadow near Trenton, N. J.[*] They were found buried with the points up, and surrounded by a sufficient number lying flat to wall them in and hold them erect had they been originally placed upon the surface. The collection numbered about one hundred and fifty specimens. As stated in the *Naturalist*,[†] we had at that time found no isolated specimens, but since then careful search has yielded several, all, however, from the immediate neighborhood of this deposit. We give elsewhere a figure of a second example of this deposit, the specimen, though, not being a lance-head, but an agricultural implement. (See chapter on " Shovels and hoes.")

Figure 38 represents the minimum size of such " chipped flints " as we would call lance-heads. It is an exaggeration of the very common leaf-shaped arrow-head, but too heavy to have been used as such. This specimen measures three and one-half inches in length by two and one-

---

[*] Abbott on " Deposit of Lance-heads," in Proc. Acad. Nat. Sci., Phil., 1863, p. 278.
[†] American Naturalist, vol. vi, p. 155.

quarter inches in width. It is chipped from bluish-gray jasper, and varies but little from the preceding except in size. The edges are still quite sharp and the point good, although the extreme point is apparently worn away. There is nothing about this specimen or the preceding to indicate in what manner a handle was attached, and yet without handles these implements seem comparatively valueless, the cutting-edges extending so far down as to jeopardize the hand if held naked when striking.

These smaller specimens of lance-heads are far less abundant than those of the larger, more slender type, which usually are made of slate, as figured in the first pages of this chapter.

Mr. Evans has figured and described several specimens of well-chipped flint implements, which he calls "daggers." They are usually longer, but otherwise identical with the average slate and jasper specimens we have called "lance-heads," particularly such specimens as figure 36. Mr. Evans mentions, however, that these same specimens are also termed spear-heads, lance-heads, &c. We cannot think they were ever used as "daggers" or "knives" by the aborigines of New Jersey; either name suggesting a short handle, and the use that of a tool rather than that of a weapon; for surely no dagger, as a weapon, would be useful with a blade as obtusely pointed as even figure 35. We have to describe in another chapter chipped flints, that we doubt not were true knives; but they differ materially from those we term "lance-heads." The whole finish, size, and shape of the "daggers" figured by Mr. Evans, and the "lance-heads" illustrated in this chapter, would show that a long shaft was originally attached, and that the weapon was then used in transfixing animals in the chase, or, giving the weapon all the force that could be brought to bear upon it, in impaling an enemy in battle. As a head for such lance, these specimens seem in every way appropriate; but we perceive nothing desirable about them as "daggers," especially after examining the beautiful flint-daggers of Scandinavia, which are in all respects admirable for the purposes implied by the term "dagger."

There are abundant instances where the use and proper name of an implement are matters of doubt; but to call such specimens as we have designated "lance-heads" by a name that expresses a use to which we could not put them only increases the confusion caused by want of some safe rule by which to be guided. So, too, these "lance-heads" have been called knives, and excellent spear-points have been so called by Nilsson. He says, "A spear is, properly speaking, nothing but a * * * knife fastened to a long shaft. It is, therefore, often impossible to judge from the blade whether it has been a *spear* or a *knife*." Of the American specimen above alluded to, he says that the handle was five inches long, and a loop was fastened to the handle. Judging from the plate, the loop and short handle were to be fastened, the one by the other, to a long shaft, which would thus make a good weapon of what seems now but a very awkward tool, and one that appears the more unnecessary as excellent and undoubted knives are quite abundant.

S. Mis. 115——18

Chapter VII.

HUNTING-SPEARS.

We may, perhaps, be charged with having carried the separation of relics into classes too far ; and that, in some cases, we have been making a distinction where none exists. Indeed, where but comparatively few specimens are found scattered over fields, the impression is natural that the whim only of the arrow-maker dictated the various shapes and sizes; and that all the smaller " pointed flints " are arrow-heads, unless the size is such as positively to render them unfit for such a purpose.

We have been fortunate enough, however, to make very large collections of these relics, (over six thousand spear and arrow points,) and have been able to satisfy at least ourselves of the correctness of the separate designations adopted, inasmuch as the circumstances under which a great many of these specimens were found show that, while the lance-heads were largely, if not wholly, a war-weapon, these so-called spear-points were as exclusively used in the chase. While lances are often abundant in a limited locality, and very frequently broken into halves, indicating a battle-field, spears are found singly, scattered over the whole country, upland and lowland, except where a great mixture of everything indicates a former settlement or an ancient arrow-maker's work-shop.

Figure 39 represents a carefully-chipped dirty-white agate, whose size, outline, shape of base, and comparative thickness render it a good type for such of our relics as are designated "hunting-spears." Figure 39 measures four and five-eighths inches in length by one and one-half inches in width at the base, where it begins to taper gradually to the point. The notches at the base are deep, similarly curved, and have the stem well shaped, projecting directly from them, but short, considering the length of the main portion of the specimen.

The size at once indicates it use : a head for a long shaft, that was intended for thrusting at an object, and then withdrawn, the attachment of head to handle being secured by the deep notches at the base of the specimen. The length of this specimen is sufficient to secure, by its use, any of the larger mammals of the period of the occupancy of the country by the aborigines, unless it be the elk or wapiti, and, even in this case, a thrust between the ribs would cause an unpleasant wound were the spear-head buried its full length in the animal's body.

More care has been exercised in making this specimen than was put upon lance-heads as a class; and as hunting-implements were more easily recovered than war-weapons, and less likely to be broken, we can readily see that pains would be taken to have more effective points and edges on specimens that were less likely to be lost or injured in using. Hunting, too, was the sole means (if we except maize-culture) of existence ; and war, although certain at intervals, was not an every-day affair, and thus is afforded another reason for the belief that these more carefully wrought specimens were set apart as a most important, if not *the* most important, implements for securing food.

Figure 40, like the preceding, represents a perfect specimen of the hunting-spear, being somewhat shorter and broader than figure 39. This specimen is chipped from a yellow jasper, veined with glassy quartz, a favorite mineral with the arrow-makers. It is very well, but not as finely cut as are many arrow-points, and shows, by its whole appearance, that it was worked with a view rather to strength and durability than to elegance of finish. The point and sides are still very sharp, and capable of inflicting a fearful wound if thrust with moderate force. This specimen measures three and three-fourths inches in length by a little less than one-half this measurement in greatest width.

Figure 41 is an elegantly-outlined and admirably-finished specimen of a spear-head, considering that the mineral out of which it was chipped is a tough, micaceous, quartz-like rock, which, in the shape of glacial bowlders, abounds in the drift about the central portion of the State. It has a most uncertain fracture, and was very little used as material for arrow or spear heads, as far as our experience extends.

This specimen exhibits a peculiarity not observable in any other of the series in our collection, but one which is seen in one of our arrow-points, viz, in having a twist to the body of the spear-point, whereby the edges are at a slight angle to the barbs, or projecting points, of the base. This feature, which is most noticeable when viewing the specimen from the point downward, extends along the whole extent of the sides. We believe this peculiarity to have been intentional on the part of its maker, and was designed to give the spear a rotary motion, by fastening to a short haft, probably feathered, and known as a dart. Although worn now, the point has the appearance of being once very sharp, so that a strong throw would enable it to pierce the skin of small mammals.

Figure 42 represents a very fine specimen of a beautiful style of spear-heads, which, however, have invariably lost their stems, suggesting that being thrust in only as far as the commencement of the stem, the animal has been able to break it there, and possibly escape. This suggestion conflicts, we know, with a previous assertion that spears were less apt to be broken than war-lances, but it would be very strange if occasional hunting-spears were not broken in the chase, and the slender stem, in comparison with the width of the blade of the implement, renders this form peculiarly frangible. This pattern of spear-head is not at all common, but having found several examples it cannot be properly considered as " quite rare."

In workmanship, the specimen in question excels that of figure 40, a characteristic possibly due to the greater tractability of the mineral, which is a dark-yellow jasper, wholly free from veins of quartz or other minerals, and therefore most favorable for working.

It will be noticed that we have outlined a base in the illustration as simply a short straight projection of the width only of the fractured surface. We think this was the shape of the complete specimen, since a few fragments of about this size and shape have been picked up, none of which, however, would fit any of the specimens that we gathered. If our hypothesis as to the shape of the stem is correct, it was probably simply inserted into a slit made in the end of the haft, and, while secure enough when being carried about, was probably dislodged in the body of the animal into which it was thrust. Since the wound it caused would almost certainly be fatal, the spear-point could be recovered. Of course, such a spear-point as this, although intended for hunting, would be valuable, and was probably used in war. Perhaps no relic (used for a single purpose) was exclusively available for several uses; but everything considered, we believe this and the preceding and following "spears" to have been *intended for hunting*.

Figure 43 is a very beautiful specimen, a very unusual form of spear-head, chipped from a pale pea-green mass of jasper. It is a pretty, regularly-outlined triangle of jasper, the base measuring two and five-eighths inches in width, which is the exact length of the specimen from the point to the commencement of the tang or stem. The stem itself is but a little over three-fourths of an inch in length, and a little broader than the length at the base of the body of the specimen. It suggests the chase rather than war. But in either, it would not require much force to drive such a spear-point through an animal, even though it might come in contact with a bone.

Figure 44 represents the ordinary hunting-spear, made of slate and other comparatively soft stone, so abundant in some portions of New Jersey. Three inches in total length by about one and one-half in greatest width, as a class they differ somewhat in the details of outline, but have a general resemblance that at once distinguishes them from everything else, unless they are looked upon as simply large arrow-heads. We have found very many single specimens of this form of spear-point in " out of the way " places along the shores of small streams, formerly and still marshy, and worthless for grain or grass, and therefore the resort of some of the few mammals that are rapidly becoming extinct by the encroachments of man. The finding of such single specimens in likely hunting-places is more confined to just such spear-heads as the specimen figured than to any other class of relics, not excepting even axes, which are pretty evenly distributed over our State.

Figure 45 represents a rude slate hunting-spear, such as is occasionally found wherever relics of any description at all occur. It seems a little curious that so few specimens of this pattern, made of slate, should be met with, as it certainly is a good form for hunting or war purposes; nor are those of this shape made of jasper very abundant. Specimens of this size, of any mineral, are not common; and nearly all that we have found, and the majority of the specimens in the various cabinets we have visited, have been in a more or less fragmentary condition.

Figure 45 is now dull along the whole extent of its edges or sides ; the point has been broken off, and a "blunt" point chipped subsequently, which is now also weatherworn ; and the entire surface is now worn and *appears* soft. The decomposition, however, does not extend very deeply into the mineral, but appears to be rather a thin coating, as rust covers exposed surfaces of iron ; and like the latter, too, the decomposed stone coating this specimen protects the mineral beneath from further decay, as the rust protects the metal.

Figure 46 well represents that even smaller form of spear-point that very nearly approaches the arrow-heads in size. We have previously considered it as the latter, but, by experiment with some of these inter-mediate forms, we are satisfied that the arrow was never tipped with specimens as broad as this, although occasionally an arrow-head was made and used with equal or even greater length. The one in question is of slate, the stem of which was formerly a little more prolonged, but the difference between the size as figured and the unbroken spear-point was trifling. It *has* measured two and one-fourth inches in length by one and one-half inches in width at the base. Any specimen, even of this length, that was narrower, we should class as an arrow-point.

Figure 47 represents an odd form of relic, bearing resemblance rather to a "scraper" than to either spear or arrow point. From close exam-ination of the base, however, we are satisfied that it was not intended for a scraper ;* the condition of the chipped edges and point indicate clearly that they were intended to be the useful features of the specimen. Figure 47 is chipped from a mass of mottled slate, and has by use or long exposure become quite smooth ; it measures two and three-eighths inches in length by one and one-half inches in width at the broadest portion of the basal half. It is not apparent how this specimen was secured to a shaft, but the evident worthlessness of the implement, unless so attached, renders it certain that, inasmuch as the form is by no means an uncom-mon one, the aborigines contrived a satisfactory way of so fixing it.

We have a large number of specimens of slate spear-points in our cabinet, besides those of jasper, but no pattern that materially varies from the eight illustrations herein given.

Judging from Loskiel's description of the Indian manner of making war, it is not probable that any considerable number of these spears were habitually used for war-weapons. He says: "The offensive weapons formerly in use were bows, arrows, and clubs. The latter were made of the hardest wood, not quite the length of a man's arm, and very heavy, with a large round knob at one end. Their weapon of defense was a shield made of the tough hide of the buffalo, on the con-cave side of which they received the arrows *and darts* of the enemy, but this is now entirely laid aside by the Delawares, &c." While noticeably the "spear" is not mentioned among the weapons formerly in use,

---

*Vidè Amer. Nat., vol. 7, p. 503, fig. 135. Here it will be seen that we have recon-sidered the specimen as a true "scraper."

the " dart" is referred to in connection with the use of the shield ; but whether this " dart" refers to spears headed with such implements as we have described in this chapter, or to the lance-heads described in Chapter VI, it is impossible to say. Probably to both ; the lance-head pattern being the more usual form of the "dart" referred to by Loskiel.* Several reasons have already been given in Chapter VI why lance-heads, or those long, leaf-shaped implements we have designated as such, were used in battle, and it is evident that since they served a double purpose, as implements of the chase and weapons of war, so, too, these hunting-spears were available in battle.

CHAPTER VIII.

FISHING-SPEARS.

In every collection of Indian relics, there will be found a few specimens of a certain long, tapering form of " arrow-head," which we designate " fishing-spears," and we propose to describe them as a separate and distinct form, fashioned for the particular purpose implied in the name given them.

The form in question is comparatively rare in the fields or associated with other weapons or implements of the chase, but quite common on the shores and in the beds of those fishing-localities that are nearest to known sites of ancient Indian villages ; hence the name chosen—fishing-spears. They are abundant in the Delaware River, in the shallower pebble-bottomed portions of the stream, but usually broken ; the same is the case at Crosswick's Creek, near Trenton, N. J.

Figure 48 represents what may be taken as the type of this class of hunting-implements. With the exception of the loss of the extreme point, the specimen is perfect. Less than three-fourths of an inch in width at the base, it measures four inches in length, and is as long, for its width, as any example of fishing-spear that we have seen. The shape itself, as it seems to us, would scarcely suggest any other use than that of fishing. Its adaptability for the purpose is admirable. Of hard mineral, sharply edged, acutely pointed, and well stemmed, to insure safe attachment to the shaft, it meets every requirement for spearing rock-fish, shad, herring, gar, chub, or even young sturgeon, all of which were abundant in the Delaware, in the bed of which stream this implement was found.

Figure 49 represents a good-sized fishing-spear, which formerly we looked upon as an arrow-head. It is admirably chipped from a bluish-gray mineral, much resembling true flint. Occasionally such a specimen as this is met with in the inland localities where relics are found ; but it is unquestionably a form used almost exclusively in spearing fish. We

---

*[In Loskiel's original work, published in German, (Barby, 1789,) nothing is said about *darts*. The passage runs thus : "As defensive weapons they used shields made of hard buffalo skin, convex on the outer side for keeping off the *arrows* of the enemy." (P. 183). The *darts* are an addition of the English translator.—J. H.]

have gathered a great many of this particular pattern about the shores of the rivers, near their mouths, where the larger and strictly marine fish are abundantly met with. In such localities, however, as the depths of the water and habits of the fish render spearing, at least *now*, a somewhat slow process, it is probable that the bow was used, the arrows being headed with such spear-points of the kind figured; or perhaps the number of the fish was formerly so much greater than now that the shallower waters were more frequented, and the fish secured therein by spearing.

Figure 50 is a style of fish-spear that is very abundant; and having occasionally met with several broken ones together in localities distant from water, the conclusion is they were most likely used occasionally in hunting small mammals. The specimen figured is chipped from a fragment of slaty rock; from great age, much use, or other cause, its extreme point has been lost, while the chipped edges are dulled. Like the preceding illustrations, this specimen has a well-shaped stem, showing thereby that, whatever its particular use, it was intended to be securely fastened to a shaft. Where spears were used in capturing large fish, it would, of course, require much strength at the junction of the head and handle, as the struggles of some fishes are very violent.

Figure 51 represents a form of fish-spear that approaches very nearly to the arrow-heads, and to a series of broad-based specimens, to be separately considered, which are by many archæologists claimed to be stones so shaped for drilling other stones. This form is usually wrought in slate, and is not uncommon. It and other similarly-shaped specimens were gathered on the Pennsylvania shore of the Delaware River, opposite Bordentown, N. J. The most conspicuous feature in its being different from the preceding patterns consists in the plain, or unnotched, base. It does not appear how this shape of fish-spear could be very securely fastened to a handle, which, it would be supposed, was the important feature of a spear for such purposes. Certainly, arrow-head making and similar work was no such easy matter, even to adepts, that the well-wrought points could be risked by insecure fastenings. Had not this pattern been found more frequently in fishing-localities than upon the uplands, associated with other relics, it would not have been classed with fish-spears; but, under the circumstances, we believe it to be properly so classed, although the others figured are far better adapted to fishing.

Figure 52 represents a variety of fish-spear that we previously have called an arrow-head. Of exactly this pattern, we have only seen this one specimen. From the locality where found we learn nothing concerning it, a very stony field that for over a century has been under uninterrupted cultivation; and it really seems incredible that a form so easily destroyed as this should finally have been picked up in its present, probably almost perfect, condition, for we doubt if there was a repetition of the symmetrical barbs. Beautifully wrought in dull-green jasper, it has the slender stem of the fish-spears generally; but, unlike these, has the depressed barb-like projections at or near the base, which add to the beauty of the specimen, and also, we suppose, to its efficiency as an implement of the chase. This specimen is much flatter than the fish-spears generally, which usually have a median ridge running the whole length of the stem, and from it uniformly are sloped the sides to the sharp edges, which seem more carefully worked even than very many of the true arrow-points. This thin condition of the stem, it would seem, must weaken the specimen very much, and so it may possibly be questioned if it *were* intended as a spear-point. If, however, we recall the comparative degrees of risk of loss to which such a specimen would be subjected, as a spear-point for fishing or an arrow-head, we will be forced to admit that an arrow-head of this size could only be used to advantage with large game, and if it came violently in contact with a bone or was but partially embedded in the body of the animal, it would certainly be broken by the creature in its endeavors to free itself from it.

One* capable of a correct opinion as to the use of any stone implement says : "I am inclined to regard them," (several specimens figured in American Naturalist for March and April, 1872, including figure 52,) "as boring-tools rather than arrow-points, though doubtless one implement passes into the other." We have ourselves given this subject of boring-tools much study, taking as the basis a very large *suite* of pointed forms in our collection, but are unable to see why *such* pointed flints should be considered tools only. There is no trace whatever of wear on the point, and if designed as tools they were never so used, not one of *all* the many specimens of drilled stones in our collection showing any indication of being bored by such a specimen as this, while all the drillings of a larger caliber than the width of the stem of this specimen have been bored with a hollow tube, probably a reed, sand and water. We see no reason to look upon this specimen as a tool; but having many others that appear more adapted as such, we class the series of "pointed forms" as tools instead of as implements of the chase, and shall consider them in detail with reference to the subject of "Drilling in stone."

Figure 53 represents a neat specimen of flint-chipping, which seems to be a fish-spear, but which has one or two peculiarities not in accord with modern ideas of a desirable implement of this kind.

In the first place, figure 53 can scarcely be said to have a point, such as would be requisite for fishing were this particular specimen depended upon for success. What point there is is blunt, and was always so. Moreover, the implement is decidedly twisted, and was so chipped, but otherwise the specimen is carefully worked, and exhibits at the base a peculiarity very uncommon to the New Jersey specimens, viz,

---

* We are glad to have an opportunity to acknowledge our indebtedness to Mr. William A. Baker, of Auburn, N. Y., through whom we have received the above-quoted opinion of Mr. Greenwell, of England.

a doubly-notched base. A third peculiarity of the specimen consists in one side being almost perfectly flat, while the other is about as ridged and sloping from a central line as in the ordinary spears and arrow-points. The flat side is not at all the result of a single plane of cleavage, but has been carefully chipped, with fully as many distinct planes as the other side. That it was intentional on the part of the arrow-maker appears unquestionable, but what the object was in thus fashioning it is a mystery.

Figure 53 measures three and three-fourths inches in length by one inch and one-half at the upper edge of the base. The material is a brownish-gray jasper, with a delicate veining of light blue.

As an arrow-point, this specimen would prove too large and heavy, and the crooked point certainly does not suggest a drill for boring.

Figure 54 is a beautifully-shaped specimen, chipped from a hard piece of bluish slate-rock. The point and slender stem are admirably finished and well preserved. The large base is also chipped to a sharp edge, as though it were also intended for cutting. While no indication exists of the use of the specimen, since it was found associated with other forms of spears in the bed of Crosswick's Creek, we believe it to be a fish-spear, or, at any rate, an implement of the chase. On comparison with the pointed specimens described in Chapter XV, it serves to show how one form of implement merges into another.

This specimen is three and one-eighth inches in length by one inch and one-half broad at the base. It is quite thin, but, unlike the preceding, is equally ridged about the center of each side.

Figure 55 is a smaller, but beautifully symmetrical, specimen of fish-spear, and forms a good connecting-link between these and the arrow-heads proper. We have seen few more admirably-wrought specimens of jasper-chipping than this one. With the extreme point, now broken off, this specimen measured two and three-fourths inches in length by one inch in width at about its middle.

That such a specimen could be used as an arrow-point is certain ; but since the vast majority of true arrow-heads are shorter, or broader if of equal length, we do not believe this to have been intended as such an implement. Glancing over our collection of fish-spears as gathered about Trenton, N. J., we find that a very great majority of them are of slate, and well provided with notched or stemmed bases. The narrow portion is not always straight, but, with very few exceptions, the edges are as uniform as chipping will secure. There is but a single specimen of fish-spear in our cabinet with a serrated edge. It is now comparatively soft from being much weather-worn, and the teeth along the sides are blunted, still they show that they were originally a marked characteristic of the specimen.

Mr. Evans has figured* one specimen of fish-spear, which is beautifully worked and is very similar in detail to the specimen from the Del-

*Anc. Stone Imp. G. B., p. 339, fig. 302.

aware River, (figure 48.) He says of it, it "is so large that possibly it may be regarded as that of a javelin, and not of an arrow." It is shorter by half an inch than our specimen, although otherwise of about the same dimensions.

In Chapter I, reference was made to the excellence of the fishing-grounds about Trenton, N. J., at the time the first settlers arrived there; and it may probably be well to note some of the more common and larger species that frequent the Delaware River. Prominent is the well-known shad, (*Alosa præstablis*, DeKay,) which enters the river, from the sea, in March, and continues to arrive and work up-stream through the spring months and June. North of Trenton, N. J., or above tide-water, they spawn in the river, and also in many of the tide-water creeks. This fish was probably more caught by weirs and other like means than by spearing, as they do not often enter shallow streams or wander from the channel of the river.

Loskiel remarks: "In Carolina, the Indians frequently use fire in fishing. A certain kind of fish will even leap into the boats which have fire in them."

We can readily see how, in "fire-fishing," the spear would be abso-lutely necessary, since few fish are more than *attracted within reach* by the light of a fire; but, as we know by experience, this attraction suffices to keep them hovering about the boat as long as the fire burns brightly, and that the "false shots" one may make in trying to spear these dazed animals does not at all frighten them off. The large cyprinoids, as *Semotilus rhotheus*, and the so-called "suckers," are the most easily speared of all our fishes when once attracted by a blazing fire.

The pike, (*Esox reticulatus*,) rock-fish, (*Roccus lineatus*,) and yellow-perch, (*Perca flavescens*,) are all species that attain to a large size, and, judging from their present habits,* were no doubt eagerly sought with the spear by the Indian. The habit of the first mentioned of the three, that of lying in shallow water, underneath the leaves of the water-lily, (*Nymphea*,) makes it a most desirable species to "hunt," inas-much as it can be got near to by the exercise of a moderate amount of care; and one cannot doubt the ability of the ancient or modern Indian to silently approach an unsuspecting fish or bird or mammal. This

---

*We say "judging from their present habits," (for it is very certain that the habits of even fish have changed since the occupancy of this country by the European,) and, although this is not the place for the discussion of this most interesting question, would add, that, so far as our observation extends, the species of mammals, birds, and fishes remaining in the neighborhood of "settled" localities have changed their habits so far as is necessary to protect themselves from the attack and pursuit of man. Mam-mals are more strictly nocturnal when living in thickly-settled farming-districts; birds also are more nocturnal in their habits, and locate their nests at greater elevations, and in thickly-tangled thickets; while fish, too, soon learn that they are safest in deep waters, and will regard with greater suspicion an unusual object when placed in a frequented portion of the stream than when the same object is deposited in remote localities where they are seldom if ever disturbed.

fact should be borne constantly in mind in discussing the probable uses of the various hunting-implements.

A stone spear, hatchet, lance-head, or arrow-point, may seem to us a most uncouth and almost impracticable weapon ; but the capabilities of the makers and users of these implements very far exceeded ours ; they knew the habits of their game better than we now know those of the same species. Traveling where we could not move, they could *silently* gain access to points that only study and mechanical contrivances enable us to reach. Remembering this, it is easy to realize how a rude spear could be utilized in transfixing a wary fish, impaling it probably while it was in rapid motion.

Loskiel says, " Hunting is the principal and most necessary employment of the Indians, and next to war the most honorable. For this reason, all Indians, but chiefly the Delawares, are very expert and experienced huntsmen.

" The boys learn to climb trees when very young, both to catch birds and to exercise their sight, which by this method is rendered so quick that in hunting they see objects at an amazing distance. In detecting and pursuing game, they almost exceed the best-trained dog in following its course with certainty. They run so swiftly that if a deer does not fall upon the first shot, they throw off their blanket and seldom fail to overtake him.

" Their contrivances for decoying and securing game are innumerable. They study this from their infancy, and many remain whole years in the woods in the way of practice."

We can see from this description how entirely familiar were the Indians with the habits of the various animals pursued ; and having all the advantages of agility, fleetness, strength, and keen vision, the rude quality of their hunting-implements was more than compensated for.

There were two species of fishes formerly very abundant in the Delaware River, still to be met with, but in rapidly decreasing numbers, viz, the sturgeon and gar, which we doubt not were most eagerly pursued by the Indian. The size of both, and the value of the former especially as food, would naturally render them attractive objects of pursuit; but no such fishing-spears as we have here figured would be available in capturing a full-grown specimen of either.

The sturgeon (*Acipenser*) frequently attains a length of eight feet, while some gars (*Lepidosteus*) taken in the Delaware have measured five feet. With such fish to deal with, the very stoutest of the *hunting-spears* we have described would alone be of use ; and even with them it would appear a laborious task to finally subdue and land these large and powerful denizens of the water.

Just as the broad-bladed, stout hunting-spear was frequently, we think, used in capturing the largest of our river-fish, so it is probable that these long, slender forms of spear-points were occasionally used for the smaller mammals, for which they are as available as any stone weapon that could be devised; yet we doubt not the principal purpose of their manufacture was that of spearing fish, and that the other uses to which they were put were governed by the custom of adaptation to circumstances.

CHAPTER IX.

ARROW-HEADS.

As almost every variety of mineral is utilized by the arrow-maker, and a great variety of forms and sizes adopted, it is almost useless to attempt any classification of arrow-heads; for, whatever series of characteristics we may select to guide us in their study, we find in every thousand specimens so many exceptions to our limited rule that we finally abandon it in despair. One peculiarity, however, as regards different localities is worthy of note, viz, that when the Indians selected a site for a settlement near a peculiarly suitable mineral *in situ*, they exclusively used this material, and thus arrow-heads of such a mineral became a feature of such neighborhood; and further, where such selected mineral could not be well worked except in the larger forms, then the feature of size would also mark such a vicinity; but when arrow-heads are in abundance—as in a locality like Trenton, N. J.—where no suitable mineral is *in situ*, then every variety of size, shape, and stone will be found.

Being evident that much skill was required to fashion these arrowheads, it is a wonder why such a variety of shapes should have been adopted, since many of them are very delicate, and yet do not show that they possessed any advantage over the plain triangular flints; especially is this the case in the long, slender barbs rounded at the end, which require greater force than a sharply-pointed barb to enter the body, but which produce no more ugly or dangerous wound.

It is observed that there is a class of so-called "rude implements" the apparent use of which preceded that of the better-known stone axes, hatchets, and flint knives. So, also, is there a series of roughly-fashioned arrow-points, which, although associated with the others, have every appearance of being older. Whether the "Indian" originated in America or came hither, which is not improbable, certain it is, however, that the arrow-points he used, and now found here, were made in this State; and as these rude specimens are the simplest in detail, made of the more easily worked minerals, and have undergone deep surface-decomposition, it may be concluded they are the first used after the thin flakes, shelled off in forming other weapons, were discarded as too primitive.

Figure 56 represents a "chance-flake," it may be, that flew off at a blow of the hammer in shaping a hatchet, knife, or rough slate lance-head. Subsequently, it was given an indented or concave base, and, thus shaped, used as an arrow-head. Just such rough specimens are picked up every day by twos and threes. None are more primitive than this, but the somewhat better outlined are scarcely more finished or indicate any greater amount of care in their manufacture. There is no fine flaking about them, while the fractured surfaces are all large.

Figure 57 represents a well-preserved specimen of rude arrow-head, with a well-shaped "tang," or stem, for insertion into the shaft of the arrow. Like the preceding, there is here a total want of delicate chipping. The detaching of a few large flakes has formed the specimen, which, notwithstanding the rough workmanship, has a well-defined point and sharp cutting-edges. It measures nearly two inches in length, the stem constituting two-fifths. If the arrow-maker who chipped this specimen was disposed to improve the quality of his work, he should certainly have felt encouraged when comparing this with such as the preceding specimen. It may be doubted by many whether figure 56 really represents an arrow-point, but no doubt certainly can exist with reference to this specimen, figure 57.

Figure 58 represents a common form of rude arrow-head, such as is frequently found in the bed of the river, (Delaware.) It is a fragment of slate-rock, roughly shaped for arrow-head purposes, the edges and point being moderately well defined. There is a rude attempt at a stem, that places this specimen intermediately between figures 56 and 57. The surface in this specimen is as rough as in the preceding examples, with as large and irregular flakes hammered or *pressed* off. The specimen apparently antedates the days of laborious jasper-chipping.

Figure 59 represents a marked improvement in the shaping of rough arrow-points. There is, in this instance, a moderately well-defined median ridge, from which the sides taper or slope to a sharp edge. The point is thin, slender, and well preserved; the base, or stem, is well defined, but there are no attempts at barbs. The specimen measures just two inches in length. The material is a compact sandstone that readily scratches glass. It is even *more modern* in appearance than the preceding figure, 57.

Figure 60 represents an admirably-shaped triangular arrow-point, that has been brought to a point and edge with more care than is usually to be detected in "rude" arrow-heads as a class. There is a shallow notch at each angle of the base, giving the specimen a stemmed appearance. It measures one and one-fourth inches in length and seven-eighths of an inch in width, and compares favorably with the jasper triangular arrow-points so abundantly met with in every part of the State.

Figure 61 represent a roughly-made slender "point," that should perhaps be considered as an "early" harpoon-point rather than an arrow-head. It is of soft material, with very crooked edges, but a well-defined point. It measures three and one-fourth inches in length, and is just one inch wide at the base.

Professor Nilsson* says, "We may divide arrow-heads into such as have, and such as have not, a tang, or projection, for insertion into the shaft." Sir John Lubbock† quotes Sir W. R. Wilde, who divides the

---

*Stone Age in Scandinavia, Eng. ed., p. 43.
†Prehistoric Times, 2d ed., p. 98.

arrow-heads of Ireland into five varieties. "Firstly, the *triangular*, which frequently had a notch on each side to receive the string which attached it to the shaft; secondly, that which is hollowed out or *indented* at the base; thirdly, the *stemmed* arrow, which has a tang, or projection, for sinking into the shaft; fourthly, that with wings prolonged on each side, this passes into the *barbed* arrow; finally, we have the *leaf-shaped* form." Mr. Lubbock continues by asserting that the true arrow-heads are about one inch in length, which we cannot but think is too small a measurement. Two inches, and less, we believe to be a more probable range in length.

The first specimen of the comparatively newer and better-finished arrow-points to which attention is called is that given in figure 62, which represents one of the most common forms of tanged or stemmed " points." The specimen is of yellow jasper, of which mineral the great majority of this pattern is made. Unlike some forms, there can be no question as to the use to which this specimen was put. It is most admirably adapted as the head of an arrow; the sharp point, well-defined edges, and deeply-notched base combining to render it secure in its attachment to the shaft, and effective as a weapon when discharged from a bow.

Figure 63 represents the most perfect and beautiful arrow-head we have as yet met with. Most admirably chipped from a mottled pink-and-yellow agate, it possesses every requisite for a most effective arrow-heading. Exactly two inches in length, it widens with great uniformity from an acute point to near the base, where small wing-like barbs project, which are themselves very nearly of a size, and rounded at the ends; a character not common among our barbed arrow-points. The notches are of equal depth and breadth, looking almost directly down. The base, or abbreviated stem, is chipped from each side to a dull edge. There are shallow but well-marked serrations down each side, more numerous and distinctly marked on one side than on the other.

The amount of labor expended in producing such an arrow-head as that given in figure 63 can scarcely be estimated. As far as killing game is concerned, there is really no advantage in such an elaborately-worked flint. The plain, triangular point could be shot with equal precision, and would prove as deadly in its effect.

Figure 64 represents a third form, with a notched base. Like figure 62, this pattern is usually of jasper, and does not vary much in size, but is not so uniformly chipped as are the preceding shapes. We have gathered many of slate, identical in form and size with the one figured; but accuracy of outline (*i. e.*, uniformity of the two halves, perpendicularly divided) and general elegance of finish were never secured in using the latter mineral. This specimen, also, has slightly-serrated edges, a not uncommon feature of many of the smaller specimens; but these serrated specimens are usually broken, the explanation of which fact is afforded by careful examination of over three hundred examples. In comparison with the same type with smooth edges, we find that they are invariably thinner. To secure the serrated edge, it was probably necessary to make them so; and, of course, these thin specimens were more frequently broken in the manufacture, and more liable to injury in the daily *use* to which they were put, to say nothing of the two centuries of plowing and other exposures to which they have been subjected since the termination of the stone age in New Jersey.

Figure 65 represents a beautiful form of large arrow-head, which we have thus far only been able to duplicate once. It is of a slaty stone, not smoothly chipped over the surface, remarkable for accuracy of outline, and is of unusual size. Another noticeable feature is the small size of the stem, or base, in comparison with the body of the specimen. The surface is so weather-worn and soft, that the exact mineralogical nature of the material cannot be determined. Exclusive of the base, the specimen measures two inches in length by one inch and three-quarters in greatest width. We believe it to be an arrow, rather than a spear point, as the stem has never been very strong for so large a specimen, and there would be less strain upon it in its use as an arrow-head than as a spear-point; in the latter case, the struggles of the animal would be likely to break it off while the shaft was being held in the grasp of the hunter. Moreover, weight is to be considered in the recognition of these doubtful specimens, and figure 65 is no heavier than many of the smaller jasper arrow-points.

Figure 66 is a form of notched-base arrow-head, more or less common in all localities. In general appearance, it is much like figures 62 and 64, but is peculiar in having a central notch in the stem. The object of this third notch is not clear. The specimen is chipped from a black, slaty stone, is very thin, and the sides have been slightly serrated. These specimens are not very variable in size, but few having been found much larger, and but two or three smaller. Inasmuch as they are very noticeably serrated arrow-points, we give two illustrations of both the larger and smaller specimens.

Figure 67 represents a tri-notched, stemmed arrow-head, perfect in detail, and particularly interesting from the deep, well-marked serrations that extend along the greater portion of the sides. The specimen measures two and one-eighth inches in length from the bottom of the central notch to the point. It is chipped from a porous, yellowish jasper or agate; the extreme point being more dense and glassy than the body of the specimen. There is no doubt this specimen was used exclusively as an arrow-point. We have a few examples similar in size and character from New Jersey, but all somewhat broken. The one figured is from Indiana.

Figure 68 represents a third example of triple-notched arrow-point; the barb on one side, however, being broken off. It is of yellow jasper, with deeply-serrated sides and an acute point. We have seldom seen an arrow-point better suited for killing birds and small mammals. With the impetus given to the arrow by the Indian bow, such a point as this would make a tearing wound that would bring down any of our New Jersey inland birds, the turkey-buzzard and wild turkey not excepted.

Figure 69 represents a fourth and still smaller example of arrow-head, with the central notch at the base. Like the preceding, it is well outlined. Mounted on a slender reed, it also would, if discharged with force, unquestionably bring down a large bird or squirrel.

Mr. Schoolcraft* says: " Boys were always furnished with small arrow-points, such as were expected to be spent against squirrels, or the lesser quadrupeds and birds. This was the second lesson in learning the art of hunting; the first consisted in using the blunt arrow, or *Beek wuk*,† which was fired at a mark."

A specimen such as figure 68 may be one of the boy-hunter's arrow-points, but there is apparently too much work upon figure 69 to have allowed the mere tyro to risk it at a passing animal.

Figure 70 represents a beautifully-shaped arrow-point that approaches figure 50 in outline, but has the ends of the slender barbs sharp; the barbs themselves are continuous with the line of the sides, and not outwardly curved as in figure 63. For delicacy of finish and general beauty of outline, this specimen is scarcely to be excelled. As will be noticed in the illustration, the base is broken off; but we are confident it was sufficiently prolonged to enable the very accurately-finished barbs to be effective. Whatever the skill of the arrow-maker, to produce this specimen was undoubtedly a tedious operation, and the prehistoric hunter equipped with arrows tipped with points such as this hardly wasted them upon small game.

Figure 71 is a fine example of a triangular-bodied arrow-point, with a long, unnotched stem, and of a pattern not very abundant in New Jersey; the examples seen are usually less perfect than this, being in outline more like the following illustration, (figure 73.) Figure 71 is of bluish-gray jasper, one inch and five-eighths long, the stem being just one-third of the total length. The specimen is thicker than arrow-points of this pattern usually are; but the point is thin and still very sharp.

Figure 72 represents a form of slate arrow-heads, very numerous and uniform in size. They are never very well finished except in outline. We recall our once coming across a site of an arrow-maker's hut in Hunterdon County, New Jersey, where the ground was covered with small fragments of a hard, slaty rock, and fragments more or less approaching the perfect arrow-point, all of which were of this pattern. A resident of the neighborhood informed us that in blasting for the road-bed of the Delaware and Belvidere Railroad a large rock proved to have in it a cavity with its entrance below the surface of the ground,

---

*Researches, &c., North American Indians, pt. i, p. 77.

† Algonquin.

which was half filled with arrow-points, "very nearly if not quite the size of figure 72 and of that shape."

Figure 73 represents a form of small arrow-point, very similar but less accurately finished than figure 71. This we suppose to be one of the "small arrow-points" intrusted to boys learning to shoot, as described by Mr. Schoolcraft. They occur in considerable numbers, and seem to be about as much scattered abroad as any of the numerous patterns. Were these small arrow-points used exclusively by boys, they should be most abundant about the former sites of villages; but such localities do not appear to specially abound in them.

Figures 74 and 75 are further examples of the abundant form of stemmed arrow-points, without notches at the base. Figure 74 is wrought out of a jasper pebble, is well made and accurately beveled from the center or middle line to the edges. During the course of an ordinary day's hunting for relics, this and the following class of specimens will be found the most abundant, except, perhaps, the triangular arrow-point, yet to be described. Specimens of this pattern and size are in a moderately good state of preservation, being pretty thick for the length, and fully capable to stand a hard blow against another stone, or the weight of a horse's foot. Ordinarily, the extreme point is broken off.

Figure 75 does not vary materially from the preceding. It is a little smaller and made of slate. The point has been chipped so as to be a cutting-edge of about one thirty-second of an inch in extent, and not a needle-like tip as is usual. In looking over a large series of arrow-points, we find very many that have such a rounded point, which might pass for broken-tipped specimens. In the resharpening of arrow-heads, we believe the rounded tip was usual instead of a fine point, as when the specimen was first chipped out.

Figure 76 represents a fine example of flint-chipping, which we call an arrow-head, although in so doing we thereby probably contradict previous assertions with reference to hunting-spears. Figure 76, however, is thin, light, and more like an arrow in appearance than like the ordinary hunting-spears. It certainly is the maximum size of arrow-points, if indeed intended as such. The base and deeply-cut notches approach figures 63 and 67 in general appearance, and the specimen, as a whole, much resembles figure 65, although the sides are here curved, instead of unusually straight, as in that specimen.

In studying the forms of arrow-heads, we have not been disposed to make any distinction between those of *war*, and *peace*, or hunting arrows,[*] but if any arrow-head was specially reserved for use in war, that figured in 76 was most likely one. Buried its full length of two inches and one-half in the side or breast of a man, it would speedily prove fatal.

Figure 77 represents an ordinary sized and shaped stemmed arrow-point, moderately well chipped from a hornstone fragment, and noticeable particularly for one feature, that of being brought to a semicircu-

[*] Anc. Mon. Miss. Valley, p. 212.

lar edge, continuous with the sides and of equal sharpness, instead of being pointed, as are the vast majority of arrow-points. The manner of flaking adopted in the manufacture of this specimen fully indicates of itself that the rounded end was intentional and so fashioned from the first, and that the specimen was not originally *pointed*, and afterward, instead of being repointed, chipped to an edge. Arrow-heads of this form, and of nearly every pattern, stemmed and without tangs, are occasionally met with, having the peculiarity of being rounded instead of pointed. Perhaps the majority of such rounded forms are those without stems, and certainly the rudest of them, and such as appear the oldest, are the triangular arrow-heads of slate and even softer minerals, that are simply rounded off, or are like the present specimen, the stem being cut squarely off.

Figure 78 represents a well-chipped jasper arrow-point, having a well-notched stem, and bearing considerable general resemblance to the preceding specimens of stemmed arrow-points. There is one peculiarity, however, about figure 78, which is worthy of attention. The end of the specimen is chipped off at almost right angles with the sides, and is sloped to a narrow, acute point at the middle, scarcely the sixteenth of an inch in length. This is not a mere accident or chance chipping, but a peculiarity frequently met with, and shown again in figure 85, which is an arrow-head of the triangular pattern. There was no doubt an object in view in so chipping arrow-points, but our limited knowledge of the bow and arrow does not enable us to discern it. It might be thought, from a cursory glance, that this specimen was originally much longer, and, the point having been broken off, that it was chipped to its present shape; but the general appearance of the specimen does not favor this view, and we cannot imagine an accidental fracture of such a character as to determine the present peculiarly-outlined pointing. We have found fully one hundred arrow-points of various patterns, which have had an *extreme* point, like this of figure 78 and figure 85.

Figure 79 represents an example of what we have considered an arrow-head, notwithstanding its size. It has been frequently remarked that arrow-heads, wherever found and of whatever age, all have very much in common; and if the labels of a collection from all quarters of the globe were lost, it would be a difficult matter to decide the locality from which any specimen was obtained, unless from the materials out of which they were fashioned. Another interesting feature is the similarity between arrow, spear, and harpoon points of an age long past and those now being used and made by the savages who are still more or less completely in the stone age. Bearing this in mind, we call attention particularly to the "harpoon-point" which we give in figure 79, which, in all its important features, is identical with one figured by Professor Nilsson,* and concerning which he says: "The stone points (for harpoons) vary in shape; sometimes they are as in Pl. iii, Figs. 45, 47. Such are like-

---

* Stone Age in Scandinavia, Eng. ed., plate x, fig. 203, and page 28.

wise found in Scania. * * * The broad head seems to indicate that they have been harpoons rather than arrow-heads. * * * It appears to me certain that Pl. x, Fig. 203, has been the stone point of an harpoon. * * * A person who had long resided in Greenland recognized it at once as such." Here we find a New Jersey, an ancient Scandinavian, and a Greenland specimen of the present day identical.

We have already described in detail and figured a series of such fishing-spears, or harpoon-points, as are characteristic of New Jersey, and suitable for the river-fishing especially that was and is to be had in our rivers. Figure 79 is not as well adapted to fishing as are those we have figured in Chapter VIII; and we have, therefore, considered this specimen an arrow-point for the larger game, its size and weight not being too great to render it suitable as an arrow-head, especially where the distance to be traveled is not great, as when large game was surprised and struck before it was many yards away.

Figure 80 is a good example of one of the rough jasper arrow-heads that appear to have been hastily blocked out for an emergency, but which probably were meant for large game, as deer, at close quarters, and intended to make a torn rather than a cut wound, which would cause the animal to bleed to death if not killed instantly. The style of rough jasper arrow-head, of this size and smaller, is common. These larger examples approach in some characters the chipped jasper knives, to which we will call attention in another chapter.

Figure 81 is a pretty white quartz form of the ordinary triangular arrow-point. There is nothing about the base to show how it was secured to the shaft of the arrow. Such quartz specimens are found in almost every nook and corner of the State. They vary considerably in the relative dimensions of length to breadth. More quartz arrow-points of the stemmed pattern occur, however, than of these plain triangular specimens. White quartz was a favorite mineral, not only for arrow-points, but spear-heads and small hatchets.

Figure 82 represents about the minimum size of plain equiangle specimens. It is chipped from a flake of dark chocolate-colored jasper, and is very pretty. In many of these smaller specimens, we find the base equally carefully chipped as the sides, and the three angles brought to such equally acute points that it is difficult to see which side, if any, was intended for the base.

Figure 83 is another illustration of a triangular arrow-point, differing from the preceding in that the base is narrower than the sides are long, and is intentionally concave. This specimen is one of the handsomest we have seen. Chipped from a pale-green jasper fragment, it is in perfect condition, and too pretty and carefully worked, it seems, to have been risked by slight insertion into the split end of an arrow-shaft.

Figure 84 represents a form of the triangular arrow-point, that is broader than long, and possibly was never sharply pointed. Such an arrow-head as this must have been shot with tremendous force to render it effective. At best, it would but bruise or crush—it could not penetrate like a pointed arrow-head.

Figure 85 represents a variation of the immediately preceding form, is of slate, well cut, and but sparingly met with. The peculiarity consists in the manner in which the little point has been chipped. A single specimen of this style would excite no comment. The peculiarity would be considered as resulting from a chance blow of the arrow-maker. This is not the case, however, as we have a number of such specimens, from one locality, each, in size and mineral, the fac-simile of the others.

Figure 86 is a pretty white quartz specimen, very smoothly chipped, and having very short but still distinct barbs, or projections of the angles of the base and sides. We have gathered numbers of this size, mineral, and peculiarity of base. They seem to have been rubbed after the chipping until the more prominent ridges were partially worn away. Occasionally rose quartz was used, forming gems among arrow-points.

Figure 87 represents a beautiful pattern of triangular arrow-head, usually of white quartz, met with in but one locality—near Crosswicks, Burlington County, New Jersey. They vary little in size, and are well made, having the edges sharp and the point slender and acute. Like the preceding example, this specimen has the sides triflingly convex, the curved outline being more pronounced near the point than at the base. It measures seven-eighths of an inch in length and three-fourths of an inch in width at the base, which is slightly concave. Like figures 69 and 73, which are both stemmed arrow-points, it would, we suppose, be classed by Mr. Schoolcraft as one intended for the boys; but, like those represented in the figures mentioned, it bears evidence of too much work to have been manufactured for so casual a purpose. As far as our experience extends in experimenting in mineral chipping, these small arrow-heads are much more difficult, both to "block out" and to finish, than are those of two inches or more in length, and we doubt not it proved so with the ancient arrow-maker. In numbers, the large arrow-points far exceed the small specimens, while, on the other hand, the great majority of the little ones are far more elaborately worked out than are the larger examples. Again, we have found very frequently that these small well-worked specimens were more numerous in graves of adults than were the larger types, a circumstance showing that they were not wholly used by boys.

Figure 88 represents a handsome form of triangular arrow-head. It has the appearance at first glance of having been barbed; but the carefully-chipped sides of the base induce the belief that it is in its original condition. With a shaft much narrower than the base of the specimen, this would be one of the most effective arrow-points we have figured. This pattern is usually of jasper, and is not abundant.

Figure 89 is a beautiful representative of a class of large triangular arrow-heads with concave base. They are mostly found of black slaty stone, and are well pointed. The specimen figured is chipped from a flake of yellow jasper, having narrow veins of white quartz, which render it very attractive in appearance. It is about the maximum size of this pattern of arrow-point.

Figures 90 and 91 represent two beautiful examples of a form of arrow-head closely allied to the preceding specimen; the difference being in the concave sides and base, and in being much more slender. Indeed, were not the body longer than the barbs, being equal in width, it would be difficult to decide which of the *three* ends was intended as the point. There is no difference in these "ends" as to workmanship or outline; they are equally slender and acute.

Figure 90 is chipped from black hornstone, the base or junction of the barbs and body of the specimen being thickest, from which point the specimen gradually tapers to a thin, very carefully-worked edge. This arrow-head measures one inch and one-fourth in length by exactly one inch in width from point to point of the barbs.

Figure 91 is chipped from a dull-yellow jasper flake, and is similar to the preceding one in size and the details of working, but is less symmetrical; the barbs varying somewhat in width, and the body being a little "bent" over to one side.

Such a shaped arrow-point attached to a shaft would make an ugly wound, and, entering the body of the animal or person shot, would very probably remain in the wound; for a more difficult object to extract from a deep flesh-wound we could not imagine.

Figure 92 is a small jasper arrow-head, with a peculiarity the opposite of that of the preceding illustration. The base is convex instead of concave. It is well chipped, finely pointed, and has notches near the base to secure it the more firmly to the shaft of the arrow. It is not an abundant variety, but one found in sufficient numbers to show it is not a chance-shaped specimen.

Figure 93 represents a pattern of arrow-point very abundant, and varying from the preceding in that the base is prolonged into a stem, and has no traces of notches, as in figure 92. This elongated base renders the specimen diamond-shaped. It is known in England as the lozenge-shaped arrow-head. As a rule, it is more slender, and has more of the appearance of a stemmed arrow-point than has the English lozenge-shaped one. We have seen some, however, from other States, which were identical with the European type.

Figure 93 is made of a sandstone pebble or fragment of rock, and has been moderately well chipped. The point is still acute, and the edges well defined and sharp. It measures one inch and five-eighths in length and a little more than five-eighths of an inch in greatest width. The base has never been as sharply pointed as the true point or extremity of the specimen, but the sides are as well tapered to a cutting-edge.

This pattern of arrow-point, of this size and mineral, are quite abundant in some localities, and seem to be a prevailing type, but, in other sections, are very rarely met with. About Trenton, N. J., they occur comparatively seldom; but about the Delaware Water Gap, and in Sussex County generally, they are numerous.

Figure 94 represents a well-chipped, lozenge-shaped arrow-point, of black jasper or hornstone. It varies but little from the preceding except in size, being two inches and one-quarter in length and only three-quarters of an inch in width at the widest point. The base is more abruptly tapered than the body of the specimen, and but one-third the length, giving the specimen a "stemmed" appearance. It constitutes a good link between the lozenge-shaped and stemmed arrow-points. The extreme point and termination of the base have been broken off, but that they were originally both pointed and slender cannot be doubted.

Such a pattern of arrow-point was probably merely inserted into a cleft in the end of the shaft, and was left in the wound when the arrow was withdrawn. It could, of course, be recovered easily from the dead animal.

Figure 95 represents a beautiful example of the lozenge-shaped arrow-point, that is *nearly* a "stemmed" specimen. The angles of the base and body of the specimen are so chipped as to make barbs of these angles, or, more properly speaking, barb-like angles; otherwise, the specimen is diamond-shaped in outline, and a true lozenge-shaped example. As a weapon, this form is an excellent pattern; the point and sides being well adapted to piercing and cutting, while the base is of a shape to make attachment to the shaft very easy and secure.

Figure 96 represents an elongate, lozenge-shaped arrow-point, admirably chipped and very symmetrical. It is of a variety of this pattern that we have found as yet but very few specimens. It measures two inches and one-half in length and three-fourths of an inch in greatest width. Notwithstanding its length, we cannot doubt that it was used as an arrow-point, and it is, therefore, an excellent specimen to show that arrow-heads were occasionally made of a length equal, or nearly so, to the average specimen of slender fish-spear. We call this an arrow-head rather than a spear or javelin point, because the means of attaching it securely to its shaft are too imperfect for utilizing it otherwise where the cleft in the shaft of the arrow is all that is required to hold the point when being shot. We have seen several specimens similar in size to the one figured, but with the base rounded instead of pointed in the middle, thus making the true lozenge-shape a leaf-shaped arrow-point, although more slender than these usually are.

Figure 97 is a pretty quartz arrow-point of the lozenge-shape and leaf-shaped patterns combined. Such arrow-heads of white quartz are very abundant, and vary but little in size. This specimen measures one inch and five-eighths in length by seven-eighths of an inch in width. It is somewhat thicker than the majority of jasper specimens of its pattern, but has a very acute point and sharp cutting-edges.

Every collection of arrow-heads will show many variations of every so-called type of these relics, but no one pattern seems to vary more than the one we have termed lozenge-shape. We notice, however, that, as a class, they are made of the harder minerals, and are small; they have no abundant representatives rudely chipped in slate and other more easily-worked minerals. This pattern is not as abundantly represented throughout the State as the true leaf-shaped type, and it has occurred to us that probably very many of our lozenge-shaped specimens were blocked out for leaf-shaped ones, but being found too brittle, or badly broken at the start, they were finished as angular at the base instead of possessing that beautifully-curved base which makes the true leaf-shaped pattern so attractive to collectors.

Figure 98 is a rare form of arrow-point as far as our experience goes in collecting them in New Jersey. It is a well-chipped jasper specimen of five instead of three angles. It is a shape apparently well adapted to its purpose, but still possesses no advantage over the plain triangle and its variations that we have been describing. There is but one other specimen in our cabinet of this shape.

Figure 99 represents a second example of quintangular arrow-head. It is chipped from green jasper, is smoothly worked, and evenly beveled from the middle to the edges. The sides are all sharply chipped, and the point has been acute. This form is not at all common, although we have met with more examples of it than of the preceding shorter and broader form. The narrow base is very sharp, and was probably inserted into a slit at the end of the shaft, and held by wrapping with sinew. This would secure it a firm hold, and, being so slender and sharp, it would penetrate deeply, if discharged with ordinary force.

Figure 100 is an average specimen of the white-quartz arrow-points of the leaf-pattern. They are very common, both of quartz and slate, but not as numerous as those of jasper, which latter mineral usually appears in the shape of stemmed or plain triangular arrow-points. There appears to be no advantage in the leaf-shaped pattern, and yet it was chosen by the arrow-maker very frequently. We have seen some " workshop sites " where it appeared to be a favorite pattern, just as the " site" in Hunterdon County was characterized by the stemmed arrow-point form. Although, as we have seen, spear-heads were sometimes leaf-shaped, the true arrow-points are not very variable in size, few being larger than figure 100.

Figure 101 represents a more symmetrical and better-finished specimen of leaf-shaped arrow-point than the preceding. It is decidedly the best-finished and most acutely-pointed specimen of arrow-head we have as yet met with. There is not a single flaw or fault in the specimen anywhere.

Figure 102 represents a third form of the leaf-shaped pattern, varying from the two preceding it in being shorter and broader. It resembles figure 101 pushed together; or, reversing the simile, 101 is 102 *drawn out*.

This shorter and broader form is more abundantly met with than the longer and more slender specimens.

Leaf-shaped arrow-points are occasionally much wider than the preceding specimen, and, of course, also longer. Figure 103 represents a large jasper arrow-point of this pattern, which is not, however, as smoothly chipped as either of the preceding nor as regularly oval in its outlines. It may be, however, an unfinished specimen.

Leaf-shaped arrow-points of this pattern of the softer minerals, as slate, are not common, although the lance-head, of slate, is only an exaggerated arrow-head of this pattern.

Figure 104 represents a fine pale-yellow jasper form of arrow-point, found scantily in New Jersey, but more abundantly in the Western States. It is noticeable, particularly, that the edges are at an angle with the point, giving it a twist, which gradually disappears as the edges reach the barbs. This peculiarity is even more marked in some specimens that we have seen, but which unfortunately were broken. Messrs. Squier and Davis, in their brief notice of arrow-heads,* say, " Some are so chipped that the line of their edges forms a large angle with their planes, as if to give them a revolving or *tearing* motion." This twisted condition of the edges in figure 104 is sufficient to produce this motion, as we have tested. Of course, the feathering at the base of the shaft can be so arranged as to help this revolving motion, and it probably was so fixed by the Indian. Whether or not this " *tearing* " motion would make a more fatal wound or not is a question ; for certainly the arrow-point itself would not penetrate as deeply.

Of the specimens of this pattern found in New Jersey, all have been smaller, but otherwise were as well-marked twisted arrow-points. The specimen figured was picked up in a field in Indiana, and is illustrated in preference to a New Jersey example only because it is in perfect condition.

Figure 105 represents a peculiar form of arrow-point, the shark-tooth pattern. This specimen is not a chance chipping or the mere whim of the arrow-maker, but is a copy in stone of a recent shark's tooth, such as was not unfrequently used by the Indians along the sea-shore. We have also met with fossil shark-teeth in graves, that when buried were probably attached, as arrow-heads, to shafts. Figure 105 is carefully chipped from a flake of black hornstone, is sharply edged, and has an acutely-chipped point. The base is somewhat thicker, but is well chipped also ; one side, or barb, being more slender and pointed than the other. We have seen more than twenty of these arrow-points all agreeing with the one figured in every important feature.

Figure 106 represents a quadrangular stemmed arrow-point, that is unique, so far as our experience extends. If we take the little projection as a stem, we find the sharp point to be directly opposite, and held or viewed in this position (as figured) the specimen appears as a stemmed

* Anc. Mon. Miss. Valley, p. 212.

triangular arrow-point, with a broad wing-like projection upon one side. It is not an unfinished specimen. The "wing" is finely and evenly chipped, with its edges as sharp as are any other of the edges of the specimen. What object there may have been in such a shaped arrow-point, we cannot imagine.

Figure 107 represents a very pretty form of arrow-point, with which we will conclude this portion of our subject. It is carefully chipped from yellowish-brown jasper, and is noticeable particularly for the exaggerated barb, which is considerably larger than the main body of the specimen. An examination of the reverse side of the base of this arrow-point shows that there has never been a second barb, but that the specimen is now as originally chipped. The barb, once beneath the skin of an animal, would be difficult to extract, and would make an ugly wound; but how such an arrow-head was attached to the shaft is not clear.

Before concluding this subject of arrow-heads, we would call attention to certain large stones found on known sites of Indian villages, which are called "anvils" for want of a more correct designation. Dr. T. S. Stevens, of Trenton, N. J., to whom we are indebted for many favors, has called our attention to one such "anvil." The stone in question is about twenty inches in height, has an hour-glass contraction at the middle, and has a level circular surface at either end of about nine inches in diameter. Where contracted at the middle, it measures about five or six inches in diameter. Sitting on the ground, and placing it before us between the legs, we found the present shape of the stone to be admirably adapted as an anvil, or "bench." Thus postured, one could easily imagine himself a prehistoric arrow-maker, resting one surface of a blade of jasper upon the upper face of the anvil, and striking off the flakes, that a subsequent laborious chipping would transform into such delicate arrow-heads as many we have figured. Whether such an anvil as this was shaped from a globular bowlder or not is a difficult question to decide; but, judging from the mineralogical character of the implement, we think that it originally bore some resemblance to its present shape, and was afterward chipped to perfect the uniformity of its hour-glass contraction. Mr. Schoolcraft has described the method of arrow-head making without the aid of an anvil, and it may be that the stone we have described was not used in resting the block upon it when broken in flakes, but as a bench for the later chipping, or in finishing arrow and spear points.

There is nothing that adds so much to the interest of arrow-heads, and indeed to that of the other stone implements of a country, as the results of their comparison with stone implements of other and distant portions of the globe. Mr. Evans's interesting volume on the stone implements of Great Britain gives us an excellent opportunity to make such comparisons with the English specimens, the work being profusely and admirably illustrated. This comparison is made at the conclusion of the chapter, and is, of itself, more instructive and interesting than any comments can be as to the weapons themselves, unassociated with the thought of their cosmopolitan character. As will be noticed, we have drawn entirely from Lubbock and Nilsson for examples of identical forms of European and American stone implements in the preceding pages of this chapter. We have read with particular interest Mr. Evans's exhaustive chapter upon arrow-heads, and are surprised to find that nearly everything that he figures under that head occurs in New Jersey, while we believe some of the forms given by us are not known to British archæologists.

We must, however, be allowed to express our dissent from some of Mr. Evans's statements concerning North American arrow-heads. He remarks,* "A prevailing type in North America, viz, that with a notch at the base on either side, has already been mentioned more than once. This form shades off into that with a central dove-tailed tang, sometimes with well-developed barbs. Others, again, have merely a central tang, with little or no attempt at barbs. The triangular form, usually but little excavated at the base, is also common. A rare form terminates in a semicircular edge. The leaf-shaped form is very rare. For the most part, the chipping is but rough, as the material, which is usually chert, hornstone, or even quartz, does not readily lend itself to fine work." With very much of this paragraph we do not agree. For instance, the arrow-point " with a notch at the base on either side," although prevailing throughout North America, is not more abundantly met with than many other totally distinct patterns. A large series of the triangular arrow-points show a fair proportion of those that have a *deeply concave* base; and some that have a convex base, passing thereby into the leaf-shaped pattern. Mr. Evans most unquestionably errs in stating that the leaf-shaped form is very rare. It is certainly abundant enough in New Jersey to satisfy any collector; and we believe the same can be said of every other of our Eastern States. We have given four examples of the leaf-shaped form, and could have added many more had it been necessary to give further illustrations of a form that necessarily can vary but little.

Further, we think Mr. Evans errs in asserting that " for the most part the chipping is rough." We do not fear comparison of our New Jersey specimens with similar stone implements from any part of the world; and especially are our quartz arrow-points as a class well finished, and this mineral is particularized by Mr. Evans as one reason why North American arrow-points are rough.

So far as *illustrations* of European and those of other countries enable us to determine, we have found within a radius of five miles of Trenton, N. J., every form of arrow-point that has been discovered and described by foreign archæologists; and we have in this chapter figured two or more patterns that European archæologists have not yet collected; and

---

* *Loc. cit.,* p. 362.

the same remarks will apply to the subject of the general finish of specimens.

Several of the specimens figured by Mr. Evans are identical with the hunting-spears and harpoon-points described in Chapters VII and VIII; and these two forms, that appear to us to have had distinct uses, are called by Mr. Evans "javelin-points." There is some advantage in studying these various forms of stone implements here in New Jersey, since they were in use down to historical times, and the writings of the travelers who visited this country nearly two centuries ago throw considerable light upon the manner of their manufacture and use. If, therefore, the same implements the world over had the same use, then those now found in America, which were the latest made and used, should decide the names and purposes of all, wherever found. A careful survey of a very large series of arrow-heads, all gathered from one limited locality, has convinced us that when the bow was first brought into use in this neighborhood, the art of arrow-point making was unknown, or in its earliest infancy, and that the first "flint" heads to the arrows were but thin flakes of slate, and possibly of jasper, that were the necessary result of shaping out the rude hatchets that primitive man mainly depended upon as a tool and weapon, for food and defense. Our reason for thus believing is that, *as a rule*, the rudest, least symmetrical arrow-heads are those which show the greatest degree of " weathering," or surface-decomposition. Very many of these rude arrow-points are now of the consistency, or thereabouts, of chalk, except in the middle, where the mineral is hard, black, and flint-like. Some of these specimens have lost nearly all trace of their original shape, but, being softened down *uniformly*, by scraping off the chalky surface, we reproduce on a smaller scale the original outline of the arrow-head. It can be set down as a rule that "rotten" arrow-points are rude, and undecomposed jasper specimens are elaborate. Will it be said that the jasper is simply not decomposable? If so, why were not those of softer stone, being so much more easily worked, made into the fantastic shapes that we find produced in jasper? The " soft" minerals will admit of it.

We have no knowledge of the origin of the bow and arrow; but we believe it to have originated here, and many years subsequently to the first appearance of those rude implements we have described in the second chapter of this work. *As* it originated here, so did it elsewhere come into use; the same surroundings produced the same result, but it is useless now to speculate on the manner and time.

CHAPTER X.

KNIVES.

The site of a former Indian village, of which there are many in New Jersey, may be recognized as the spot of a once busy community, by the "mixed" condition of the relics there found. While lately searching through such a heap of broken tools and weapons, a carefully-chipped flint (Fig. 108) of oval outline, sharply edged at every portion of the circumference, was found. Although not a novelty, it was better finished than others found singly in the fields.

It measures three and one-quarter inches in length, and one inch and seven-eighths in its greatest breadth. One side is straighter and much more finely chipped than the other, and has a sharper edge. The coarser-chipped side evidently was not intended for any use. A glance at this implement shows that, with a handle at the *back*, or coarsely-chipped *side*, it would be a beautiful " scraper." The typical scrapers having a totally different form, however, the proper designation for figure 108 would probably be a knife.

Figure 109 is a second example of a chipped-jasper knife, not as finely finished as figure 108, but evidently identical in character. Such a specimen might at first seem to be simply a rudely blocked-out arrow-head, which was subsequently thrown aside, but as the like are found singly, scattered over a large portion of the State, and are not very similar to the rejected specimens so abundant where an arrow-maker has worked, it cannot be doubted that they are finished specimens.

Figure 110 is a third example of these knives, and varies but little from the others, except in being somewhat thicker, and having the two sides more uniform than usual.

To what cutting purpose such knives were put is a pertinent question, but one to which my only reply is that I do not know. I have experimented with them to some extent and find that with patience they will cut a green twig, and even flesh.

Considering savage dexterity with flint, figure 108 appears fitted for use as a scalping-knife, though we have never met with any flint implement which archæologists have classed as knives used for this particular purpose.

Figures 109 and 110 may be looked upon as quite serviceable knives when we consider the skill evinced by savages in using flint tools. Sir John Lubbock states,[*] quoting Mr. Galton, that the dexterity with which the savages of Southern Africa butcher and cut up large beasts with the poorest knives is really extraordinary. The Dammaras had usually nothing but bits of flattened iron lashed to handles, or the edges of their flat spears. Yet with these imperfect im-

---

[*] Prehist. Times, 2d ed., p. 536.

plements they would cut up giraffes and rhinoceroses, on which, even with excellent knives of European manufacture, Mr. Galton had much difficulty in making any impression. Other savage tribes readily cut flesh with pieces of shell or of hard wood. After all, some of these jasper knives are not mean tools; and, guided by the same skill, we doubt not flesh and hide would yield as readily to the specimens we have figured as to the " bits of flattened iron " just referred to.

Figures 111 and 112 represent examples of long, narrow, and finely-edged implements, which we have called knives. Such specimens, which are always broken squarely off at one end, are very abundant in some localities. We have experimented somewhat with them, and are of the opinion that they were used as " fish-knives," being very well adapted to scaling fish; moreover they have been found most abundant on the shores of the larger creeks and on the river-banks. They are usually smooth, or comparatively so, on one side, and roughly chipped and ridged upon the other. Both sides are brought to a cutting edge, and the square end is also chipped to an edge. Those we have found have generally been of slate and minerals of like character. There are a few, however, of jasper, but they do not vary in any important particular from the two examples figured, which are of slate.

Mr. Evans has figured two specimens of " flint " knives from Scotland, which bear a marked resemblance to those here given.* The Scottish ones are usually worked upon both faces, and have but a single edge sharpened by grinding. Figures 111 and 112 differ from this description, in having two equally well defined edges, " chipped" and not subsequently ground. The " bases" of the specimens figured by Mr. Evans seem to be " worked," while ours are broken. As all the specimens of this style of knife have been similarly broken, we are inclined to think it intentional rather than accidental. Again, a careful examination of this broken end shows that it has undergone much weathering, and must have been broken very long ago, if not, indeed, when the knife was manufactured. This form of knife-blade seems to be rare in Great Britain, but with us it is fully as abundant as are the more elaborately chipped jasper specimens, such as figures 108, 109, and 110.

Figure 113 represents a small chipped fragment of hornstone, in itself a completed implement, but of exactly what kind, it is difficult to determine. It combines the arrow-point, knife, and the " semi-lunar flake" which was used as a knife in Scandinavia. Of this form, also, Mr. Evans† has given an illustration very similar to ours in all respects. The English specimen, however, is one-fourth longer. Mr. Evans calls such specimens " trimmed flakes," which describes precisely what the specimens are; but as their use was " to cut," we see no objection to classing them as " knives," especially as the so-called " trimmed flakes " and the " knives " blend so gradually that no line of demarcation can be drawn between them. Although much ruder and smaller, figure 113

---

* Anc. Stone Imp. Great Brit., p. 303.

† Evans, l. c., p. 294, fig. 236.

bears considerable resemblance to certain "semi-lunar knives" figured by Nilsson.* These Scandinavian forms are, however, usually of a toothed or serrated edge, and are more decidedly curved than is the case with figure 113. Although such specimens have not yet occurred, we doubt not we shall be able to find knives of the true semi-lunar pattern before the supply of specimens is exhausted in the localities which have yielded so bountiful a series of stone implements of the various types.

The chipped-jasper knives, figures 108–110, vary materially from "flints" that have been designated "knives" by Professor Nilsson and Sir John Lubbock; still we think they are true knives. One consideration to be borne in mind is, that there was scarcely a single instrument which was confined to a single purpose; and, as the modern pocket-knife is frequently a combination of tools, so the chipped-jaspers had a multiplicity of uses. The edge being the prominent characteristic of the specimens, cutting must have been the principal design in the making; therefore, figures 108, 109, 110, are called "knives."

Commenting on a collection of Indian stone implements forwarded to him by the writer, from this neighborhood, (Trenton, N. J.,) Sir John Lubbock remarks: "The absence of flakes and true scrapers surprises me. How do you account for it? Is there no flint in the neighborhood?" There is no flint in the neighborhood, and as jasper, slate, and sandstone do not flake off as readily and conveniently as flint proper, so we do not have in that abundance characteristic of European "finds," *true* "flakes" and "scrapers," such as may have been fashioned by almost a single blow; and so, too, our knives, if those implements which we have here figured are such, have not a smooth edge as is produced by a single plane of cleavage; nevertheless, they would surely be effective for most of the purposes to which a knife of "flint" could be used. As we have noticed, both sides have the surface equally chipped. None that we have seen are identical with the semi-lunar knife found in Sweden, figured by Professor Nilsson,† but some few approach a shape that might be termed semi-lunar. Occasionally a specimen is met with that is concave on one side and convex on the other. In such instance the outer, or convex, side has the cutting edge.

Sir John Lubbock has figured‡ an Esquimaux knife, that we can certainly duplicate without difficulty, excepting *the handle*. Comparison of figure 113a with that given by Sir John Lubbock, as quoted below, will at once indicate the similarity, if not identity, of form. Many of the more elongated leaf-shaped arrows which had lost their points, might have been thus used, by placing the broken end in a bone handle, and so converting the base and sides into the edges of a (double-edged) knife-blade; but, besides these, we have occasionally met with chipped jaspers which were identical with Mr. Lubbock's figure above referred to. Instead of being as thin and as nearly flat as an arrow-point, they had a

* Stone Age, Eng. ed., pl. v, figs. 87, 88, 89.
† Stone Age, pl. v., fig. 80, Eng. ed.
‡ Prehist. Times, p. 490, fig. 214.

well-defined middle ridge down one side, and were flat upon the other, thus presenting, in section, a triangular outline, which would increase the strength very much over an ordinary arrow-head.

Messrs. Squier and Davis* assert that "knives of flint and obsidian have been taken from several of the mounds;" and one figured is nearly (in shape) identical with an accompanying one from a Scandinavian barrow. We have not met with any of this pattern in New Jersey, which are, according to Squier and Davis, "not less than six inches in length (*i. e.*, some of them) and three-fourths of an inch in breadth; others are not more than two inches long, and of exceeding delicacy. Besides these, and constituting a much larger class, are found cutting-implements chipped with great neatness, so as to produce as clear and smooth a cutting-edge as practicable." These latter, in being "chipped," approach our New Jersey specimens, and we doubt not the other pattern, if it does not *now* exist in some of the large private collections in the State, will yet be found. Obsidian, in the shape of arrow-points, but always broken, has been picked up in New Jersey.

CHAPTER XI.

SKINNING-KNIVES.

When it is remembered that the primitive people whose stone implements we have been describing were perhaps wholly dependent upon the skins of the animals captured in the chase, not only for clothing but for shelter, it is not strange that much care was exercised in fashioning and finishing implements for detaching the skin from the carcass and for its subsequent preparation for domestic use. We are prepared, therefore, to find in skinning-knives and in scrapers, to be separately considered, stone tools that have been elaborately worked out from the most desirable minerals.

Wherever there is unquestionably the site of a village or town of the aborigines, there will we find specimens, sometimes many, of carefully-polished stone implements, having a well-defined cutting-edge; these we have called skinning-knives; a designation embracing the whole ground of use to which they were put by the race of men who made them.

Figure 114 represents a very fine example of skinning-knife plowed up in a field bordering the Crosswicks Creek, Burlington County, New Jersey. This polished implement is made from a large pebble of yellowish sand stone, of such fine-grained consistency as to be capable of the high polish which is still to be seen in one or two places on the specimen in question. This skinning-knife measures six inches in length at the thick back, but the blade, or cutting-edge, starting at an acute angle with the ridge-like back, makes a gentle, perfect curve, which, at the middle of the specimen, is but one inch and a half distant from the lower

---

* Anc. Mon. Miss. Valley, p. 215, fig. 105—(No. 2.)

margin of the back. The back itself is but seven-sixteenths of an inch in thickness, and tapers to a blunt point at the ends. The blade is only one-fourth of an inch thick where it joins the back, and from thence tapers to a very fine and really sharp edge. The edge is uniformly sharp throughout its whole extent. Taken as a whole, it is the best example of a skinning-knife we have met with, and its shape indicates its use as unquestionably as does the most symmetrical arrow-point suggest the use of the bow.

Although centuries have elapsed since its last use, it is still available for separating animal skins from the carcass, and comparatively little was gained in substituting for it a metallic knife. It is the only specimen of this pattern we have found; not even fragments referable to this form have been gathered among the thousands of relics found in the same neighborhood.

Squier and Davis figure* a cutting-instrument somewhat like the preceding in general appearance, and remark : " A variety is occasionally found in the Eastern States, of which figure 170 is an example. They are sometimes composed of slate, and are of various sizes, often measuring five or six inches in length. They are very well adapted for flaying animals and for other analogous purposes."

Figure 115 is a remarkably pretty example of a skinning-knife of totally different shape and character, being a long, slender stone, edged at one end, instead of on the margin of one of its longer sides. The illustration will convey a better idea of the specimen itself than can any description. The specimen is a hornstone pebble, beautifully polished over the greater portion of its surface. One end is blunt, as though abruptly broken off, but is now equally well polished with any of the other parts. From this blunt end, the width of the specimen gradually increases, with about a corresponding decrease in the breadth or thickness for the distance of an inch, when the width decreases by a beautiful curve more marked upon the upper margin, which margin becomes the edge at the descent of the curve, continuing so until it joins the straighter portion of the lower outline of the specimen. The blade, or edged end of the knife, is slightly bent, or, at least, has that appearance, from the edge not being in a line with the middle of the thickest portion of the implement. If the specimen is held with the straighter side (*lower side*, in our description) up, then the blade is bent to the right and has just the proper " twist" to most readily separate the skin from the muscles. On experimenting with this knife, in skinning a lamb, we found that when once an incision was made in the skin, the detaching, by breaking away the thin connective tissue, was easily done, but that the edge was not sufficiently sharp to cut a tendon or the skin itself. When used in deer-skinning, by the Indians, no doubt the flint-knife was brought into play in incising, as, in our experiments with this knife, we found that

---

* Anc. Mon. Miss. Valley, p. 215, fig. 107.

the implement figured in 108 would cut the tendons of a lamb, and also the skin, but not with as clean an incision as was desirable.

Figure 116 represents a comparatively common style of skinning-knife, made from a piece of serpentine, pecked to a blunt point at the back, and from about the middle of the implement to the edge is very smoothly polished. The specimen measures a little less than three inches in length, and two inches in width along the cutting-edge, and is a very good average specimen of this class of implements. It approaches in general character the cylindrical hand axes with pointed butt, but is considerably flatter and somewhat broader. It does not appear as well adapted to skinning as does either of the preceeding examples.

Figures 117 and 118 represent two more skinning-knives, one from New Jersey, figure 118, and the other from Indiana, figure 117.

Figure 117 is a better specimen than the other, inasmuch as it is thinner, and originally had a better edge. It is of very compact stone, similar to serpentine, but not exactly like this mineral as found in New Jersey. Figure 118 is also of a very compact mineral, approaching porphyry, but very heavy, as though largely charged with iron. It has been carefully polished over its whole surface, to accomplish which, considering the mineralogical character of the specimen, must have cost much labor. The specimen measures just three inches in length by one inch and three-quarters in width, along the cutting-edge. As figure 116 approaches the cylindrical, pointed hand-axes, so does this specimen come near the square-ended, ungrooved axes, of which figures have been given. Such skinning-knives as these appear to be common over the whole territory of the United States. We have seen them from nearly every State in the Union. Messrs. Squier and Davis[*] give illustrations of two such specimens, differing only in mineral, and remark: "There is another variety (besides knives proper) of cutting-instrument, which it may not be out of place to notice here. These consist of hard, compact minerals, worked into a chisel-shape. Some have a very sharp, smooth edge, and form quite a good substitute for metal. Engravings of two, of full size, (both are much smaller than our specimens of a similar shape, *i. e.*, figures 117 and 118,) are herewith presented. They are formed of very compact nodules of brown hematite, which have been ground into form and polished with great labor. They have a submetallic luster, and very nearly the specific gravity of iron. A file produces a scarcely perceptible impression upon their rounded surfaces." We have, as yet, not collected any specimens of these skinning-knives or other implements made from nodules of known hematite, although this mineral is abundant in the northern portion of New Jersey, but probably there are specimens in collections made in that section of the State, not only of knives, but of grooved axes, and other of the larger implements of stone. Figure 119 is a rude skinning-knife, ground down from a globular porphyry pebble, and, considering its thickness at the com-

---

[*] Anc. Mon. Miss. Valley, p. 215, fig. 106.

mencement of the polished surfaces, one inch and three-eighths, the labor upon it must have been enormous. We have, elsewhere,* called this specimen an ax, but on comparing it with a large series of undoubted skinning-knives, we are induced to place it with them; and, indeed, it may be that two other of the smaller ungrooved axes, which we have figured, should really be included in this chapter rather than under their present heading; but nowhere in the range of stone implements is it harder to draw the dividing-line satisfactorily than between axes proper and true skinning-knives.

Figure 120 represents the smaller-sized skinning-knives found throughout the length and breadth of the land. Usually, those found in New Jersey are ground into form from a hornstone or porphyry pebble, and polished. The specimen in the figure has been pecked into shape from a fragment of serpentine, and subsequently highly polished on the sides. The cutting-edge is very good. It is very nearly equal in size to the smaller of the two hematite implements figured by Messrs. Squier and Davis, and referred to in our description of figures 117 and 118, but somewhat more irregular in outline. Polished skinning-stones as small as figure 120 are as useful for the larger mammals as are those given in figures 114 and 118, and we do not understand why there should be such a variation in size, unless, in their making, stones of suitable shape were selected irrespective of size, and an edge, the length of which was decided by the original breadth of the stone, was given to them.

In the collection of M. Newbold, esq., of Burlington County, New Jersey, to which we have frequently referred, there is a fine series of skinning-knives, all gathered from the immediate neighborhood. The largest, we should unquestionably class as a hand-ax, as its length, nine inches, renders it too unwieldy for skinning-purposes, but it stands at the head of a series which lessens in length very gradually down to two highly polished specimens scarcely two inches in total length. By placing these specimens in a row, it is difficult to decide where the ax ceases and the knife begins.

The smallest specimens of Mr. Newbold's collection are flat, sharply-pointed triangles, very highly polished, and, altogether, exhibit far more work than any we have figured, excepting, possibly, figure 115. The object of this sharply-pointed end is not easily determined. Certainly it does not render the implement any more "handy" in the operation of skinning, and is not likely to have been needed to puncture the hide, especially as great care was taken to preserve the skin as entire as possible.

The skinning-knives in the above-mentioned collection are made of porphyry, serpentine, and hornstone, the majority being of the first-named mineral, and those from the other two materials are about the same in number.

The skinning-knives which we have figured, as well as those referred to in collections other than our own, vary considerably in outline, though but little in general finish, and may all be described as polished pebbles, with some portion of the rim brought to a cutting-edge. It has also been shown that these and the hand-axes, or those without a groove, have many features in common, and, indeed, that they (the skinning-knives and hand-axes without grooves) are identical, except in size; but whether some of the specimens are classed as the one or the other implement depends much upon the fancy of the collector.

We now propose calling attention to the apparent identity of the more common forms of skinning-knives and of some of the smaller hand-axes with the class of stone implements known to European archæologists as "polished celts."

Mr. Evans* says: "The general form of stone celts is * * * * usually that of more or less flat blades, approaching an oval in section, with the sides more or less straight, and one end broader and also sharper than the other. In length they vary from about two inches to as much as sixteen inches."

It will be seen from this description of "celts," as a class, that the specimens represented by figures 116, 117, 118, would be called in England "celts," as would also all the "hand-axes" that we have figured. If, therefore, it were proper to separate the two forms in America, why should they not be so separated when studied abroad? Is it not probable that these implements, being identical in everything except the mineral of which they are made, had identical uses?

Some of the illustrations given by Mr. Evans of polished celts are very similar to those we have given; and, in fact, he speaks† of "hematite *celts* found in North America of much the same size and form" as those occurring in Great Britain and France.

As to the uses to which our "skinning-knives" and the European celts were put, Mr. Evans remarks: "They were used chiefly for cutting down timber, and for scooping canoes out of the trunks of forest trees; for dressing posts for huts; for grubbing up roots and killing animals for food; for preparing fire-wood; for scraping the flesh from the bones when eating; and for various other purposes in the domestic arts. But they were also employed in times of war as weapons of offense and defense, as a supplementary kind of tomahawk."

We see here, indeed, a wide range of uses, and so varied are they that we should think their separation might easily be based upon such a list of purposes for which these implements were intended. Surely a "celt" a foot in length, perhaps, available for cutting down trees, would rather be in the way than useful "for scraping the flesh from bones when eating," while one two inches in length would scarcely be fitted for digging up roots or killing animals sufficiently large for food; yet such celts occur, and *are* moderately well adapted to skinning animals when once

---

* Anc. Stone Imp. of Great Brit., p. 51.   † L. c., p. 116.

an incision is fairly made. While many specimens may have had
various uses, certainly the extremes in forms cannot be confounded;
and our ungrooved axes or true "celts" on the one hand and polished
skinning-knives on the other are well-marked types of stone implements
that are properly distinguished by names suggested by their probable
uses, notwithstanding the varying forms which little by little effect
a blending of the two types.

<h2 style="text-align:center">CHAPTER XII.</h2>

<h3 style="text-align:center">SCRAPERS.</h3>

Among the very numerous "flint" specimens of Europe are certain
rudely-chipped objects, of various sizes, which have received the name
of "scrapers." Of these, Sir John Lubbock* says: "The so-called
'scrapers' are oblong stones, one end of which is rounded and brought
to a beveled edge by a series of small blows. One side is flat, the other
or outer one is more or less convex; sometimes they have a short handle,
which gives them very much the appearance of a spoon. They have
been found in England, France, Denmark, Ireland, Switzerland, and
other countries. They vary from one to four inches in length, and from
half an inch to two inches in breadth. * * * Modern specimens
(Esquimaux) are in form *identical* with the old ones." We have said
that they are "rudely chipped," and, judging from the general appearance, as represented in the illustrations, they unquestionably are; but
this is very far from being the case with the New Jersey specimens. As
a class, they are as well chipped and as uniform in shape as the majority
of arrow-points. They usually have the "short handle" mentioned
by Sir John Lubbock, but are not commonly as spoon-like in appearance, being similar in outline to the "sheaf of wheat," especially if
viewed with the "handle" down. They vary somewhat from this typical form of the "sheaf of wheat," however, especially in the character
of the handle, which is sometimes pointed; and, again, there are other
examples, having no distinct handle, but the edge of the scraper is
receded from at a gentle slope, making the complete specimen a triangular flint, with the peculiar beveled edge which characterizes all
such implements as "scrapers." One feature of the European scrapers
is having one side flat or uniform, the result of the breaking away of a
large flake, thus giving on one side the smooth surface of a single
plane of cleavage. We have all our specimens chipped upon both sides,
unless it be those of about the minimum size, which appear absolutely
identical with the European specimens.

During the summer of 1871, I forwarded a number of "sheaf-of-wheat"
scrapers to Sir John Lubbock, who kindly wrote me, concerning them:
"None of your specimens are 'true' 'scrapers,' according to our ideas,
nor have I ever seen one from a red-skin area." Since then we have

---

* Prehistoric Times, 2d ed., p. 92.

gathered hundreds of our scrapers; and of one of the smaller ones, smooth upon one side, Mr. Lubbock has written: "I should certainly regard it as a scraper." During the present summer I forwarded specimens of the scrapers found about Trenton, N. J., to my friend, Mr. Wm. A. Baker, of Auburn, N. Y., and of one of them he writes: "The smallest (black) one is, in everything except material, an exact duplicate of my Yorkshire scrapers."

Scrapers vary, in the minerals from which they are made, to the same extent as arrow-points; but the majority of them, unlike arrow-points, are of hornstone, chert, jasper, and quartz. Many, however, are of slate and sandstone, and are carefully shaped, but have not the same degree of finish as the harder minerals; but it may be possible that the slate and sandstone specimens were originally finished with the same care, but have been broken in the rough-and-tumble existence to which they have been subjected during the past two centuries. They have all softened upon the surface by the years of weathering, and, if judged by the surface only, would be considered much more friable than they really are. If the external coating of rotten stone is scraped off, the body of the specimen is found to be still sufficiently hard to turn the edge of the penknife.

These remarks upon the surface-decomposition of slate and sandstone relics are, of course, as applicable to arrow-points of these materials as to scrapers. To what extent decomposition is indicative of age cannot well be ascertained; but that the very much worn, deeply rotted, and sometimes scarcely recognizable relics are considerably older than others of identical material, but hard upon the surface, there can be little, if any, doubt.

Figure 121 represents the largest scraper in our collection and one of the largest that we have seen. It is of slaty rock, and is rudely chipped on both sides, quite hard, and in color very dark. The whole surface is much weather-worn, and is of a grayish hue, similar to the yellow-gray Jersey sand in which it has been lying for so long a time. The specimen measures a fraction over four inches in length and a little more than two and one-half inches in width. The handle is exactly one inch long, and one inch wide at the end, but increases a little in width as it nears the body of the specimen itself. The scraping end is rounded, and equally edged with the sides. There is, in this specimen, no beveling of the front edge, as is the rule with scrapers; but that this is anything but a scraper no one will contend. We suppose that the short handle of this specimen was intended to be inserted in a bone handle of greater width than the body of the implement, since otherwise such a narrow and short projection would only be in the way in using the specimen as an ordinary scraper.

The other slate scrapers in our collection are all of the true "sheaf-of-wheat" pattern, having the beveled edge at the front, but as a class are thinner than those made from other materials. As slate was certainly more easily worked than jasper or quartz and equally as good for a scraper, we cannot imagine why the harder minerals should have been used so much, unless that once made they were less liable to be broken— a probability which would seem of little moment when we reflect upon the little wear and tear on a stone solely used in scraping the soft fat from a scarcely harder skin. Nine-tenths of all the scrapers we have gathered, however, were of the various kinds of jasper and quartz. While our slate and other scrapers vary considerably in length, there is not this variation in width, and several in our collection are fully two-thirds as wide as figure 121, but less than half its length, and in some cases only about one-third as long.

Scrapers are seldom found singly, but are abundant on the former sites of Indian villages, and where arrow-makers had their workshops.

Without making any distinction between true scrapers and stretch-ing implements, as suggested by Professor Nilsson,* we proceed to the consideration of the average jasper scrapers as we have found them about Trenton, N. J.

Figures 122, 123, and 124 are excellent specimens of the pattern we have called the " sheaf of wheat." To recognize the similarity in out-line, the specimen must be viewed with the handle *down* and not as here given, which is, however, the true position of the scraper, considering its use. Two of these specimens have the beveled edge; but in figure 123 the edge is equally chipped from either side, which fact inclined us formerly to consider this a blunt arrow-head,† but more careful study with an enlarged collection makes us confident that we were for the time in error. We have seen that figure 121 was so chipped at the edge, and certainly no one will class that as an arrow-head. Occasionally the butt-ends of the scrapers will be curved and give the specimen much the appearance of a barbed arrow-point, the tip of which has been squarely broken away. In many specimens, too, the blade is much shorter than these we have here figured, being but a third or a quarter of the length of the handle, instead of equal in length or longer.

Figure 125 is a well-cut jasper scraper, with a narrower front, or scrap-ing edge, than usual. The specimen bears a general resemblance to Esquimaux examples that we have met with and have also seen figured. The handle does not join the body of the implement as abruptly as in the four preceding figures.

Figure 126 is a beautifully wrought example of a jasper scraper, hav-ing much in common with figure 125, but is more symmetrical. The scraping edge is broader and flatter, and is beautifully beveled along the whole front, but the object has an ordinary straight or cutting edge along the sides. The handle is about one-third of the total length of the specimen, and is neatly chipped and brought to a sharp edge on both sides and at the end.

It is seldom that we see a chipped-jasper implement with its use stamped

---

* Stone Age in Scand., p. 77.   † Amer. Nat., vol. vi.

upon it as in this instance by the shape, size, and manner of finish. The beveled edge is very marked, being sharp on one side and blunt on the other, so that with the sharp edge the fat may be removed, the skin being softened by rubbing with the rounded edge—two implements, really, being combined in the one stone.

Figure 127 is a specimen of jasper scraper that more nearly approaches the European form of this implement. It is smaller than the usual find of our New Jersey specimens. The scraping edge has been produced by a single flake being detached from one side along the whole width of the specimen. The handle is a short, narrow, stem-like projection, terminating in a blunt point.

Figures 128 and 129 represent two forms of scrapers possessing many points in common and which are also allied, but more remotely, to the preceding pattern. These two specimens were classed as arrow-heads in our paper in the American Naturalist; but, as with the scraper previously called a blunt arrow-point, so with these, additional specimens rendered their peculiar forms intelligible. They are unquestionably scrapers. Why they should be so shaped is not known; but we were not a little astonished to find, during the present summer, other specimens *exactly* like the two figured, and varying among themselves just as these vary. Both figures, 128 and 129, have had very good points at the ends of the handles, and the additional specimens of these patterns are even better pointed. The chipped beveled base, however, of these supposed arrow-points furnishes a clew to their true character, and the additional examples, genuine duplicates of the preceding figures, are as evidently scrapers as any specimens we have figured. The only specimens we have met with have been gathered from a single field, and were associated with the common style of this implement, with arrow-points, &c.

Figure 130 is a most interesting example of jasper scraper, having all the peculiarities of our sheaf-of-wheat pattern; it is, however, exaggerated, and the stem or handle, instead of being straight, has side projections, which make the specimen, when viewed upside down, a blunt, deeply notched, stemmed arrow-point. Its true character, however, is that of a scraper, inasmuch as the edge is very carefully beveled, which would not be the case were it intended as a blunt point for an arrow. The object of the arrow-head-like " handle " is not at all clear. In its present condition it does not offer a good hold for skin-scraping, and to attach a long slender shaft like that of an arrow to it, would render it only more embarrassing for skin-dressing. This specimen, figure 130, was found in Indiana, and forwarded to the author with a number of others. They have all proved interesting for purposes of comparison with our New Jersey specimens, but no one of them differed in any important particular from those of this State. We have seen a New Jersey scraper similar to this, except in being a little larger; but being broken we preferred figuring the Indiana example.

Figure 131 represents a beautifully chipped jasper scraper of the triangular form, and is the smallest specimen we have met with. It is a little less than one inch in length, and almost three-fourths of an inch in breadth, and is, therefore, of the minimum size according to Sir John Lubbock. Although chipped upon both sides, as is the rule with New Jersey scrapers, it is very nearly flat upon the under side, the sloping from the middle toward the edges being very gradual. The front, or scraping edge is carefully chipped at about right angles with the upper surface of the specimen. A ridge extends along the upper side of the whole length of the specimen, and from it, the surface slopes uniformly to the edge. The object in fastening a handle on an implement so small as this, the use of which is supposed to have been that of scraping, in rendering skins pliant and available for clothing, does not appear, unless it was used for skins of the smallest mammals.

Mr. Evans[*] has figured no example of a scraper that is equal to this, figure 131, in general finish and workmanship, and only one that is as short. His specimen is broader, however, although otherwise it bears much resemblance to that from New Jersey.

Mr. Evans, in his most interesting chapter[†] on "scrapers," has advanced many reasons for his belief that some of our so-called scrapers were used in producing fire, in connection with pyrites, remarking of the English specimens, "we find some of these instruments with the edge battered and bruised to such an extent that it can hardly have been the result of scraping, in the ordinary sense of the word."

We have many scrapers with battered edges, and of a quadrangular outline, very similar in general appearance to the modern "strike-a-lights," which we doubt not were used, as Mr. Evans suggests. Figure 132 represents such a specimen of "scraper." It is of yellow jasper, an inch and a half long, an inch wide, and half an inch thick near the middle of the specimen. The front edge is much battered and has every appearance of having been struck against a mineral as hard as pyrites.

Pyrites, in masses of various sizes, is very abundant about Trenton, N. J., where these short, thick scrapers are found. It occurs in the beds of clay which crop out of the hillsides along the New Jersey shore of the Delaware, being there attached in large masses to the fossil trees imbedded in these strata.

In closing this chapter, an illustration is given of a slate specimen, figure 133, which has particularly interested me from the very marked resemblance it has to a specimen of scraper, found by Sir John Lubbock at Bourdeilles, in the South of France, and figured the natural size in Prehistoric Times.[‡] Our New Jersey specimen is identical with it in length, while the handle is immaterially broader, the only noticeable difference being that our specimen is chipped upon both sides.

There is, perhaps, nothing so interesting connected with the study of

---

[*] Anc. Stone Imps. of Great Britain, p. 277, fig. 220.
[†] l. c., pp. 280–286.
[‡] 2d ed., p. 92, fig. 103.

the "flint" implements of New Jersey as this identity in the more important features with those of distant countries. We have seen this similarity in the axes and arrow-heads; and now in the scrapers, we obtain an example of identity in a specimen from the South of France, and one from Central New Jersey; the former has existed as many centuries as the latter has years, and yet the latter must be more than two hundred years old.

CHAPTER XIII.

HAMMERS.

There are occasionally found about our fields, slender oval stones and some of more irregular shape, with grooves entirely around them, as in one pattern of axes, which stones would serve as good axes had they a cutting-edge. Being without such edge their use as hammers is unquestionable. Such an oval, grooved pebble is well represented in figures 133, 133*a*. There has been no chipping or pecking of this specimen other than was necessary to produce the narrow, shallow groove, to better secure the handle. This hammer is seven inches in length, about three inches wide in the middle, and tapers quite uniformly to the somewhat narrower ends. To what uses such grooved stones were put it is not easy to determine. In this instance there is not the battered appearance at the ends, indicating use as a hammer for striking other stones, as in the ends of chisels and gouges. Very probably it was a weapon, as its weight and size certainly do not suggest any heavy mechanical works, such as the ancient copper-mining, where immense stone mauls were largely used.

Figure 134 represents an interesting form of stone hammer, being peculiar in that one portion has been pecked into such shape as to answer as a handle, instead of being so shaped as to require a wooden one. Probably the stone originally bore some resemblance to its present shape. There has been a rude edge chipped upon the lower margin of the head of this hammer of about one-quarter of an inch in width. When this specimen was first described by us,[*] it was suggested that a handle had been attached to the present stone stem or handle; but this is improbable. Whether it was used as a weapon or a domestic tool is indeterminable. This is the only specimen we have met with of this style.

Figure 135 represents the more usual shape and size of these stone hammers, as we find them in New Jersey. Of course occasional specimens of this and other styles occur that are several times larger. This specimen is exactly five inches in length. It was originally of the ordinary oval outline so common to the cobble-stones of the river-bed, and afterward pecked at the head to make it flatter. It has a very shallow groove pecked irregularly about it; the dressing down was apparently more with a view to obliterate projecting angles than to secure a de-

* Amer. Nat., vol. vi, p. 158.

pression or groove for the handle-fastenings. At the end or point there is a small pecked surface which may have been intended to produce a blunter end, or caused by hammering upon other stones, as in using the chisel or gouge. We have sometimes thought it possible that such hammers as figure 135, which are by no means rare, may have been intended as axes at first, but in consequence of the amount of work required, or from other cause, they were rejected by the implement-maker. Were there not also hammers to which these remarks cannot be applied, and tools that require the use of hammers of some kind, we should be inclined to adopt this view of "unfinished axes," especially since, at *that* time, as now, any stone of suitable weight and size, and conveniently manipulated, might serve as a hammer.

Figure 136 represents a cobble-stone hammer, which has puzzled us considerably. There is a well-defined depression extending all around the stone at one end, but it is so smooth, and uniform in color with the natural surface of the stone, that we are a little puzzled to determine whether the groove is natural, or whether the whole surface of the specimen was polished or worked. That the stone is well shaped for a hammer is undoubted, whether it be a chance bowlder or not; also, it is equally available for hammering purposes, with or without a handle, not being too large to enable one to secure a firm grip about its head, or grooved portion. There is no indication of pecking at any part of this hammer, nor does it show those slight inequalities which indicate use against other equally hard or harder stones. This specimen was found near Lambertville, N. J., and was presented to the author by Mr. William Dean, of that place, whose interest in Indian antiquities has resulted in preserving many valuable specimens. The neighborhood from which this hammer came is quite rich in the various classes of relics, and the fact of this specimen being found associated with other implements is largely in favor of the idea that it, at least, was in use as a hammer by the Indians, even if it was not grooved by them in the manner in which it now appears.

Figure 137 represents a very handsome form of stone hammer, found near the Delaware River, at Scudder's Falls—a locality quite rich in the commoner form of relics. This specimen, kindly lent by John H. Scudder, esq., of Trenton, N. J., for purposes of description and figuring, was found some forty years ago, and has been used as a nut-cracker ever since. The specimen is a finely-grained sandstone, and has been carefully worked out into a very handy shape for hammering purposes. It measures eight and one-quarter inches in length, about four of which form the handle. The head of the hammer is quadrangular in outline; the whole outer and inferior inner lateral outline being at an angle of about forty-five degrees with the line of the handle. Both head and handle have a uniform thickness of two inches. There are now but few traces of tool-marks upon any part of the specimen, the inferior outer angle and extremity of the handle alone showing a roughness of the surface which has been so produced. It is probably an accidental fracturing of the cobble-stone which furnished the general outline of the specimen as it now exists, and that the uneven surfaces were ground down to make the stone available as a hammer. But there is no doubt that the aborigines could fracture stones into pretty much the shape they desired, as will be seen in the sculptured animals' heads, which were first broken and then smoothed down to correct dimensions.

The outline drawing given above, of another specimen of "handled" hammer shows a decided variation from this example in that the handle was, and is, cylindrical, whereas in figure 137 the handle is flat, pecked only at the end, and smoothed down with a polishing-stone. In figure 137, also, there is no trace of an edge; as in the example above mentioned, there is nothing but blunt hammer-head surfaces throughout. This specimen may have been used as a weapon for close combat; but if examined in connection with the beautiful specimen of gouge represented in figure 139, it will be seen that one supplements the other admirably, and that, with the two, charred wood could be easily removed, or a "dug-out" canoe readily made. This specimen of hammer bears some general resemblance to a not uncommon form of pestle, where a portion of the length has been "split," as it were, giving the specimen a canoe-shaped handle and a nearly circular head. Such a specimen is always rough on the extremity, showing that it was used as a pestle, the blow being struck with the specimen in a vertical position, and not as a hammer. We give a figure of such a pestle in chapter xxiv.

We have never seen perforated hammers of the general shape of figure 133 from New Jersey, except in one instance, where a fragment was found that much resembled such a perforated stone hammer as Nilsson figures,[*] and of which he remarks, "it is of diorite, and of a very convenient shape. It was found in a bog in Scania, and fell into the hands of a carpenter, who provided it with a handle and used it a long time in his workshop as a hammer." The New Jersey fragment was not as elaborately ridged and fluted, but was far more carefully shaped than any perfect ones we have seen. The specimen, however, was too fragmentary to determine positively whether or not it was a hammer. Inasmuch as we have so many specimens of carefully-drilled "banner-stones," "gorgets," and some stone pipes, it appears strange there should be such an absence of tools that have been drilled for handles. We have never yet seen a perfect or even recognizable fragment of an ax or hammer sufficiently large to be useful as a tool, that was drilled for a handle instead of having the ordinary groove.

Stevens[†] figures a stone hammer found in Ireland, not materially differing from figure 135, to which we refer as another example of the curious identity of the specimens of stone-work found in distant quarters of the globe. We have not collected any specimens of very large stone mauls,

---

* Stone Age, pl. viii, fig. 172, p. 69.   † Flint Chips, p. 557, fig. 121.

and it is to be presumed that they were exclusively used for mining purposes. Dr. Wilson describes* those found in the copper-mining regions of Lake Superior, as "water-worn bowlders of green-stone or porphyry, roughly chipped in the center, so as to admit of their being secured by a withe around them. But others are well finished, with a single or double groove for attaching the handle by which they were wielded. They weigh from ten to forty pounds." It will be noticed here that his description applies also to the majority of the specimens we have found in New Jersey, where probably there was no mining, though copper occurs about New Brunswick, Middlesex County, New Jersey, and the surface lumps of native copper were eagerly sought for and utilized by the Indians. We do not remember ever having met with a stone hammer exceeding ten pounds in weight, the minimum weight of the stone mauls described by Dr. Wilson; but they may occur, however, as the weight of the largest grooved ax we have seen was twelve pounds lacking two ounces.† The hammers found in New Jersey are usually made of sand-stone; but the "mauls," as described by Dr. Wilson, are sometimes of porphyry, a mineral generally used for fine axes and "skinning-knives," but to our knowledge not at all for hammers.

Grooved hammers, *for mining purposes*, are described by Mr. Evans;‡ they are similar to many of the surface-found hammers of New Jersey, but are smaller generally than the Lake Superior "mauls."

Chapter XIV.

CHISELS AND GOUGES.

Messrs. Squier and Davis,§ in describing the various forms of stone axes from mounds, as well as from elsewhere throughout the United States, remark that "the form of these relics seems to have been determined entirely by the manner in which they were designed to be used. Those intended for deadening trees, or as war-axes, have grooves for the adjustment of handles. There are many which are destitute of this feature, and which were probably designed for *chisels* or *gouges*." The specimens of "chisels" figured, however, are there also called, and very properly, "hand-axes," and are identical with those we have figured as "celts." No *true* chisel or gouge—and they are different—is illustrated or, we believe, referred to. The implement we have called a "chisel," is an elongated, oval, cobble-stone, that has been pecked over the greater portion of its surface; it is well rounded at one end, and at the other has been carefully ground to a sharp cutting-edge. The under side is rounded, very uniform throughout the whole length, and curved toward the ends, so that, while lying on that side, it will rock to and fro, if touched. Two-thirds of the upper surface have been smoothly

---

* Prehist. Man, 2d ed., p. 161.
‡ In the cabinet of Michael Newbold, esq., of Burlington County, New Jersey
‡ Anc. Stone Imp. Great Brit., pp. 208–210.
§ Anc. Mon. Miss. Valley p. 217.

split off, making it, not a hollowed "gouge," but a smooth chisel. Figure 138 is such a specimen. We have gathered a large series of the kind, showing that they were intended for some chisel-like use, and not merely a chance variety of the ordinary cylindrical celt.

As we meet with no stone-work that has been fashioned by such an implement, the natural inference is that they were used in connection with wood; and no wood-work of the aborigines suggests itself other than boat-building, and we have no doubt that logs were converted into canoes with some stone hammers, such as we have figured in connection with this chisel. It must have been a laborious process, comparing the stone chisel with modern ones; but how else could figure 138 have been utilized? Moreover, this view of the use of chisels is upheld by Dr. Daniel Wilson.[*] He writes in his fascinating work: "On the banks of the Scottish Clyde the modern voyager from the Old World looks with peculiar interest on the growing fabrics of those huge steamers which have made the ocean, that proved so impassable a barrier to the men of the fifteenth century, the easy highway of pleasure and commerce to us. The roar of the iron-forge, the clang of the trip-hammer, the intermittent glare of the furnaces, and all the novel appliances of iron-ship building, tell of the modern era of steam; but, meanwhile, underneath these very ship-builders' yards lie the memorials of ancient Clyde fleets, in which we are borne back, up the stream of human history, far into prehistoric times. The earliest recorded discovery of a Clyde canoe took place in 1870, at a depth of 25 feet below the surface, on a site known by the apt designation of Saint Enoch's Croft, when digging the foundation of a church dedicated, by a strangely apposite misnomer, to the antediluvian father of Methuselah. This canoe, hewn out of a single oak, rested in a horizontal position on its keel, and within it, near the prow, *lay a beautifully-finished stone ax or celt, * * * doubtless one of the simple implements with which this primitive ship of the Clyde had been fashioned into shape.*" It cannot be urged that there is no evidence of "dug-out" canoes having been used in New Jersey. We know from historical data that the aborigines of this section had canoes of some sort; and, that some dug-outs were used, we learn from the fact that one was found in Savannah River swamp, concerning which we have the following:[†] "In 1845, while digging a canal on one of the rice-plantations on the Savannah River, only a few miles distant from the city of Savannah, at a depth of three feet and a half below the surface of the swamp, the workmen came upon a canoe imbedded in the soil. It answered to the description of what is familiarly known as a *dug-out*, and had been fashioned from the trunk of a cypress tree." If Dr. Daniel Wilson is correct in considering the oak log on the Clyde as hollowed by the celt found in it, which celt is analogous to ours, (see figure 26,) then surely such a chisel, with a hammer, could effect as much with a cypress log, or even the white oak, which grows to such perfection in New Jersey.

---

* Prehistoric Man, 2d ed., p. 103.
† Jour. Anthrop. Inst. of New York, vol. i, p. 67, 1871–72.

Figure 139 is a curved chisel or "gouge" proper, and is a most beautiful specimen of workmanship in stone, being an absolutely perfect tool fashioned for some single particular purpose. It needs but one glance to see what the implement is and what was its use. It is a gouge (figure 139) of exactly five inches in length; is polished over its entire surface, and hollowed throughout the upper side. The depth of the depression is uniform, but it narrows equally with the slope of the sides of the implement, giving the ridges above the depression a uniform thickness. At about one inch from the cutting end, the depression descends rapidly until it meets with an upward curve of the bottom or under side of the gouge. At this angle is a sharp edge, beautifully worked and still well preserved, which describes mathematically nearly one-half of a circle. No modern gouge of steel is more accurately outlined than is this one.

Figure 140 represents one of a pair of very beautiful gouges on the cabinet of Michael Newbold, esq., of Burlington County, New Jersey. It is of serpentine, very accurately cut, and highly polished. It measures three and three-quarters inches in length, and one inch and seven-eighths in width at the blade, which width does not alter as it nears the cutting-edge. The blade is just two inches long, and is headed with a curved knob, which is separated from the blade by a "neck" measuring about two-thirds of the width of the head or "knob." The back of this implement is moderately curved, but less so than the gouge we have already figured. The *front* side is hollowed out, and shows, by the character of its edge and the curved surface of the blade that the specimen was intended as a gouge; but there is no indication of hammering upon its head, and this, we think, gives occasion for the question whether it *could* be used as a gouge in the absence of a hammer. It is just possible that wooden mallets were sometimes used, but we do not believe they were, as, with the tools in use, a piece of wood of suitable size and shape would be difficult to procure, and we know stone hammers were in use. We shall find that this objection is urged with reference also to another curious implement figured in chapter xxv, which bears much resemblance to a chisel.

We have seen no other specimens of this style of "gouge," except the two mentioned as in Mr. Newbold's cabinet; and that gentleman informs us that he has seen no other specimens from his neighborhood, where these were found, or in any cabinet. The ridges at the sides of the blade in the one figured are quite thick and uniform, while the whole appearance of the specimen is that of a well-finished metal tool.

Mr. Squier has figured in his monograph on New York aboriginal monuments,* a very symmetrical "stone ax," which has a well-marked rim about it, and an edge very similar to that of figure 140. Although there is so great a difference in the size, we doubt not there was a similarity in the uses to which the two implements were put. The one

*Abor. Mon. of New York, p. 77, fig. 16.

figured by Mr. Squier is, of course, not an ax at all, and should never have been so called.

The implements of themselves are not, we find, sufficient to give us a correct or complete insight into aboriginal ways of living during the stone age. It may be that implements and ornaments of perishable material were made wholly or in part with some such a tool as figure 140; and that only the tools are left to us.

Mr. C. C. Jones, jr.,* in his description of the Savannah River Swamp canoe, further states: "While there were no marks of sharp-cutting tools, the evidence appeared conclusive that the charred portions of the wood, both within and without, had been carefully removed by rude incisive implements, probably of stone;" and still further on, "It is entirely probable that the ordinary stone ax or chisel was the only implement at command for the removal of the charred surface, as the cypress tree was by degrees converted into the convenient *dugout.*" We agree with the author as to the *chisel* being used as he suggests; or better yet, the gouge, as represented in figure 139; but not the " ordinary stone ax." It is very undesirable, certainly, to call an "ax" a " chisel", or vice versa, if there is really the difference between the two forms that we claim. Do not a stone ax and a stone chisel, or gouge, differ as much as do these forms of tools made of steel, and in use at the present time ? Certainly, when such forms as figures 138, 139, and 140 were made, no Indian would undertake to hollow out a cypress log with an ordinary ax, such as we have described in the third chapter of this work.

Some of the English stone chisels figured by Mr. Evans bear much resemblance to the specimen we have figured on page 154; but none of the gouges can in any way compare with the beautiful examples we have given in figures 139 and 140.

CHAPTER XV.

DRILLING-STONES.

There is nothing more interesting to the archæologist than drilled implements of stone. It is scarcely necessary to remark that such drilled stones are rare, but only comparatively so, since the number of specimens now in museums and private collections is considerable, yet they are as nothing to the tens of thousands of arrow-points and allied implements. Their relative abundance may be apparent from the statement that during two summers of collecting we have secured but twenty-four specimens for our collection of about eight thousand objects, and of the twenty-four only five can be considered perfect.

The object of drilling holes through any of the stone implements used by the aborigines was to afford a convenient means of suspending such articles. This particularly applies to thin objects, that have two or

---

* L. c., p. 68.

more holes of small diameter, such as those thin, quadrangular plates so commonly found in graves, and which were apparently breast-ornaments.

"Mr. Wallace has * * * found that * * * plain cylinders of imperfect rock crystal, four to eight inches long, and one inch in diameter, are made and perforated by very low tribes on the Rio Negro." "The perforating of the cylinders crosswise, or even lengthwise, is said to be done thus: A pointed flexible leaf-shoot of wild plantain is twirled with the hands against the hard stone till, with the aid of fine sand and water, it bores into and through it, and this is said to take years to do."*

We shall find that in New Jersey also stone was drilled by wood, with sand and water, but not exclusively, for, on the site of an Indian settlement which was not merely the locality of a temporary or periodical sojourn, we find in comparative abundance slender-pointed stone instruments, arrow-points in appearance, but which were probably never used for weapons. We have figured some of these specimens of so-called "arrow-heads" in the American Naturalist,† but reproduce them here with a number of others, under the name of "drilling-stones." That the two forms of arrow-points and drilling-stones merge into each other is very certain, it being but another instance of that gradation from one form to another so noticeable in most of the classes of stone implements we have thus far considered.

Figure 141 is an unbroken specimen of the slender-bodied, square-based, jasper implements, which we suppose to have been designed for drilling. We were once confident that such an implement could have had no other significance than as an arrow-point, and wondered why Sir John Lubbock should "express this opinion only under reserve," in stating the possibility of their being arrow-heads. This specimen, with a number of others, gathered during the summer of 1871, were all characterized by a comparatively small base, which did not seem to interfere with their use as arrow-heads. During the summer of the present year we made careful search in a former Indian town, and gathered a very large series, and two constant features of the series convince us of the propriety of calling them drilling-stones. First, the majority have bases entirely *too* large for arrow-points, and all have bases which would be a defect in the arrow-head, if such they were; secondly, none have sharp points, while many have been broken square off at the point, showing that when in use the strain was there; and again, in many the points are rounded *by rubbing*, and are *highly polished*. Figure 141 is carefully chipped and has never been used, the edges of the flake-marks being still sharp. The base has been chipped to a sharp edge, showing it was inserted into some kind of handle, and not held between the fingers as was sometimes the case.

Figure 142 is a much smaller specimen of drilling-stone of the same

---

* Early Hist. of Mankind; Tylor, 2d ed., p. 190. London, 1870.
† Vol. vi, pp. 205, 6–14.

general outline. It is carefully chipped from slate, has the base sharply edged at its lower margin, and less so upon the sides. The stem or drill has probably been longer, is nearly cylindrical, and is highly polished at the end, which we think clearly indicates the use of this little implement. The size of this specimen suggests the probability of its having been attached to a handle, and that it was then driven by a to and fro motion. In some of the specimens of "breast-plates" which we have, there is a series of "half" ridges in the hole, showing apparently where the drill stopped to make a return motion. These ridges are similar in appearance to those in the larger drilled holes of "banner-stones," which, being perforated with a hollow drill, (probably a section of reed,) have unbroken circles lining the holes; while, when the stone drill was used, it has produced, at least in some cases, a broken or half circle.

Figure 143 is another example of the square-based drill; it is of slate, well chipped, and more fancifully outlined at the base. The stem or drilling portion is quite long and unbroken, except the extreme point, which was probably never very sharp. The stem is flatter than usual, but quite stout, with a well-defined median ridge the whole length. This specimen has a very arrow-head like appearance in its general outline. It is large enough to be held in the hand for use in the manner suggested. Why the base should be made somewhat flaring, or "barbed" at its junction with the stem, is not clear, for, even if the object was used as an arrow-head, such a feature would not be of any value. Such a shaped base is not uncomon, however, in the slate drills; but the specimens of this mineral are usually nothing but bases.

Figure 144 is a beautiful piece of carefully chipped yellow jasper, a "drill" unquestionably, but the drilling portion is unfortunately gone. This instance, however, is instructive, inasmuch as the size of the remaining portion of the specimen throws light upon these implements as a class. If any doubt existed in the minds of others about the smaller specimens, certainly it is clear that figure 144 is *not* an arrow-head. Nor can it be said that it is unfinished. The edges of the quadrangular base are carefully chipped, and the lower margin in this specimen, as in the preceding one, is brought to what would be considered in a knife a good "cutting" edge. Such a chipped jasper, inserted into a wooden handle, and operated with a bow-drill, or held in the hand and operated by a wrist-motion, would prove satisfactory to the savage, to whom time was a matter of no importance. Many of the drilled stones, however, were of much softer material than this jasper, and so would be perforated without much difficulty.

Figure 145 is an instance of how readily the drilling-stone passes into the arrow-point proper. We incline to the opinion that this is a drilling-stone and not an arrow-point, as the point or stem is well defined, and appears to have been worn rather than broken. This specimen possesses peculiar interest, in that it has decomposed to such an extent as to now scarcely possess the consistency of chalk. Whether this degree of softening is a matter of years or not we will not conjecture; but it is strange that a stone once hard enough to be used for drilling other stone should become so rotten.

Figure 146 represents one of those specimens which we have before described* as an arrow-point. The specimen is of slate, and varies from the square-based specimens, only in having the junction of the stem and base less distinctly indicated.

Figure 147 represents a specimen of slate drilling-stone with the largest base we have as yet met with. The specimen at present has much the appearance of a short-handled, large-bowled spoon. As in figure 144, there can be no confounding this fragment with an arrow-point. Judging from the slight bend in that portion of the stem which remains, we should consider the end of the stem to have been turned very considerably "to one side;" a peculiarity, however, not confined to this specimen or its class. Some arrow-points have a similar bend at their points, which appears usually to be due to some peculiarity in the mineral rendering this shape necessary. We recall picking up a small slate arrow-point, that had both the point and the base, which were narrower than the body of the specimen, twisted in the same direction, making the specimen describe a part of a circle. This specimen was well chipped, and not crooked, because "the work of a beginner," as was suggested, but its shape was rather owing to the the whim of the arrow-maker—a shape more difficult to chip successfully than if it were straight. The base of this specimen is well chipped, being at every portion of the margin brought to a good edge. The flakes struck off were unusually large, but five being taken from one of the sides.

Figure 148 is a finely-shaped fragment, chipped from yellow jasper. In this example, the base is quite wide, but not long, not exceeding the fragment of the stem which remains. It is well chipped on both sides, and has a beveled, and not a cutting edge. Held by the remaining portion of the stem, this specimen would make an excellent scraper, and possibly these broken specimens, with this shaped base, were thus utilized. The stem exhibits a well-marked median ridge, so far as the fragment extends, from which it is equally chipped to the edge, giving the stem, viewed in section, a diamond shape; the median angles being nearly as well defined as the outer ones.

Figure 149 represents a small specimen of chipped jasper drill, classed previously† as an arrow-point. This specimen is somewhat interesting from the fact of its strong resemblance to specimens of arrow-heads from Scandinavia, figured by Professor Nilsson.‡ The only variation in the specimens from the two countries is, that the one from New Jersey is better chipped than the other; the latter not being, we think, used as an arrow-head.

Figure 150 is a crooked, rudely-shaped specimen, noticeably flat upon

---

* Amer. Nat., vol. vi, p. 206.   † Amer. Nat., vol. vi, p. 214.
‡ Stone Age, pl. ii, fig. 36, and pl. xvi, fig. 266.

one side, and unusually ridged, uneven, and roughly chipped upon the other. This specimen had long been lying in our drawer of arrow-points, but in experimenting with it on a breast-plate, its crooked point was found to take hold admirably, and by twisting it to and fro we made such progress in drilling slate, and that without much wear upon the specimen, that we at once classed it as a drilling-stone.

Figures 151 and 152 represent two forms of jasper drilling-stones which are, however, nearly allied. They present a marked difference from the others, in that the bases are not so different in breadth from the stems of the implements.

Figure 151 is remarkably straight, beautifully chipped, and has, as usual, the edges quite sharp. In fact the base, in its shape, suggests the possibility of its having been used in drilling out the bowls of soap-stone smoking-pipes. The base is bowl-shaped in outline, and readily cuts soapstone. Were the stem a little more slender we should incline to the opinion that *it* was used to drill the stem of the pipe, and the base the bowl of the pipe. Figure 152 is much smaller, and like an arrow-point. The base is oval in outline, the width decreasing gradually as it passes into the stem portion of the implement. We doubt not the mode of using figures 151 and 152 was identical, and also that both were used in drilling other stones.

Figures 153 and 154 are " points ", or the drilling-ends of such specimens as we have been describing. They are quite abundant, wherever the bases with or without " stems " occur, and occasionally we have been able to find two fragments that " fit." These " points " are always rounded or blunt, and the sides, for a short distance only, are smooth, as though they were intended for drilling only very thin plates of stone. The *thin, polished* slate " breast-plates," are by far the most numerous examples of perforated stones that occur in New Jersey ; next come the thicker, flat, quadrangular stones, with a single perforation at one end. We think it very probable that such specimens were drilled exclusively with the species of implements we have been figuring in this chapter. These shallow drillings have never that wonderful accuracy characteristic of the banner-stones, and the two depressions, which meet in the middle of the stones, in the breast plates, are not always opposite each other, while they have just such an amount of irregularity as might be expected from a stone drill, held in the hand, and which had as crooked a point, for instance, as figure 150. Certainly, in the same stone, there is frequently a difference in the character of the perforations, as though the boring of one-half the hole dulled the drill, and a new one was used upon the opposite side ; and this difference appears to be explained when we look over a series of these pointed arrow-head-like implements which we have considered as the tools wherewith the perforations were made.

Figure 155 represents a perfect example of a form of implement of which we have collected three specimens. We have classed it as a drilling-stone, because it *might* have been used for such a purpose; but it was apparently *never* used, but lost or discarded as soon as made. The specimen is a chipped piece of slaty rock, four and seven-eighths inches in length. The head or point is narrower than the main portion of the implement, oval in outline, and somewhat pointed. About an inch from the point there is a slight contraction of the outline, when it again widens and retains a uniform width of an inch and one-fourth. The sides are well chipped and brought to a good edge, as is also the base of the specimen, which is slightly rounded.

Figure 156 represents a beautiful example of chipping in white quartz, the specimen being the head, apparently, of such an instrument as figure 155. As the three preceding examples are all of slate, this one is figured to show that the same instrument occurs in different materials. Although there is no indication of polish upon the point of this specimen, we believe it to be a drilling-stone—possibly one which was broken before being used. We find, by experiment, that with it but little time and labor are necessary to drill through the ordinary "breast-plates," such as those described in the following chapter.

We would also call attention to the similarity of this specimen with the "scraper," figure 129. There is indeed little or no difference, except that in figure 156 there is no chipped or beveled edge for scraping, as in figure 129. It suggests, in itself, therefore, that when an implement like figure 155 became broken, such a fragment as figure 156 would usually be chipped smooth upon the broken surface and thus converted into a scraper. This would explain the presence of points, such as the scrapers, figures 128 and 129 have, which features do not appear to have any value so far as the use of the specimens as "scrapers" goes, and indeed, to us, they seem a great objection as they make the instrument much more difficult to hold.

Figure 157 represents a very roughly-chipped implement of slate, which bears some resemblance to the specimen, figure 155. We unhesitatingly pronounce it to be a drilling-stone, inasmuch as at the pointed end there is a polished surface, which has escaped the general weathering which the specimen has undergone. In this specimen it will be noticed that the narrow portion or waist is nearer the middle than in figure 155, so that the "head" is very nearly one-half the total length of the instrument itself. The sides of the specimen throughout their whole extent are brought by chipping, to cutting edges as sharp as those of the majority of arrow-points or "flint" hatchets. If viewed horizontally, figure 157 appears to be a slender tomahawk, and allied closely to some of the forms of "rude implements" which we have described; the narrow middle appearing to be notched for the better fastening of a handle. If such was the use and object of this specimen, then what we now consider the "base" was the front or cutting edge, and this it has certainly never been, inasmuch as it is by far the most blunt and irregular portion of the margin of the implement.

The polished point, to which we have alluded, shows that the purpose of this implement was to drill other stones, and, although the mineral of which it is made has suffered softening to some extent by long exposure, still with sand and water it will now drill ordinary breast-plates.

Figure 158 presents another form of chipped slate, bearing some resemblance to figure 155, which we have classed with the drilling-stones, but whether correctly or not we are by no means certain. They are abundant; almost always associated with the preceding forms, and always made of slate. The one figured is a good example of this class. It is rudely chipped, three inches long, and two wide, at the widest portion of the specimen. The point is sufficiently sharp to drill the thinner "breast-plates," one side at a time.

Mr. Evans has figured* six specimens of flint implements, which he denominates "borers, awls, or drills." Four of them are very nearly identical with several we have figured in the foregoing pages of this chapter. Probably the most noticeable difference is, which in such of Mr. Evans's figures as have broad bases, they are much less elaborately chipped than the New Jersey examples of the same implement. Whatever may be the advantage of true flint, which we do not have, over some veins of jasper, which we do have (not in New Jersey, but near it) in abundance, it is certain that the majority of our specimens, as scrapers, drilling-stones, &c., are manufactured with greater elegance, and evince a more thorough knowledge of the "flint-chipping" art. The English specimens of "drills" appear to be all "flakes" which have had their edges chipped, that the requisite shape might be given to the specimen. The New Jersey specimens, on the contrary, are, like arrow-heads, chipped entire, from a fragment of jasper, or, it may be, from a jasper pebble, and no portion of the surface is a part of the natural surface of the rock.

Two of the specimens figured by Mr. Evans are quite blunt at the ends, but not more so than some of the drilling-stones which we have figured. These blunt forms Mr. Evans thinks may have been arrow-points, and not drills. Prof. Charles Rau, of New York, has given us a most interesting paper on drilling in stone,† in which he claims that a wooden drill, with sand and water, was one method in use during the stone age, for perforating stone. We do not doubt that he is correct as to the larger holes drilled through polished stone ornaments, banner-stones, and pipes; but we hold to our opinion as to the use of the specimens we have described in this chapter.

We quote one paragraph of Prof. Rau's paper, as bearing upon the question of the purpose of the specimens illustrated in this chapter. Prof. Rau writes: " Mr. Desor thinks it probable that the drilling was effected by means of very thin flakes of flint fixed around a stick, which

* Anc. Stone Imp. of Great Brit., pp. 288–291.
† Smithsonian Report for 1868–'69, p. 392.

was made to turn in such way as to separate a portion of the stone, which, when the perforation was accomplished, would fall to the ground.* A drilling-stick of this description really *may have served for perforating soft stones*, but could not be successfully applied to hard materials." We have carefully examined in detail all our specimens of "breast-plates" from slate and other minerals, and find that the holes through them can be duplicated by the aid of any of the specimens we have figured, merely twirling the drill between the thumb and fingers.

Figure 159 represents a flat slab of very hard, finely grained sandstone, which in outline bears some resemblance to a small mammal, crouching down; as a muskrat or small rabbit. This resemblance may be accidental, and the outline produced in the more prosaic use of a whetstone, as the margins are all polished and cut by contact with other stones. The five deep cuts upon the side of the specimen have been artificially produced, and while they bear some resemblance to grooves on polishing-stones, such as were used in sharpening celts and skinning-stones, we rather incline to the opinion that they were made to give the stone a more animal-like appearance.

We shall again refer to the specimen in chapter xviii.

The object of placing the specimen in the present chapter, is to refer more particularly to the hole drilled through it, which, if the stone be a representation of an animal, corresponds to the eye.

When the specimen taken from a grave was procured, there was on each side of the stone, where the perforation now is, a shallow circular depression, with a "nipple" in the center, showing that a perforation had been commenced; the drill used being a hollow reed. This of itself added to the animal-like appearance. By the aid of the two stone drills (figures 161, 162) we completed the perforation; accomplishing it after eleven hours of not difficult but rather tiresome labor. While drilling, which was done by simply twirling the drills to and fro, we kept the specimen under water. The drill, figure 162, is of slate, and comparatively soft, but it did not wear away more rapidly than the jasper specimen, in consequence of the latter continually splintering; the splinters amounting to about the same as the gradual wear of the softer specimen. Figure 160 represents a fragment of a large "breast-plate," very carefully polished along the edges, and smooth on the broad surfaces. When found, there was a single hole drilled through it, the uppermost one in the specimen as now figured. The mineral is a dense sandstone, but more yielding than the "animal" carving, figure 159. With the softer drill, figure 162, we made the nine perforations seen in the illustration. The time occupied in drilling each hole varied from a half to three-quarters of an hour; the wear upon the implement was scarcely appreciable. Considering that thin plates of stone were so frequently perforated by the aborigines that they might be suspended to the person, and that

---

* Palafittes, &c., p. 359.

implements of stone admirably adapted to such work are so abundant, we are of opinion that our suggestions as to the use of the latter are substantially correct.*

CHAPTER XVI.

BREAST-PLATES AND GORGETS.

On the site of ancient Indian towns, throughout the whole State, or wherever evidences occur of a fierce battle, and in every grave we have opened, are found tablets of easily-worked stone, varying in length and outline, and, as a rule, carefully polished, and perforated with one, two, or more holes. Such stone ornaments—and they were intended merely as ornaments—we have called "breast-plates," because found lying near the breast of skeletons in the graves which we have examined, or "gorgets," a good name for them, suggested by Squier and Davis.

We have said that these breast-plates or gorgets vary in shape and size, which is the case, but those found in New Jersey are most usually of the shape of our first illustration, (figure 163,) and vary only in other details from this, which may be considered the typical form. The mineral of which they are made varies much, but none have been found of stone as hard as porphyry.

Figure 163 is four and five-sixteenths inches long and one inch and five-eighths wide at the middle; this specimen has been drilled in two places from each side until the depressions met, the distance between the holes on one side being exactly four-fifths of an inch, a distance noticed particularly by Squier and Davis,† in several of the specimens they figured. They remark, " It is a singular fact that the holes in the three specimens first noticed, as also in some of those which follow, are placed exactly four-fifths of an inch apart. This could hardly have been the result of accident. These relics were found at different localities, several miles distant from each other." If this similarity of distance between the perforations was intentional, it would seem that the stone had some use other than merely as a breast-ornament. Certainly, in such case, the mere distance separating the holes could have had no special use. In figure 163 this distance is variable, inasmuch as the hole is obliquely drilled, and so produces a greater space between the two perforations on one side than on the other. This crooked drilling and unequal interspacing is quite common, and seems more strange when the accuracy of the drilling in "banner-stones," which were much more elaborate ornaments, is taken into consideration. The rude drilling of some breast-plates may indicate that they are older than banner-stones, and were fashioned when the art of drilling was not much advanced.

---

* Mr. John Evans, of England, referring in detail to the various forms in a small collection of antiquities forwarded to him by the author, writes of a slate drill, a *fac simile* of fig. 142 : "I imagine it to have been an awl or boring-tool for soft substances, such as leather." While this is very probable, we think we have shown clearly that these "soft" drills are capable of drilling in stone.

† Anc. Mon. Miss. Valley, p. 237.

On one side, at the extreme end of this specimen, figure 163, is a row of short notches carefully cut, and of a size throughout. Such notches being better preserved on the next figure, we will reserve our remarks concerning them until that specimen is described. Figure 163 was probably considerably harder when fashioned into a gorget. It has undergone a process of decomposition which has made it chalky on the surface, while the interior has not been unaffected. The specimen is of a reddish-brown slate with a greasy feel, similar to that experienced by the collector in handling milky quartz, but to a greater degree.

The length and general shape of such breast-plates as figure 163 have rendered them peculiarly liable to be broken, especially when lying near or upon the surface of our long-cultivated fields. Usually such specimens, when so found, are but halves, or even smaller fragments; and whole ones are to be looked for only in the graves. Figure 163 was taken from a grave, in a little natural mound, on the tract of marsh known as Bear Swamp, near Lawrence, Mercer County, New Jersey. Associated with this breast-plate were several arrow-points and an ax. Figure 164 represents a most interesting specimen of breast-plate. Its shape is peculiar, the number of holes unusual, and the series of notches at the rounded end a marked feature of the specimen. The upper margin measures two and three-fourths of an inch in length; the lower, a trace over one inch and a half. The notched end is rounded at the angles, and the curves thence continue as a reversed and longer curve along the sides. The oblique end has been as carefully polished as the flat surfaces. The holes, four in number, were roughly drilled and evidently in pairs, and not promiscuously or even at one time. The pair quite near together are larger than the others, irregularly drilled, and are in the center of the plate. The other pair, better drilled, and smaller, are at the angles of the oblique end of the specimen. The chief feature of interest connected with this specimen is the series of carefully cut notches, very regularly distributed along the curved end of the plate; eleven on one side and nine on the other. The nine notches upon the under side are not mere continuations of the others, but are distinct, in some instances not being opposite the others. The thought naturally arises, what do these notches indicate? We believe that, as the specimen was a breast-plate or a breast-ornament, these notches were a record of the number of fights in which the wearer was engaged, or of scalps taken. The notches cannot be said to be either useful or ornamental for a breast-plate, they are not requisite at all, as are holes for suspending the same, while they are too inconspicuous to be considered merely ornamental markings. The natural inference, therefore, is that they are intended as a "record."

Figure 165 represents a different form of stone ornament which may have been suspended by a cord so as to hang in front of the breast, or was suspended from the terminal lobe of the ear. At any rate, it was designed for ornament and not for any other purpose, as has been suggested, such as a fishing-line weight or a sinker. This specimen is not smoothly finished, nor accurately outlined, as is usual with this pattern of ornamental stones. The hole is nearly uniform in width, from side to side, being somewhat more flaring upon the "wrong" side, or that which is not marked with ornamental lines. These lines are an interesting feature of this specimen. They are much less distinct than the notches in figure 164, and are more than double their length ; the spaces between them are much wider, and the lines themselves are engraved upon the sides of the stone, instead of on the end ; yet, with all these differences, their object was no doubt identical with that of the notches in figure 164. About the perforation of this specimen are also four lines, similar in depth and width to those upon the sides, which are drawn at such angles to each other as to meet above, at each side, and beneath, making a diamond-shaped figure. Whether this was merely for ornamentation, or, like the side markings, for a record of certain events, is not determined, but the probability is that it was only to compensate for the general roughness of the specimen both as to shape and surface.

Figure 166 represents a polished serpentine specimen of the same general character as the preceding one. It is longer, but of the same width ; it is considerably thinner, flat upon both sides, and more highly polished along the edges than over the sides. The perforation is quite different from that of figure 165, being a cup-shaped depression, made upon each side, and meeting at the middle of the stone, the hole there being but one-third the diameter of the drilling upon the surface. There is no trace of any " record" mark whatever upon this specimen ; it being, in this respect, different from all the preceding examples, and similar to one of the seventeen specimens figured by Messrs. Squier and Davis,* except that the hole is nearer the end than that of the Ohio specimen. Of the relics of this class, from New Jersey, the specimen figured is the usual size ; but occasionally they have been found greatly exceeding it. Mr. Newbold, of Burlington County, New Jersey, has one specimen exactly twice the length, but otherwise like the one figured.

Figure 167 represents a small, but very handsome gorget, which has a marked peculiarity in the ornamentation upon one side. The specimen itself is short, being but one inch and three-quarters in length. The upper or perforated end is but three-eighths of an inch in width, and from this upper margin the specimen increases uniformly in width until near the bottom, when it rounds off in an almost regular curve. The hole appears to have been drilled wholly from the plain, or under side, being wider there at the surface than upon the opposite side, which has a slightly worn edge occasioned by the rubbing of the cord that suspended it. We believe this specimen to have been pierced with one of the smaller stone drills figured in the preceding chapter.

The ornamentation of figure 167 differs from any that we have ever seen elsewhere. The surface of the stone has been smoothly worn off,

*L. c., p. 237, fig. 136, No. 14.

leaving, a short distance below the perforation, a quadrangular figure that may be called a hollow square, there being a cleanly-cut depression in the center of the projecting "square," the width of which is just double the depth. Below this figure commences a second, which can be compared to an inverted pick-ax, with the iron arms straighter than usual. It is simply a "raised" ridge, the surrounding surface being cut away to leave it in bold relief. It is not exactly in the center of the specimen, but near it, the upper ridge or handle of the pick being slightly inclined to one side. Below this the specimen is smoothly polished and somewhat sloped to the end. We cannot see how any doubt can be entertained as to the nature of this specimen. If *not a suspended ornament*, it is safe to express doubt as to an arrow-head being an arrow-head or an ax being an ax.

Figure 168 is another most interesting specimen of this class of relics. It is a piece of black, well-worn stone, but with no polish ; it is thin, but irregularly so, and has a greasy feel which is most deceptive. One can almost smell the grease, now stale, with which the object seems to be saturated. The specimen is leaf-shaped, more pointed at one end than at the other, and, when viewed horizontally, has a striking resemblance to our common sun-fish (*Pomotis vulgaris*). We believe that this fish was intended to be represented, and that it was the tribe mark of the original possessor of this ornament. If such was the case, then the hole which represents the eye of the fish was used to suspend the specimen from the person who carried it. Notwithstanding the unworn condition of the hole, which is of uniform width from one side to the other, we believe that a soft string, probably a sinew, was passed through it and the gorget suspended from the neck. That such was the use of this specimen cannot, as in the preceding example, be doubted.

Figure 169 represents a split, water-worn jasper pebble, of somewhat irregular shape, with an extensive perforation through it. The hole is about one-half the diameter upon the under or split side that it is upon the upper. The under side, however, has an equally weather-worn polish with the upper, indicating that the perforation was made subsequently to the splitting of the pebble, or that many years have elapsed since the "split" pebble was drilled, the peculiar gloss of the fractured surface indicating great age. The somewhat irregular outline of the perforation upon the "split" side of the pebble favors the belief that the fracture occurred *after* the drilling. This specimen is interesting from its resemblance to an African example figured by Sir John Lubbock.[*] This African drilled stone is square instead of pentagonal, and the drilling is of much less diameter at the junction of the two depressions which, together, make the perforation.

Squier and Davis[†] seem to be in doubt as to the use of such specimens as the preceding seven figures of this chapter. They remark, "at first glance it seems obvious that they were designed for suspen-

---

* Jour. Anthrop. Inst. of Great Britain, vol. i, pl. i.   † L. c., p. 238.

sion; but there are many circumstances which it is not easy to reconcile with that conclusion. In common with the perforated copper
plates, already described, they exhibit slight traces of friction upon the
edges of the holes, which, for the most part, are as sharp as if newly
cut. This could hardly be the case had they been worn suspended from
the neck, or upon any part of the person." Notwithstanding this objection
we have considered these perforated plates to have been ornaments for the
person, from the fact of their position, which is always the same when
found in graves. On opening a grave, the invariable position of the
trinkets and weapons has been as follows : weapons on the right side ;
pipe on the left ; small vase (pottery) at the feet, and the ornaments
near the region of the breast. If these " breast-plates," as we have
termed them, had been some domestic implement, as a " bow-string
twister," it seems strange that they should have been invariably placed
upon the breast of the person buried. Again, why so large an amount of
ornamentation, as is sometimes seen, if the stone relics in question
were not used for decoration ?*

Figure 170 represents a not very abundant, curiously-wrought stone
ornament or implement, we cannot determine which, but one which was
once used over a large extent of territory.† This specimen is a fraction
over four and a half inches long. The body, or main portion, is very
accurately sloped to the back, which is a narrow flat ridge, of a uniform
width of one thirty-second of an inch. The " head " of the specimen is
nearly square, and not unlike the head of a blunt muzzled mammal in
shape. The knob-like protuberances stand out from the head one-third
of an inch, and have a narrow neck, about one-half the width of
the " knob " itself. The bottom of the implement, as the illustration
shows, is flat. There is at each end of the bottom of the specimen a small hole, drilled obliquely upward and outward, meeting
another drilled hole, made from above, and extending downward
until it meets the other. These holes are characteristic of this class
of relics. There appears to be a considerable diversity of opinion
as to the nature of these relics, all of which are about the same size as
the one figured, and, as a class, they are more than usually uniform.
No illustration of this pattern of ornament that we have met with has
the knob-like protuberance, or head, so noticeable as this.

170. Schoolcraft‡ has designated this form of relic as a handle for a
knife, the blade of which was obsidian or jasper. One of these "knife-
handles" is figured, found on Cunningham's Island, Lake Erie, New
York, which is considered to be " apparently a sacrificial or a flaying

---

* Figures 169 *a–b* represent the two sides of breast-plate, found near Freehold, N.
J. The very elaborate ornamentation on each side, and the careful notching certainly
are to be taken as proofs that the specimen itself was an ornament, and not a mere
implement. This specimen was received from Rev. S. Lockwood, of Freehold, N. J., too
late for further description.

† Squier & Davis, Anc. Mon. Miss. Valley, p. 239.

‡ Hist. Condit., &c., N. A. I., vol. iv, p. 175, pl. xxiii, fig. 2.

knife." The relic is so described, although there is no indication of a blade.*

We believe that Messrs. Squier and Davis† correctly cover the whole ground concerning them, in stating that "it may reasonably be concluded from the uniform shape of these articles, and from their apparent unfitness as implements, as also from the wide range of their occurrence, that they were invested with a conventional significance as insignia, or badges of distinction, or as amulets. We know that the custom of wearing certain stones as preventives of disease, or as safeguards against accidents or the malice of evil spirits, has not been confined to one continent, or to a single age. It is not entirely obliterated among certain classes of our own people. Regal authority is still indicated by rich baubles of gold and gems. It matters little whether the index of royalty be a scepter or a simple carved and polished stone, so that it is sanctioned with general recognition."

CHAPTER XVII.

BANNER-STONES.

The love of display that has survived the changes in human culture, and which is witnessed in some civilized communities in all the glare and glitter of barbarian times, was and is a marked trait in the character of the American aborigines. And, although in their painting there is nothing but harshness and most violent contrasts of gay colors, and in their pipe-sculpture but little to commend, we nevertheless have, in the series of stone relics which we have here called "banner-stones," a beautiful illustration of the fact that symmetry could be obtained in more complicated forms than the shapes of arrow-points; and elegance of design and accuracy in details were sought and acquired by this untutored race, their banner-stones being the more remarkable in that they are frequently of hard stone, to fashion, carve, and polish which the only tools available were those of the same material.

The variety of forms in this class of stone ornaments is very extensive, and so scarce are unbroken specimens that we have been unable to present any great number of figures. Of the more common shape, which may, perhaps, be considered typical of the class, we have but one absolutely perfect specimen. (Figure 172.) Of the varying examples we present one which is of peculiar shape—a broken specimen, "done up" for duty again as an ornament.

We have classed these relics as " banner " stones or ornamental stones, either used in the decoration of weapons or for suspension from the body, after the manner of breast-plates.

Figure 172 is a beautiful example of the more usual form of banner-stones, as found in New Jersey. In outline, finish, and perforation it is faultless. Of a very fine-grained sandstone it was first carefully chipped and then polished until no trace of uneven surface can be detected in it. The upper or convex margin is accurately curved from end to end, with

---

*L. c., vol. ii, pl. 45, fig. 1.   †Anc. Mon. Miss. Valley, p. 239.

the exception of a very slight depression at the opening of the perforation. One end is somewhat flattened, the other less abruptly outlined. The under or concave margin is less defined than the upper, and more sloping from the center toward each end than a segment of a circle. Both the upper and lower margins are flat, the width of each decreasing from the perforation at the middle of the specimen toward each end.

The hole which passes entirely through the middle of figure 172 is a very noticeable feature. It measures a little less than nine-sixteenths of an inch in diameter; it is perfectly circular, of uniform dimensions from end to end, and faintly exhibits those rings that characterize holes drilled with a hollow instrument, as a reed, as this perforation must have been.

Professor Rau, of New York, has so fully and accurately gone over the whole subject of drilling in stone without metal, that we refer our readers to his paper [*] for the details of the modus operandi of making these larger perforations which characterize such relics as we have called banner-stones. A superficial examination of the hole drilled through figure 132 shows that such perforation has been made with a hollow instrument. We presume it to have been a reed, and Professor Rau states, in the paper above mentioned,[†] " It is very likely that the *hollow* drills of the aborigines of North America were pieces of that hard and tough cane (*Arundinaria macrosperma*, Michaux) which grows abundantly in the southern part of the United States, mostly along the banks of large rivers, and forms at present an article of trade, being used for pipe-stems and fishing-rods. This cane varies considerably in thickness; sometimes as thin as a straw, it assumes, when fully grown, the diametral proportions of a strong rifle-barrel, and even of larger cylindrical objects, in which cases it reaches the enormous height of 25 or 30 feet. A piece of this cane, from which the knotty joints have been cut, forms a regular hollow cylinder sufficiently strong to serve as a drill. I learned from Dr. Davis that many years ago a stone pipe with an unfinished hollow, partly filled with vegetable matter, was sent from Mississippi to the late Dr. Samuel P. Morton, of Philadelphia. When subjected to a microscopical examination the vegetable substance exhibited the fibrous structure of cane, and thus appeared to be a remnant of a drill broken off in the bore. Squier and Davis [‡] figure one example of a banner-stone, very similar to figure 132, and say of it, and others somewhat similar, " It is clear, both from their form and material, that they were not designed for use. They may be regarded as having been intended simply for ornament or display."

Whatever may have been the manner of exhibiting such stone ornaments it is impossible to determine, but the fortunate possessor of such a specimen might well be proud of it. May it not be that such stones were the " charms " of the " medicine " men ? Stones that were concealed from the general gaze of the crowd, and only brought to view

---

[*] Smithsonian Rep. for 1868, p. 392. [†] L. c., p. 399.
[‡] Anc. Mon. Miss. Valley, p. 218, fig. 114, No. 3.

with elaborate coverings on great occasions. They do not seem sufficiently abundant to be simply the ornaments of chiefs or warriors.

Figures 173 and 173a represent a second example of this form of perforated ornament, or banner-stone. It is shorter and broader than the preceding, but is well made, and drilled with that smoothness and beauty which are marked features of figure 172. The outline drawing of a sectional view of the specimen shows that the perforation is somewhat oval, instead of perfectly circular, and the diameter of the drilling is a little less at the apex than at the base. The drilling of this hole must, therefore, have been done with something different from a section or a number of sections of reed of identical diameter. This specimen has probably been drilled by the application of sand and water, in connection with a solid drill, as a pointed wooden stick, but the perforation begun below has been continued from thence, but only half the distance on each side as is usual in such cases.*

Figure 174 represents a very interesting form of banner-stone, of a totally different shape from either of the preceding examples. This specimen is an oval or ovoid polished pebble of a soft mineral, approaching, but not identical with soapstone. The two halves, if we divide it through the center of the perforation which extends from the top to the bottom, will be found identical in every particular of shape and dimension. The base of the specimen is somewhat more flattened than the top, and appears to have been in contact with another stone, as it is worn off smoothly, but with a variable width. This worn surface is of a lighter tint than the other portions of the specimen. The perforation is a little less in diameter than that of figure 172, but it is of equal beauty of workmanship. The diameter is the same throughout, the perforation being accurately circular, and showing the rings which indicate drilling with a hollow tube. For a short distance from the base, extending upward along the sides of the perforation, the "rings" are not distinguishable, except by the closest scrutiny, and appear to have been worn away by the rubbing of whatever passed through the hole as a handle or suspensory cord. From point to point, this specimen measures two and five-eighths inches, and across the middle one inch and a half. The diameter of the perforation is just one-half an inch, or one-third of the total width of the specimen itself.

Figure 174 is quite similar in general appearance to a specimen of this character found in Mississippi, and figured by Squier and Davis, which specimen, however, "measures six inches in length. The hole is half an inch in diameter at one end, *but less at the other ;*" which latter feature is met with in figure 173, but not in either figure 172 or 174.

Figures 172 and 174 were both found in Burlington County, New Jersey, but not together, and were kindly presented to the author by Joseph Newbold, esq., to whom we are indebted for several favors of a similar character.

---

* *Vide* Rau, l. c., p. 92.

Figure 175 represents a form of banner-stone allied to figure 172, but is noticeably different in not being perforated for a handle or suspensory cord, but simply grooved upon one side; the groove, too, being narrow and very shallow. The specimen is of hornstone, and was first pecked into its present shape, and subsequently polished over the whole surface of one side and one-half of the surface of the other side. The groove is polished over its entire surface. The margins are all blunt, and, although quite regular in outline, have had no care in finishing.

We have met with no other specimen of banner-stone that was grooved on only one side, and it may be, indeed, that we err in considering figure 175 under this heading; but its size, shape, and general appearance show very plainly that it was never intended either as a weapon or a domestic implement, unless it is unfinished and was intended to be a double-bladed skinning-knife. This conjecture, however, we do not believe to be in any way correct.

Figure 176 is the half of a banner-stone of the pattern of figure 172, but much smaller than that specimen, and pointed, instead of bluntly rounded at the end. This fragment is interesting, as it shows that such banner-stones were highly valued by the people who fashioned them, and that a piece of one was not to be discarded if it could at all be utilized. The broken edges of this specimen, which has been fractured along the perforation, has been carefully smoothed down, and through the middle of one of these projecting edges a small hole has been drilled. This hole has been drilled from both sides, showing that the specimen was broken after the large hole had been completed. Along the lower margin, on one side only, is a long row of narrow, closely-placed lines, which appear to have been carved there by design as a "record," such as we have shown on specimens of the breast-plates.

As a class, these banner-stones are found scattered over the country, at or very near the surface. They are turned up occasionally by the plow or spade, but are not found more numerously at one point than at another, as at localities known to have been sites of Indian villages formerly. We have not met with any specimens of this stone in graves, as we have with the breast-plates described in chapter xvi.

These elaborate banner-stones bear witness to the great patience possessed by those who fashioned them. Although it is true that time was not taken into consideration in the various undertakings of the aborigines, yet, in view of their well-known aversion to labor, these specimens are the more marvelous, since steady hard labor was required to bring them to their present respective conditions.

It must be noticed that these banner-stones are now no longer made by any of the western tribes. The rude brass trinkets obtainable at the trading-posts, and the bright-colored beads, have taken the place of these less gaudy, but far more beautiful ornaments. The contact of the Indians with the whites has certainly been fatal to their taste for art, from the banner-stone to the bead being a long step backward.

The stone implements of Great Britain do not include any forms which are analogous to our banner-stones. In Mr. Evans's work there is nothing in any way similar to the specimens figured in this chapter, excepting, perhaps, an oval perforated hammer-head,* which, however, is double the size of the banner-stone, (figure 174,) which it resembles.

CHAPTER XVIII.

STONE-AGE SCULPTURE.

Lubbock says: "The earliest traces of art yet discovered belong to the Stone age—to a time so remote that the reindeer was abundant in the south of France, and that probably, though on this point there is some doubt, even the mammoth had not entirely disappeared. These works of art are sometimes sculptures, if one may say so, and sometimes drawings or etchings made on bone or horn with the point of a flint."[†]

We recalled this statement on finding our first specimen of New Jersey Stone-age sculpture, and could not but feel astonished to see so rude an attempt at art, when the pipes of the western mound-builders are so elaborate in all their features. The date of the production of these "animal carvings" is as yesterday, compared with the sculptures and etchings of the reindeer people of Southern France, and yet they are even ruder, and far ruder than the pipe-sculptures of the mound-building people. From these facts we conclude that the Atlantic coast Indian was inferior in art capabilities to the people of the western mounds, which may or may not have antedated them in their occupancy of American territory, and that, at one time, the aborigines of New Jersey were, in art capabilities, scarcely as far advanced as the reindeer people of the south of France.[‡]

Were we guided by the excellency of workmanship in our estimate of the comparative antiquity of stone implements and art productions of a Stone-age people, the rude profile carvings, of which but four examples have as yet occurred, would be far older than the mounds of the Mississippi Valley, or the elaborately carved pipes they contain. As the photographic portrait is a later achievement of the ingenuity of man

---

* Anc. Stone Imp. of G. B., p. 203, fig. 154.

† Lubbock. Orig. of Civil., 2d ed., p. 30.

‡ *Works of art of the cave-dwellers.*—"With   *   *   evidences of easy living, it is not surprising to find there was leisure for less necessary work, and that spare time found occupation in works of pleasure, as instanced in the sketches and sculpture before alluded to. And it is curious to trace how they passed from the simple exercise of industry to ornament, and at last to something of art, for such may well be termed the sculptured poniard handle, representing the figure of a reindeer, and which, while clever in its adaptation of the material to the purpose intended, preserves at the same time all the characteristics of the animal." (Reliquiæ Aquitanicæ, p. 22.)

The foregoing remarks are equally applicable to the early Indians of New Jersey in matters of art and ornament. They too, notwithstanding frequent wars with neighboring tribes, appear to have found time to carve or, at least, *shape* slabs of compact stones into good resemblances of those animals with which they were familiar.

than the silhouettes which still adorn many old walls, so these profile carvings *should* be older than the useful and so ingeniously carved pipes. Such, however, is not the case; and the differences in the two classes of relics indicate different peoples as their respective producers—the one an older, it may be, but certainly a more advanced people; the other at the very outset, as it were, of human culture.

We must conclude, therefore, that the two peoples were wholly unlike and independent in origin; or, originating from a common center, that they proved very unequal in their progress in culture. The latter appears to be the correct view, inasmuch as in all other respects their stone implement productions were identical, both in the variety of form in each particular weapon, and the skill exhibited in the flint-chipping art.

We say "in all other respects," because the art capabilities of a people are an index to their intellectual advancement. No better guide can be had to a proper estimate of the relative advancement of a race or tribe. More modern, less advanced, Indians, however, have occasionally proved themselves capable of the imitative art to a degree commensurate with the mound-builders of an earlier date; and the Chippewa pipe, figured by Dr. Wilson,[*] certainly equals any animal carving the mounds have yielded, or the even more complicated and fantastic illustrations of Babeen pipe sculpture which the same author gives us.[†]

It is to be regretted that so few examples of this profile-carving have, as yet, been met with; and, further, that they should all have come from a single limited locality, since this gives rise to the thought that they are all the work of some one ingenious savage.

One of these specimens, a pebble of unusual shape, and one requiring but little alteration to make it what it is, can scarcely be considered an "animal carving;" but the ingenuity displayed in utilizing nature's freaks to secure a result similar to carving, shows skill akin to that requisite in carving.

Figure 177 represents the specimen above referred to as the first example of its kind we have met with. It is a plate of slaty stone, and has a nearly uniform thickness of half an inch. The margins have been carefully polished, as also have the two surfaces of the specimen, which latter, however, are less smooth than formerly, owing to scratching by the sand and gravel among which it was found. There is no attempt whatever at even an outline drawing of an eye or other feature; the whole attention of the artist having evidently been to correctly outline the stone, in which respect he has been successful. The curvature of the cranial outline and the neck, and the commencement of the back are correct, while the nose, lower jaw, and under outline of the neck are equally so. From the highest point of the arch of the cranium downward the specimen is narrowed along the edge, being thinnest at the point of juncture of the neck and back. It is supposed that the animal

---

[*] Prehistoric Man, 2d ed., p. 319, fig. 27.   [†] L. c., p. 320, figs. 28, 29.

intended to be represented by this carving is the seal, of which, at the present day, a single one will occasionally wander up the Delaware River, one being killed during April of the present year, at Salem, Salem County, New Jersey. Formerly the seal was not uncommon in Delaware Bay, and, at the time of the settlement of Littleworth, now Trenton, New Jersey, in 1680, they were numerous about the rapids, or so-called Falls, of the Delaware.

This specimen of stone-carving is by far the finest of the three examples we have been able to secure, and shows in every detail that much care was expended in its production. How a block of stone of its density could have been cut in the age in question is impossible for us to determine. We have found nothing in the way of weapon-making tools that would answer for such stone-cutting; and it seems incredible that it should have been pecked into shape and the margins and surface afterward polished. A few fresh fractures of small extent show the body of the stone to be of a dark lead-blue color, but the surface is a dull brown. Upon one side are four irregularly-shaped patches of small crystals in a matrix of apparently silicate of lime. These have formed upon the specimen after it was lost or thrown aside, and indicate considerable lapse of time since the date of its fashioning by the aboriginal artist. What could have been the object of a carving such as this? How was it used when finished? The holes in breastplates and ear-drops explain *their* nature and the method of utilizing *them*, but in the present instance there is nothing by which to suspend the object, nor an indication of any method whereby a handle could have been attached, which latter, however, would scarcely have added to the value of such a specimen. Again, the aborigines were of too migratory a nature for stationary idols or ornaments for the walls of their wigwams. That the three examples figured are the work of the aborigines, and that they are intended to represent animals, cannot be doubted, but as to the meaning of the carvings, and the use to which the specimens were put, we can only conjecture.

Figure 177, 177*a* is a small, oddly-shaped pebble of a reddish-brown color, which, while it originally bore some resemblance to the head of a bird, has had that resemblance increased by the rubbing away of certain points about the margin, and the grinding of the convex surface on one side until it was flat, leaving in the center of the worn surfaces a circular projection, which correctly represents, in size and position, an eye of a bird. The under surface is irregularly concave, and has no such eye-trace or other markings upon it.*

Figure 178 represents the head and neck of a bird-like animal, rather than of a bird or mammal exclusively. Were it the only specimen of this kind we had seen, we should doubt the propriety of considering it an indication of stone-age art, although it has marks of human workmanship in the polished margins at the slope of the back of the head and

---

* Figure 177 does not correctly represent the specimen, the artist having omitted the "eye."

neck and on the lower or basal outline of the specimen. The projecting point in front much resembles the beak of a bird, and although rough in finish does not appear to be merely an accidental fracture. This specimen was found within a few yards of figure 176, and we do not doubt that it is an unfinished specimen of the same nature. Two-thirds of the original surface, upon one side, has been broken off in a single piece, and this newer surface has now nearly the same degree of weathering, and is of nearly the same tint as the natural surface of the specimen. There are no grooves, scratches, or other markings that appear to have been made when the stone itself recieved its present shape.

This specimen is a finely grained, compact sandstone, readily scratching glass, but is more easily worked than the jasper(?) pebble, figure 177. With the exceptions of the two portions of the margin above referred to, there is no indication of any attempt to polish or smooth down the surface of the stone.

If it be objected that these stone figures are too rudely shaped to be considered specimens of animal sculpture, we can only say, in reply, that they are not accidentally fractured stones, as shown by their polished and ground surfaces at different points. Again, they are not more crude than those wonderful " animal mounds" mentioned* by Lapham, as existing in Wisconsin; and it may not be inappropriate here to refer to a figure given by this gentleman, and called " the stone bird." Mr. Lapham† remarks: "At Hustisford a stone was shown us, which, by the aid of a little imagination, may be supposed to represent the head of a bird, and which was held in great veneration by the Winnebago Indians, who have but very recently been removed from this part of the State. It is a gneissoid granite, of accidental form, caused by the unequal decay and disintegration of the different layers of which it is composed." Here we see that an accidentally shaped stone was venerated because of some resemblance to a bird; and if a modern Indian could see the resemblance in the case of the stone figured by Mr. Lapham, would it not require a less fertile imagination to see the resemblance in the specimens we have figured, which are recognized as animal carvings by those who have seen them, and which, unlike the Wisconsin stone bird, are not chance shapings but designed cuttings.

We have in Squier and Davis's‡ great monograph an account of several "singularly sculptured tablets," one of which is figured. " It represents a coiled rattlesnake; both faces of the tablet being identical in sculpture, excepting that one is plane, the other slightly convex. The material is a very fine cinnamon-colored sandstone." We have here a near approach to the general character of our specimen, figure 176; but the Ohio tablet has elaborate carving upon the sides, which alone enables the specimen to be recognized as a snake, while in the three figures we have given, the recognition of the intended likeness to animal heads is through the outline alone.

---

* Antiq. of Wisconsin, Smithson. Contrib., vol. vii.   † L. c., p. 51.
‡ Anc. Mon. Miss. Valley, p. 276, fig. 196.

Mr. Squier[*] also, in his memoir on the aboriginal monuments of New York, figures a terra-cotta head of a fox and two other specimens of an indefinite character, which are also more elaborate in the details, but not more accurate in outline, than is figure 176 compared with the fox-head figured by Mr. Squier, or the two figures 177 and 178 as compared with the two ruder figures given in the above-mentioned monograph. We conclude, therefore, that our New Jersey specimens bear to those of the West the same relation that the old-time silhouettes bear to the modern photograph.

Considering that the difficulty of shaping hard stone is much greater than molding terra-cotta, surely the New Jersey outline carvings exhibit an equal amount of skill to those described from other States and required a greater amount of patience; but there was little difference in the capabilities of the aborigines of New York and New Jersey, the advantage in most respects being, probably, with the more northern tribes.

On page 140 we briefly referred to a "slab of hard sandstone," which, it is thought, may properly be called an "animal carving," although, on our first examination of the specimen, its outline did not impress us as being very animal like. Our impression then was that the ground, or semi-polished surfaces upon the edges of the specimen, were produced in polishing weapons and repointing them; and, therefore, that the outline of the whole stone was accidentally formed. A subsequent examination, however, and a comparison of the specimens with the ones already described, added to a better knowledge "of true" polishing tools, led us to a different conclusion. The stone has been split to render it thin enough for ready working, while its original (if such there was) resemblance to a small mammal was increased and rendered somewhat perfect by subsequent grinding and polishing. The faint, eye-like depressions make the resemblance to an animal more striking and unmistakable.

In a subsequent chapter, we shall call attention to "pestles," some of which have *carved heads*. They are referred to here, merely to show that the disposition to imitate animals by figures in stone is evinced in ways other than by "outlines" such as we have figured, and that while these outline works are much ruder than the carved head of a wolf upon a pestle found in Vermont, they are not probably older, but show that at about the same period in the average progress or degree of culture of the red man there was the beginning of that art which was but little advanced at the period of the later pictorial writings of these same people, when a warrior would publish his autobiography by means of a long series of grotesque sketches upon his blanket.[†]

---

[*] Abor. Mon. of New York. Smithson. Contrib., vol. ii, p. 76.
[†] Catlin's N. A. Indians, vol. i, p. 148, fig. 65.

CHAPTER XIX.

PIPES.

In Eastern and Western stone weapons and domestic implements there is apparently but little difference, except in smoking-pipes, where the difference is very great; although the two kinds of pipes, those of baked clay and those of stone, both occur in New Jersey.

Figure 179 represents the common shape of the stone pipes which are occasionally picked up in New Jersey. This nearly perfect specimen, like the majority of pipes of this shape, is made from a fragment of ordinary soapstone, and bears no trace of ornamentation. It is an elongated oval bowl two and a half inches in length, and a little more than one inch in diameter at the mouth and five-eighths of an inch in diameter at the base. The front of the bowl is somewhat convex in outline; the opposite outline is more nearly straight. A little above the middle of the front of the bowl commences a projection a quarter of an inch in width and a little less than an inch in length. The hollow of the bowl extends throughout its whole length, the opening below being in the center of the base. This pipe-bowl was evidently intended to be set on a flat, hollow tube, closed at the outer end, and the mouth-piece* placed at or made of the opposite extremity. The " projection " would be useful in holding the bowl securely to the stem, by affording a hold for the cord that wrapped the tube and crossed the upper end of this projection on the bowl.

We have said that figure 179 was the common shape of the stone pipes; but the pipes themselves are not common nor abundant, even where relics are plentiful. Of the majority of soapstone pipes that we have met with, the pattern figured is the prevailing one; but of the thousands of relics we have ourselves gathered, or seen in the cabinets of others, there were not probably two dozen specimens of stone or clay pipes.

Figure 180 represents a somewhat fragmentary specimen of a calumet or pipe of peace, carved from soapstone of even less density than the material of the preceding example. It bears a general resemblance to the calumets figured by Lapham† and Squier‡; but in no wise approaches the artistic elegance of the mound-builders' pipes. This specimen, figure 180, consists of a flat stem, one inch wide at the bowl, where it gradually narrows toward the end, or mouth-piece termination. This stem is of a uniform thickness of seven-sixteenths of an inch. The hole for the passage of the smoke is smooth, and decreases in caliber as it nears the opening into the cavity of the bowl. The bowl-

---

* We have seen two specimens of short, drilled stones, that may have been used as "mouth-pieces," when a long reed has been used as a "stem."

* Antiq. of Wisconsin, pp. 83, 84.

† Abor. Mon. New York, p. 76.

cavity is exactly half an inch in diameter, and half an inch deep. As, however, the margin of the bowl is broken throughout its entire extent, it is possible that the depth of the cavity may have been greater. This form of pipe is not as frequently met with as the preceding one, although not what might be called a "rare" pattern. We have seen several plain fragments of carved and drilled soft stone, which were certainly referable to the stems of this style of pipe.

Figure 181 represents a form of small clay pipe, of which fragments are occasionally found, but very seldom is a perfect or even nearly perfect specimen met with. In the splendid cabinet of Michael Newbold, esq., of Burlington County, New Jersey, are several fragments of this form of pipe, of fine yellow clay, which had been very carefully baked. The stems were perfectly cylindrical instead of flat on the under side, as is the case with figure 181; the bowl, also, of this specimen figured is ridged and somewhat flattened upon the sides and front, which gives it a much less neat appearance than those referred in the Newbold collection or than similar clay pipes found in New York.*

Figure 182 represents a very large, though roughly made, stone pipe, found near the shore of the Delaware River, at Beverly, N. J. It is apparently carved out of a serpentine pebble, the bowl pecked out and then polished inside and out. The stem is flat, with rounded angles, while the whole surface is somewhat polished. The nearly circular bowl is two inches in diameter, with sides varying little from an average thickness of about three-eighths of an inch. The bottom of the bowl and the stem, which are continuous and straight, or flat, have not been polished, and appear to be the unaltered surface of the pebble of which the pipe is made. The only attempt at ornamentation consists of a number of oblique lines, pretty deeply cut, which are crossed by similar ones extending across the spaces between the long lines. The cross-lines are all short, none extending to, or encroaching upon, the others. These have been cut with a sharp-pointed tool not recognized in any of the large series of pointed forms, as drills, &c., which we have collected.

There is in the cabinet of Rutger's College, at New Brunswick, N. J., a large stone pipe similar to this specimen in every particular, figure 182, save that of ornamentation, of which there is none. These two specimens are the largest we have seen, that have been discovered in the State. We have heard of the existence of several specimens of large stone pipes, some with elaborate carving, but on tracing them up they have invariably proved to be either much less "extensive" than was represented, or undoubted pipes of the mound-builders, brought from the Western States.

Figure 183 represents an interesting fragment of a "pottery" pipe, and is made of the same mixture of clay, shell, and mica as are most of the scraps of vessels that we find scattered over fields where Indian villages formerly existed. This fragment is unquestionably the front of

* Squier, l. c., p. 76, figs. 9, 10, 11.

the bowl, which was quadrangular instead of circular—a character quite uncommon in the pipe-bowls of "pottery."

The amount of surface ornamentation in this fragment is unusually great; and although composed of straight lines only, the human face was evidently intended to be represented in the three short transverse lines; the two upper ones representing the eyes, and the lower one the mouth. This is the more probable since the lower line is the widest, largest, and really somewhat mouth-like in shape. Besides these three there are eight lines, four upon each side, extending obliquely upward and outward. This fragment measures one inch and one-quarter in width, and one inch and an eighth in depth.

While we have been far from successful in collecting an extensive series of fine pipes, there is no doubt that large and finely-worked specimens were made by the Indians on the Atlantic sea-board. Such pipes have been discovered elsewhere,* and it is fair to presume that what is occasionally met with in the Eastern States, in the way of "relics," will yet be found somewhere in New Jersey. Mr. Perkins has described " a very pretty pipe" which " was dug up not far from Burlington, Vt., and is now in the museum of the University at Burlington." It is shaped like a common clay pipe, but the bowl is smaller and thicker, and the stem shorter. It is wrought from a piece of dark-clouded gypsum, and is nicely polished. The bowl * * * is encircled by two rows of oblong cavities, about one-fourth of an inch broad, and from three-tenths to one-half of an inch long, and one-eighth of an inch deep, no two being exactly alike. There are seven of these in the lower row and eight in the upper, and they were probably inlaid with some ornamental substance." We have quoted this entire description of the Vermont pipe for the reason that we remember having seen such a pipe some years ago, which was said to have been found at or near the Delaware Water-Gap.

The comparative rarity of aboriginal smoking-pipes is easily explained by the fact that they were not discarded, as were weapons, when those by whom they were fashioned entered upon the iron age. The advances of the whites in no way lessened the demand for pipes, nor did the whites substitute a better-made implement; therefore, the pipes were retained, and used until worn out or broken, excepting such as were buried with their deceased owners. What was the ultimate fate of these can only be conjectured. Certain it is that in every instance an Indian grave in New Jersey does not contain a pipe. If the practice of burying the pipe with its owner was common, we must believe that the graves were opened and robbed of this coveted article by members of the same or some other tribe. A serious objection, however, to this supposition is that the stolen pipes would be recognized; but while this is possible, we do not think the fear of detection deterred the ancient grave-robber, and, besides, it should be borne in mind that a pipe could

* Amer. Nat., vol. v, p. 13.

be easily altered in its general appearance, and, further, that the great
majority of pipes were probably of a plain character, no single one being
especially distinguishable from its fellows. But for the few lines upon
the specimen figured in No. 182, it would not differ noticeably from that
in Rutger's College Museum; and might not a dozen others be but fac-
similes of figure 180?

CHAPTER XX.

POTTERY.

In certain localities, fragments of black, brown, and red pottery are
almost as abundant as arrow-points in others. Unfortunately, these fragments are generally too small for determining the shape of the vessels to
which each belonged; they are, however, large enough to show one
characteristic of aboriginal pottery, viz, profuse ornamentation. This
was principally by lines and dots, but the variety of the combinations of
these is so inexhaustible that we have seldom met with two fragments,
not of the same vessel, which were identical.

The lines and square "dots" have been formed by removing a small
portion of the clay while soft, and not by mere displacement by pressure with a cord or sharp stick or bone. The edges are sharp and
well defined, and never merely elevated ridges, which give the intervening depressions the appearance of carved lines.

Figures 184, 185, 186, and 187 are good examples of the usual "find"
of pottery-fragments, both as to size and general character of ornamentation. These specimens are all formed of the blue clay ("triassic"),
as determined by Prof. T. A. Conrad, of Philadelphia, which underlies
and constitutes in part the bluff running parallel to the Delaware
River and skirting the meadows from Trenton, N. J., to Bordentown
and beyond. This clay, which is now used in terra-cotta establishments,
was not used by the aborigines in its pure state, but was mixed with
sand, mica, or pounded mussel-shells, or with all of them. The mixture
of other materials does not appear to have affected the color, since we have
found pieces of every shade of brown, black, red, &c. Judging from
the degrees of curvature of even these small fragments, the vessels of
which they are pieces were originally small, globular, and would hold
not more than a quart, but usually they were of about two-thirds this
capacity.

Figure 188 represents a fragment of pottery peculiarly ornamented.
Besides a narrow line which is met near the middle of the fragment and,
at nearly a right angle, by another, showing that but few lines were engraved upon the vessel, there are rows of curious "dots" formed by
pressing the clay, while soft, with a hollow tube (in this case a spear of
grass); the clay rising into the tube leaves a bead-like formation on the
pottery. We have not met with any other fragment with bead-like
markings similar to these, either in rows, as in this instance, or scattered about.

Figure 189 is another instance of interesting ornamentation. In this case the intervening lines and spaces are of equal width, but the depressions or "lines" are curiously "broken" by transverse, narrow ridges, uniformly distant from each other. These transverse ridges are of the same size, distinctly carved or molded, and nearly on a level with the *true* surface of the fragment. The vessel to which this little piece belonged was, evidently, broken intentionally, there being, where the fragment was found, a mass of blackish powder and more than a quart of pieces, all smaller than that in the figure, but equally covered with ornamental lines. Although no stone was in the immediate neighborhood of this and the other fragments when found, the mass of pieces indicated that the pottery was crushed by a large flat stone.

Figure 190 represents a perfect specimen of a small vase, such as is occasionally met with in the graves of aborigines, and, if buried by themselves, always in the immediate neighborhood of graves of adults. This vase measures three and three-fourths inches in height, and is of equal width at the mouth, including the flaring of the rim. The clay has but a slight admixture of shell, and is identical with much of the pottery found in fragments upon the surface of the ground. The ornamentation is the rudest we have seen. It consists merely of lines in series of four each, at an angle with the rim of the vessel and of different lengths, the longest being not over one and a half inches. These lines appear to have been produced by drawing a pointed stick over the clay previously to baking. The capacity of this vase is one pint and five fluid-ounces. When taken from the earth it was filled to the brim with a black dust which, on examination, proved to be burnt bone and animal matter unmixed with earth. On exposure to the atmosphere this "black" powder became gray, and shortly afterward, absorbing moisture very rapidly, formed a dull, lead-gray, pasty mass. The top of the vase, as it lay *in situ*, was covered with a plate of mica about one foot square and half an inch thick. Such plates of mica are quite common about the fields in the neighborhood of Trenton, but are seldom met with in as large size as that covering the buried vase. This vase is in size similar to those found in the western mounds,[*] but is not ornamented with the care which distinguishes the latter. It should be borne in mind, however, that difference in ornamentation is scarcely a safe guide in the separation of pottery into the production of the mound-builders and that of the modern Indian. In gracefulness of outline the New Jersey vase is the equal of that of the mound-builders, while we have seen a drawing of a large vase found in Vermont[†] which exceeds in elaborateness of details any figured by Messrs. Squier and Davis. The mound-builders were never inhabitants of what is now known as New Jersey nor of the State of Vermont, but pottery is sometimes found in these sections the equal, in some instances, of the pottery of the West in style of decoration, while in all cases it is as hard and durable.

---

[*] Anc. Mon. Miss. Valley, pp,. 188, 189, pl. xlvi.
[†] American Naturalist, vol. v., p. 14, fig. 1.

We have seen one example of pottery which presented several peculiar features; it was, however, unfortunately broken up and lost previously to our interest in aboriginal remains. It consisted of a quadrangular box of black pottery mixed with mica, about fifteen inches long, ten wide, and six or seven deep. It was ornamented on all four sides with fine lines, closely engraved, and extending from the top to the bottom of the box. When taken out of the ground it was full of a reddish powder of a faint aromatic odor, and contained many of the smaller bones of a deer, (*Cariacus virginianus.*) These bones had apparently not been exposed to heat at any time, but were probably the remains of venison buried with and intended *as food* for the deceased, whose skeleton was found within a few feet of the "box."

Of course pottery, in fragments, is most abundant at localities where the aborigines had their villages, as near Trenton, N. J., but we have always found some fragments wherever we have chanced to search for relics in general. Especially is this the case along the old "Indian trails" or the routes they used for their annual trip to the sea-shore.

Under the heading of "pottery," we now call attention to certain fragments of vessels which, instead of being formed of clay molded into the desired shape, were "pecked" out from a solid stone. When we come to the consideration of "corn-mills" we shall find that basins of considerable capacity were pecked in stationary rocks, and smaller stones were hollowed for portable corn-mills, and therefore it is not strange that vessels for other purposes should also have been made. We have not met with any perfect specimens of such stone vessels. Our knowledge of them is based solely on two fragments, one of which we figure. It is an ordinary sandstone bowlder, probably of an oval shape; being first broken into halves, the broken surface has been pecked at until a basin of some capacity has been formed.

Figure 191 represents the fragment referred to. The inner side of the bowl is noticeable from the fact of its being of a decided red tint, which is in marked contrast with the light gray color of the stone itself. Along the side of this reddish interior is a deeply cut groove, which extends downward a distance of nearly an inch and a half, and then bending at a right angle to its former course extends to the broken edge of the specimen. To what use such a stone vessel was put can only be conjectured. The other fragment which we have shows even more plainly that the vessel has been "pecked" out with a stone hammer, but it is so irregular in shape—so fragmentary a fragment—that the indications of its having been a portion of a vessel are not as clear or unquestioned as are those of figure 191.

Mr. Evans[*] says of Great Britain, with reference to vessels of stone being found there: "Vessels without handles were also occasionally formed of stone. Six or seven of these, of various sizes and forms, were discovered in a 'kist-vaen,' in the island of Unst, and are now for

---

[*] Anc. Stone Imp. of G. B., p. 403, and fig. 368.

the most part in the British Museum. Four of them were of a rude quadrangular form, with flat bottoms, and from 3½ to 7 inches high. The other three were oval. They were formed of schistose rock, and some of them still bear traces of the action of fire." Mr. Evans also figures a stone cup, which seems to be but a "restoration" of the fragment we have figured, and of that which we have in our cabinet.

There is really more difference in degree than in kind between such stone cups as figure 191 has been, and the "paint-cup" and "corn-mills" yet to be described; in the former, a vessel to hold a liquid has been required, and so was pecked at and hollowed out to a greater depth than were the mills and paint-cups, which were needed only to reduce small portions of grain or lumps of clay to a fine powder. If the red color of the inside of figure 191 is a trace of the red paint which was so abundantly used in the toilets of the aborigines, then, indeed, the specimen is a fragment of a "paint-cup," such as we shall more particularly describe in the following chapter; but if such were its use it probably is an exceptional case, as paint-cups, according to our acquaintance with them, were small vessels for individual use only, and certainly such a fragment as figure 191 would hold enough paint to cover the entire body of the most stalwart warrior.

Fragments of the ordinary pottery are frequently abundant in the fresh-water or inland mussel-shell heaps, associated with slabs of stone and rounded or oval cobble-stones, on the former of which, and by means of the latter, the Indians crushed the *Unios* and *Anodontas* so numerous in our rivers and larger creeks.

CHAPTER XXI.

PAINT-CUPS.

When it is remembered how elaborately the warriors of our modern Indian tribes are painted when on the war-path, it is not strange that we should find traces of this custom among the relics of the older Stone age of New Jersey. The traces to which we refer are certain hollowed stones, or diminutive mortars, in which the mineral mass of colored clay was reduced to powder and prepared for application to the body. Such paint-cups or small mortars are not common in the localities with which we are most familiar. They are usually only water-worn pebbles which have had a *natural* hollow or depression upon one side, which was either enlarged at first, or the original hollow was utilized as a paint-receptacle, and gradually increased by the rubbing action of the little pestle. Messrs. Lartet and Christy have figured a series of mortars from the caves and rock-shelters of France. Of these "mortars," we have many identical specimens; but it is curious that the most perfect or undoubted paint-cup in our collection should be so very similar to a specimen which they include among their "mortars" as doubtful. This "doubtful" mortar or paint-cup is described as "a water-worn, irregularly-shaped fragment of soft friable gray sandstone, bearing a part of the natural impression of a bivalve shell which had ribs and prickles, such as *Spondylus santonensis;* but these markings caused by the shell have been nearly obliterated, either by the natural action of water, or by artificial rubbing, probably by both. Some slight ferruginous stains remain in little hollows in the cavity; but they may be due rather to the imbedding material than to the use of this saucer-like stone as a paint-mortar or ocher-pot."* It is safe, we judge, to presume such stones to be true "relics" when found associated with others of which there can be no doubt. Its presence with undoubted relics may have been accidental, but probably not, and if *brought* to a cave-dwelling or rock-shelter, it was for the purpose of using it just as has been suggested, as a "paint-mortar or ocher-pot."

The similarity of the weapons between the cotemporaries of the reindeer of France and the aborigines of North America has been frequently pointed out by the authors of the Reliquiæ Aquitanicæ. It would seem, too, that the custom of painting the face and body was also common to the two peoples, if such hollowed stones as Messrs. Lartet and Christy have figured from France, and the two figured in this chapter, were used, as we believe, for paint-mortars.

Messrs. Lartet and Christy remark: "With these early cave-dwellers the art of painting was, as far as we know, limited to that favorite aboriginal color, red. Various pieces of soft red hematite, covered with scratches, indicate how they scraped off a red powder, which, mixed with grease, would furnish as good means of personal adornment as is employed by many Indians at the present day."† We should think that the finding of the red hematite and the paint-mortars both would render the fact of their having painted the face an absolute certainty, and that the presence of the mineral indicated the use of the hollowed stones as mortars. The particular one we have referred to, as figured by Messrs. Lartet and Christy, appears more unquestionably a "mortar" than do some of the discoidal stones which have merely flattened sides and not a well-marked depression.

Figure 192 represents a medium-sized paint-cup, made of a water-worn pebble. Three and three-fourths inches long by two and one-quarter inches wide, this specimen has sides and ends of a uniform width of half an inch, giving thereby a *large* cup-shaped depression for the total dimensions of the specimen. It may be objected that the size of figure 192 is too small for the supposed use. Undoubtedly many paint-mortars were larger, but this specimen is not as small as some we have found; and, in favor of the theory of its having been used as a paint-cup, is the fact that it was found in a grave, with a series of arrow-points, an ax, a knife, and some fragments of pottery. The locality and the evidently artificial character of the cup-shaped depression prove beyond a doubt that it is an Indian relic; and that its use was for paint-

---

* Rel. Aquitan, p. 109, pl. xxiii, fig. 2.   * L. c., p. 22.

mixing seems more probable than any other that can be suggested.
Associated with this delicate paint-cup was the little club-shaped
pestle, drawn as resting in the cup. It is a pretty pebble, three inches
in length, slender and oval at one end, and flat, oval, and double
the width at the opposite end. This pestle has probably been worn
away considerably in its use with the accompanying cup. The width of
the club-like end, and that of the slender stem, seem to agree perfectly
with the width and depth of the cup's hollow, and the slender portion
with the points of contact of the rim of the cup and the handle of the
paint-crusher.

Figure 193 represents a very small paint-cup made from a water
worn pebble, which has received its present hollow, or cup-shaped
depression, wholly by pecking, after the manner of working the
deep grooves of the common stone ax. This paint-cup is circular in
shape, being a little flattened on one side only. It is one inch and five-
eighths in diameter, and has but a depth of three-eighths of an inch at
the center or deepest part of the depression. There are still marks of
the stone hammer in this hollow, which, however, feels perfectly smooth
to the touch, and has the same color and amount of polish as the exterior surfaces of the specimen. This specimen, like the preceding, was
found in the grave of a child, with a number of much-decayed bone
beads (?), and a highly-polished black stone, having a number of small
holes through it. Reference will be made again to this specimen.

As in the preceding example of paint-cups, so in this instance, a long,
slender pebble, of considerable polish, and more worn at one end than
at the other, was found with the cup. The two certainly seem fitted-
for use with each other.

Similarly with arrow-heads and skinning-knives, which merge gradually into spear-heads and ungrooved axes, do these paint-cups or small
mortars gradually increase in size until their use as paint-cups becomes
doubtful and they assume the size, &c., of corn-mills. We have seen a
few which were large enough for *small* corn-mills and yet small enough
to suggest that at any time masses of red clay sufficient for a party of
warriors might have been ground in one of them.

Loskiel says :* " They bestow much time and labor in decorating their
faces ; laying on fresh paint every day, especially if they go out to dance.
They suppose that it is very proper for brave men to paint, and always
study a change of fashion. Vermillion is their favorite color, with which
they frequently paint their whole head. Here and there black streaks
are introduced, or they paint one-half of their face and head black and
the other red. Near the river Muskingum, (State of Ohio,) a yellow
ocher is found, which, when burned, makes a beautiful red color. This the
Huron warriors chiefly use for paint, nor do they think a journey of one
hundred miles too long to provide themselves with it. Some prefer blue,
because it is the color of the sky, when calm and serene, and, being

---

* Mission to North American Indians, p. 49, London. 1794.

considered as an emblem of peace, it is frequently introduced as such in their public orations. Therefore, when they wish to show a peaceful disposition toward other tribes or nations, they paint themselves and their belts blue. The figures painted upon their faces are of various kinds. Every one follows his own fancy, and exerts his powers of invention to excel others and have something peculiar to himself. One prides himself with the figure of a serpent upon each cheek, another with that of a tortoise, deer, bear, or some other creature, as his coat of arms and signature."

We have not been able to determine what minerals were used as paint prior to the advent of the European settlers. That it was some mineral, naturally red, or made red by burning, we have no doubt, as we have found faint traces of a reddish powder in many of the Indian graves, which latter are usually only to be recognized by the black stain in the soil—naturally a light-colored sand—by the decomposition of the body, or by the relics which they may chance to contain. This reddish powder is always, as found, so mixed with the surrounding soil that we have not been able to separate a sufficient quantity for conveniently determining its composition. It has, however, invariably a marked pungent odor, not at all disagreeable. To what extent this may be due to chemical action that may have been caused by the decomposition of the body, with which the pigment had been buried, it is not possible to tell.

Describing an Indian burial, Loskiel says:* " They used formerly to put a tobacco-pouch, knife, tinder-box, tobacco and pipe, bow and arrows, gun, powder and shot, skins and cloth for clothes, *paint*, a small bag of Indian corn or dried bilberries, sometimes the kettle, hatchet, and other furniture of the deceased, into the grave, supposing that the departed spirits would have the same wants and occupations in the land of souls."

Seeing that not only paint but such a multitude of other articles were placed with the body in the grave, it is not to be wondered at that the light-colored soil should be stained black, but that any trace of the red paint should now remain. Of course, as the practice of burying the paint and other effects of the deceased with the body is still continued, it cannot be doubted that these reddish patches of earth which we have described as still existing in the almost obliterated graves of Indians, are really deposits of paint, such as Loskiel mentions as one of the list of articles usually buried.

CHAPTER XXII.

HOES AND SHOVELS.

The cultivation of maize or Indian corn was carried on extensively by the aborigines throughout the southern, or more properly the central counties of the State. The fertile tract, comprising Burlington

* L. c., p. 120.

and Monmouth Counties, known as Cream Ridge, was a favorite spot with the Indians, as shown by the abundance of relics found throughout this section, and especially by the occurrence of certain implements wholly used in the cultivation of their corn. These implements, of which there are two varieties, we have designated "hoes and shovels," the latter being used by the women in preparing the soil, the former to keep down the weeds after the corn had sprouted.

Implements known as "hoes," both of stone and elk-horn, have been figured and described by Prof. Nilsson,* which differ, however, from the New Jersey specimens in being perforated for the insertion of a handle, a feature wholly unknown in Indian antiquities, other than as regards those used for mere ornamental purposes. The Scandinavian hoes differ principally in being perforated instead of grooved for the secure attachment of a handle. Of the use of such "hoes," Prof. Nilsson says, "It must be acknowledged that if agriculture, as seems most probable, consisted originally in burning tracts of forest, and then sowing among the ashes, these rude hoes must have been very suitable for such operations."

Figure 194 represents a very beautiful specimen of a New Jersey stone hoe. It is admirably ground into proper shape from a light-gray sandstone pebble, mineralogically not similar to any other relic in our possession, except a corn-mill, to be figured and described in the next chapter. This relic is now five and a quarter inches long by a little over two and a half inches wide. It was originally much longer, and, by the wear it shows, was much used. The under surface was almost perfectly flat. The upper or outer surface is ridged, the height decreasing as it approaches the front edge of the implement, thus making the greatest thickness, one inch and a half at the head, which is separated from the body of the implement by two deep grooves, or notches, which do not meet on the under or the upper surface; but the ridge that extends the whole length of the hoe has a shallow depression where it passes between the two side notches.

This hoe, therefore, has been attached to a handle at right angles to the blade, the handle being placed in contact with the hoe at the under surface and well lashed by raw-hide strips passing around it and over the side notches; or the handle has been split, or a forked stick, the ends being drawn about the hoe at the notches, and firmly bound by raw-hide strips at the central notch, after the manner of securing handles to the ordinary grooved cobble-stone ax. The shape of the specimen at once indicates its use as an agricultural implement. We do not see the advantage of a modern hoe over this one, except in being lighter and less liable to be broken on coming violently in contact with large stones. We have seen no other specimen from New Jersey as well shaped as that sketched in figure 194, but the few specimens coming under our notice were all similarly shaped in the essential parts.

---

* On the Stone Age in Scandinavia. London, 1868. P. 74, and pl. viii, figs. 180, 181.

Professor Rau, of New York, has twice published* notices of agricultural implements, which he has called " shovels and hoes," which latter bear much resemblance to the example here figured, but differing in being chipped instead of ground, or " pecked," and then smoothed, either intentionally or by constant use. The hoe figured in Professor Rau's later paper (1868) " is seven and a half inches long, nearly six inches wide, and about half an inch thick in the middle. The rounded part forms a sharp edge. The material of which these implements (also, shovels) are made is a peculiar kind of bluish, gray, or brownish flint, of slightly conchoidal fracture, and capable of splitting into large, flat fragments. I never succeeded in finding this stone *in situ*. The agricultural implements of my collection were all found in Saint Clair County, in Southern Illinois." It will here be noticed that the New Jersey hoes, while bearing a marked general resemblance to, differ considerably from, the western forms. The western specimens are all larger, or at least broader. The side notches are deeper, and the head is of a uniform thickness with the blade of the implement. Mr. Rau further says, and our specimen agrees entirely with his statement, that " if the shape of the described implements (shovels and hoes) did not indicate their original use, the peculiar traces of wear which they exhibit would furnish almost conclusive evidence of the manner in which they have been employed; for that part with which the digging was done, appears, notwithstanding the hardness of the material, perfectly smooth, as if glazed, and slightly striated in the direction in which the implement penetrated the ground." The New Jersey specimen has the polished surface and the striations perfectly, but being of a very different material, the specimen in question probably does not show them as plainly as described by Professor Rau. These hoes appear thus far to have been overlooked by archæologists, except as occurring in the West. Professor Rau mentions them as "rather scarce, and merely confined to the States bordering on the Mississippi River." We have seen none from Pennsylvania or the New England States, and, as regards New Jersey, they seem to occur only in the favorite corn-fields of the aborigines, now Burlington, Monmouth, and Ocean Counties. This hoe, illustrated by figure 194, was kindly presented to the writer by Joseph Newbold, esq., of Plattsburgh, N. J. It was the only specimen of hoe in his large collection of American antiquities. In the collection of Michael Newbold, esq., of the same neighborhood, which is one of the finest and largest we have seen, are two implements, bearing much resemblance to figure 194, but so much smaller that their use as hoes is doubtful. One of them is of serpentine, the other of fine-grained porphyry. That of serpentine measures three and three-fourths inches in length, and one inch and seven-eighths in width. The head of this small, beautifully shaped, and polished specimen is narrower than the blade, which is the case also, though to a much less extent, with the

* Smithson. Ann. Reps., 1863 and 1868, p. 379, and p. 401.

hoe figured in 194. The cutting-edge of the serpentine implement is almost as curved as the gouge described in chapter xiv. This peculiarity, however, does not militate against its use as a hoe, although, considering its size, such was probably not its use. The porphyry does not differ materially from the serpentine example. Professor Rau,[*] in the two papers from which we have so freely quoted, in describing hoes, mentions a large oval, flat, flint implement, found by himself only, in the West, which he designates as a shovel. We have seen that the New Jersey hoes differed in some respects from those the professor has figured and described, but no question could arise as to the identity of their uses. We will now present figures of "flint" implements bearing some resemblance to the "shovels" of Professor Rau, which we believe were used as such, although the circumstances under which one was found would seem to class it with "implements not in a state of completion, but roughly-edged fragments which were destined to be made into arrow and spear heads at some future time." We cannot think this of the examples we have figured, although they certainly do not exhibit at their front edges a high polish and striation, the result of use as shovels and as hoes. Shovels of sandstone also occur, in New Jersey, a foot or more in length, and six or seven inches wide. These are carefully chipped, flat upon one side, and have a less regularly oval outline than the jasper examples. We have seen that the jasper lance-heads are reproduced in this common sandstone, in a less careful manner; and so is it with the shovels of sandstone, as compared with those of jasper. These, like all other forms of relics, also vary in size, but we have met with none that were too small for practical purposes.

Figure 195 represents a beautiful specimen of chipped jasper which we have twice referred to elsewhere, once as a lance-head[†] and once as a hatchet;[‡] but which, we now fully believe, was not designed as either, but as a shovel. It was, however, never used. It is one of a hundred and fifty which were discovered in plowing a piece of newly-drained meadow near Trenton, N. J., in 1860, and is shorter and broader than the others, which might have been hatchets, war-club teeth, or lance-heads, probably some for one purpose and some for another. They were certainly all *finished* specimens, being carefully chipped to sharp edges, many of them having well-defined points and bases. None were as crude as a " rudely-shaped flint article * * * discovered * * * on the bank of the Mississippi, between Saint Louis and Carondelet," and figured by Professor Rau. [§] Most of these buried jasper specimens, when discovered, had their points up, being surrounded by a sufficient number of the series to wall in and hold in position those that were erect. We stated in the Naturalist that we had not met with any isolated speci-

---

[*] L. c., 1863 and 1868.

[†] Abbott on "Lance-heads," in Proc. Acad. Nat. Sci. of Philadelphia, 1863, p. 278.

[‡] Stone Age in New Jersey; American Naturalist, vol. vi, p. 155.

[§] Smith. Report for 1868, p. 405, fig. 4.

mens similar to those in this "deposit;" but since then we have found three in widely different localities, two of which were of the lance-head pattern, if not unquestionable examples of that weapon; the other was a shovel, similar in all its details to figure 195. This collection, which was of great interest as a whole, was unwisely divided soon after its discovery; but the bulk of the series formerly in the museum of the Philadelphia Academy, has fortunately been placed for safe-keeping with the American Philosophical Society at Philadelphia, where the specimens are open to examination.

On comparison with the measurements given by Professor Rau, figure 195 will be found to be much smaller than the western specimens, its greatest width being three and three-fourths inches, its total length six inches, while the western specimens measure "above a foot in length, a little more than five inches in its greatest breadth, and is about three-quarters of an inch thick in the middle;" but just as our hoes, though considerably the smaller, are yet unquestionably "hoes," so it is equally probable that such a specimen as figure 195, though much smaller than the western examples, is a shovel. In *width*, there is no important variation in these specimens, but as there *is* a decided difference in the depth of the soil in the Mississippi River bottom-lands, as compared with that of the corn-grounds of New Jersey, this may account for the difference in their *length*.

Figure 196 represents a large "flint implement" of "shovel" shape, carefully chipped from yellow jasper, measuring nine inches and a quarter in length, by five inches and a quarter in greatest width. It is somewhat more pointed at one end than at the other, but is too broad and blunt to have been put to any other use, and too finished in appearance to warrant the idea of being unfinished. This very large specimen of jasper chipping was presented to the East India Marine Society at Salem, Mass., by William Story, esq., and was found in New Jersey so long ago as 1824. It is much larger than any specimen we have found or seen in this State, but otherwise is identical with such as figure 195 and the lance-head figured in chapter vi, figure 35. Professor Rau mentions[*] with reference to several of the agricultural implements found at East Saint Louis, that "their material is a yellowish-brown variety of the flint" to which *he has* already referred. In shape they correspond with the tools of the same class previously described by him; most of the shovels, however, instead of having the end opposite the cutting-part worked into *a rounded edge*, terminate in a more or less acute angle. This answers admirably for a description of this specimen from New Jersey, figure 196, which is a *new* shovel, not having been worn and striated, as used shovels of flint always are; but the base of this specimen would soon become "perfectly smooth, as if glazed, and slightly striated in the direction in which the implement penetrated the ground."

---

[*] L. c., 1868, p. 403.

All the shovels from New Jersey, that we have seen, were from localities where the aborigines cultivated maize; the jasper specimens from Mercer County, exclusively, and those of sandstone and slate from Burlington, Monmouth, and Ocean Counties. There may be an exception in figure 154, which is simply labeled " New Jersey," in the Salem collection, it not being known from what part of the State the specimen came.

In the collection of Michael Newbold, esq., is one specimen of shovel, which in finish, shape, and dimensions, is identical with that figured by Professor Rau, in the Smithsonian Annual Report; but is of sandstone instead of " flint " or jasper. It was found in the very richest locality for Indian agricultural relics in this State.

Mr. Evans, in the fourth chapter of his work, has described in detail and figured many specimens of so-called " chipped or rough-hewn celts," which have every appearance of being " shovels" such as we have described; or our shovels are " celts." Certainly they could not have been put to a cutting use, while they are unnecessarily large for bone-splitting. Mr. Evans himself remarks of some of these celts, " as has already been suggested, it is by no means improbable that some of these ruder unpolished implements were employed in agriculture; like the so-called shovels and hoes of flint of North America, described by Professor Rau."

Considering that the polished celts are quite as abundant in those localities where implements of this character occur at all, it seems fair to presume that the "chipped or rough-hewn" specimens were thus made for some particular purpose, and not that they were rejected specimens, intended to be polished but for some reason thrown aside. These chipped " celts" such as we have figured under different names, as suggested by their size, are all carefully shaped and finished, but have no polished surface, and yet the art of polishing stones was well known to the Indians, as illustrated in the beautiful " skinning-knives " we have figured, and which would be considered as " polished celts" in England.

Mr. Evans does not figure any specimen of " rough-hewn celt" as large as the brown jasper shovel, figure 196, which bears more resemblance to many of the " drift implements" of France than any other American " chipped flint " we have seen, and exceeds in size the river-drift implements, figured by Mr. Evans; the nearest approach to it being his figure 472, from Midford Hill, Salisbury.*

Figure 196a represents a specimen of agricultural implement closely allied in general appearance to the "rude implements" in chapter II. It is a rudely-formed instrument for digging or hoeing roots or cultivated corn; is of sandstone and chipped over the greater portion of its surface, with one side, throughout its whole length, more rounded and even than the other, as though it formed the back to a rudely-edged blade.

* Anc. Stone Imp. of Gr. Br., p. 554.

The width of the implement decreases somewhat at one end, giving the narrower portion the appearance of being itself a handle for the instrument. The total length of the specimen is nine and seven-eighths inches. The width, for two-thirds of the length, varies but little from three inches. The width of the "handle" or narrower end is within a trace of two inches. The broad end, or that opposite the handle, is chipped from each side about equally, but on one side of the specimen, at this end, there is a more uniform slope, and a degree of smoothness which indicates a rubbing motion at this point, as in digging in loose soil. If held by the so-called "handle" or narrow end, with the smooth side of the opposite end *down*, it will be evident that this instrument was in all probability used as a spade ; if held with the handle from and the *smooth* end toward the person, then the implement becomes a hoe. In either case the polished end is thereby easily explained; otherwise, it is inexplicable and the rude implement is an enigma. This implement was plowed up in a field from which a majority of the specimens figured in this volume were obtained ; and, although from this locality some *truly* rude implements have been secured, yet we have not considered this as belonging to that more archaic class of stone implements, although so greatly resembling them in general appearance and workmanship, and being identical as to mineral material. We ourselves have no doubt that its use was to dig up those roots and bulbs which the Indian used as food; or it may be that, with this and similar implements, the ground was prepared for corn-planting, and, as we have shown, may be called a shovel or a hoe in accordance with the manner ner in which it is held.

Of the Delaware and Iroquois Indians Loskiel* mentions that "they used formerly the shoulder-blade of a deer, or a tortoise-shell sharpened upon a stone, and fastened to a thick stick, instead of a hoe ;" and we readily see, on comparing such "hoes" with the one of stone, which we here figure, that the latter is fully as capable of doing the same work, and of doing it as well; and we doubt if there was as much work in flaking figure 196*a* into its present shape as there would be in sharpening a tortoise-shell or a bone by rubbing, and then fastening the "blade" to a thick stick.

We have seen that among the rude implements of chapter II, was one which we considered as probably an agricultural tool; but we must limit its agricultural use to that of merely digging such roots as were used as food by the primitive people of this region. In the implements which have been described in this chapter, we see a wider range of work intended in their manufacture, even including figure 196*a*; all of them being designed for use in the cultivation of vegetables and grain, as well as in the mere gathering of the latter when fully grown. We have seen also that, according to Loskiel, both bone and shell implements were formerly used, and this explains why stone hoes and shovels are

---

* Loskiel, l. c., p. 66.

not abundant, as they certainly should be, considering the amount of maize grown, had stone been the only material out of which agricultural implements were fashioned.

CHAPTER XXIII.

CORN-MILLS, MORTARS AND PESTLES.

The Indian women, upon whom fell all the drudgery of aboriginal life, reduced the hard kernels of maize to coarse meal by pounding them in hollows of rocks, natural or artificial, with globular pebbles, or with long cylindrical stones, carefully chipped for the purpose, and known as pestles. Wooden mortars and pestles also were used. We have, perhaps, made a distinction where none exists, in saying "corn-mills" and "mortars," but it appears proper to make this distinction, as the plan pursued in meal-making in the two varieties really differs. By corn-mills, we mean small, portable bowlders, that have a shallow hollow pecked in them, and with which were used oval pebbles held in the hand and revolved around the hollow or basin of the mill. This motion *ground* the corn into coarse meal. By mortars, we refer to the deeper hollows, or basins, which were made in permanent rocks, and with which were used the long, slender, cylindrical pestles, which *pounded* the grain into meal, or, if used *for grinding*, were held upright in these deeper basins and a revolving motion given to them. The vast majority of the pestles which we have gathered were polished upon the end only, showing that this part alone of the implement was made use of.

Somewhat south of a line separating New Jersey into its upper hilly and lower level portions, a very marked peculiarity occurs with reference to corn-mills and mortars. In the northern or upper section of the State, where rocks *in situ* abound, the large flattened stones with cup-shaped depressions (corn-mills) are rare, while deep basins hollowed in immovable rocks are very numerous, which is evidence that in the rocky sections of the State the site of a village was chosen with reference to the "mill." Throughout the lower part of the State, on the contrary, rocks *in situ* are not at all abundant, while in many sections they are entirely absent, especially those suitable for "mills," and here are found stones weighing twenty or more pounds which were brought from a distance; a receptacle was first chipped on one side, which gradually by use became both deep and smoothly worn. The largest of these portable corn-mills that we have seen was a bowlder of conglomerated sandstone and iron-ore; it was a cubical mass, two feet by nineteen inches on the upper surface and twenty inches in height. The "basin" measured nine inches in diameter by six in depth.

Figure 197 represents a fine example of the small mortars, or portable corn-mills. It is a flat, triangular piece of sandstone, somewhat less than nine inches along each side. The upper surface has been ground out until a depression was formed about an inch deep. Associated with it was figure 198, an ordinary water-worn pebble. The under side of this stone is worn smooth by rubbing against the sides and bottom of the basin of the corn-mill.

Of the large stationary mortars, but little can be said that has not already been mentioned in reference to the portable examples. They are generally larger in diameter and of greater depth, and could be used only with the long pestles. The vast majority of these stationary mortars are natural "pot-holes;" possibly, in some cases, deepened intentionally, or by long usage in crushing corn. Such a "pot-hole," used as a mortar, formerly existed in a large glacial bowlder in Centre street, Trenton, N. J. (Figure 199.) That this was used as a "pot-hole" is evidenced by the circumstance that on excavating to remove the rock, several broken pestles were brought to light, also a stone ax and several dozens of spear and arrow heads of various sizes.

"Hunter informs us that in some of the Indian villages visited by him, there were one or two large stone mortars for pounding corn, which were public property. These were placed in a central part of the village, and were used in rotation by the different families."*

Wooden mortars were also used by the aborigines, stumps of hardwood trees being worn off and hollowed out. With these a stone pestle, sometimes suspended to an elastic branch of a tree, was used; but it would seem that such a mortar, necessarily yielding to the blows of a stone pestle, would but very slowly reduce corn to meal.

As even the smaller of these corn-mills are quite heavy, and the true mortars, of course, immovable, it is probable that two stones, of moderately smooth surface, were used as a "corn-mill" when merely a dish of mush or a cake was demanded. While there were a few permanent towns, the great bulk of the aborigines were constantly changing their quarters, and we doubt, therefore, if the majority of their corn was ground either in portable corn-mills or stationary mortars. Besides maize, other articles of diet were reduced in the "corn-mills." Loskiel states that they grind the maize "as fine as flour by means of a *wooden* pestle and mortar;" so, possibly, the stone mortars were intended for other articles, such as shell-fish, nuts, and berries.

Of the Delaware Indians† the same author says: "They are fond of muscles and oysters, and those who live near an oyster-bed will subsist for weeks together upon them. They also eat the land-tortoise, which is about a span broad, and rather more in length; and even locusts are used for food. These come frequently in large swarms, covering and destroying even the bark of the trees."

As the oysters and muscles were also dried in large quantities for winter use, it is very probable that portable corn-mills were used to reduce the dried shell-fish to a sort of powder or pulp. This, mixed

---

* Flint-Chips, p. 546, quoting from Hunter's Manners and Customs of Indian Tribes, p. 269.

† Mission to North American Indians, p. 67. London: 1794.

with the corn-meal, made a dough, or batter, not unlike the modern "fritters." It was a common practice with the Indians to mix other articles of food with the meal made from maize, and for this both corn-mills and mortars are admirably adapted. Loskiel mentions their mixing dried bilberries with corn-meal, and also smoked eels chopped fine.

Pestles, very abundant throughout the whole State, are those long, cylindrical stones, which, as a class, have been chipped, or chipped and ground, until their length is many times greater than their diameter. Of course, so simple an instrument will not vary much except in size. We have seen none in New Jersey showing any attempt at ornamentation. Mr. Perkins,[*] describing some Indian relics from Vermont, in speaking of pestles, says: "I have seen only one that had any kind of ornament upon it. This is a large one, over two feet long, in the museum of the University of Vermont. It is cylindrical, as usual, and is rounded at one end, while the other is carved to resemble the head of some animal—it may be a wolf." Mr. F. W. Putnam, in a foot-note, referring to the above, adds: "In the collection of the New York State museum at Albany, there is a long 'pestle,' of identical pattern and having the same rough carving as the one described from the Burlington museum. These are the only ones that have come under my observation having the handle carved to represent an animal, though most of the longer implements of this character have a knob at the handle, as if for the purpose of suspension." We have seen pestles from New Jersey twenty-five inches in length, but all are plain throughout; not a single example, with even "a knob at the handle," having occurred in any collections in this State which we have visited.

Figure 200 represents an excellent average specimen of the stone pestles as found in New Jersey. This example measures seventeen and a half inches in length and nearly eight inches in circumference. It is somewhat polished and beveled at either end, which would indicate that the ends were used in the deep mortars, and not the sides, by rolling in the saddle-shaped corn-mills. There is no indication whatever of the sides having been used, they being now as rough, or nearly so, as when the implement left the hands of its maker. The marks of the stone-hammer are plainly visible even to the very ends of the specimen, showing that a great amount of labor was expended in producing the implement. Its weight is seven pounds, enough to make it a cumbersome article for carriage. As such pestles were useful only where there were stationary mortars, it is probable that this and allied specimens were used principally in the permanent towns, as, for instance, the one where Trenton, N. J., now stands, which, according to Haeckwelder, was the headquarters of a great chief. Figure 200 was found within a mile of the big mortar we have mentioned as in Center street. We have, however, seen several fine specimens of long and heavy pestles in the cabinet of

Michael Newbold, esq., of Burlington County, New Jersey, which were found in the immediate neigborhood of his residence; and here the small portable corn-mills are quite abundant, and were probably used solely in reducing grain to meal. This fact somewhat induces that collector to believe that these long " pestles " were in reality war-clubs; but we do not think it can be shown that they were ever used as such. Neither does the fact that Indians now use wooden clubs of a very similar shape and of about the length of figure 200 favor the belief that these so-called pestles were used as clubs. Indeed, the largest corn-mills we have seen in Burlington County could not be well employed in the ab sence of a pestle, as, for instance, the one we have described in this chapter, the basin of which is nine inches in diameter and six inches deep.

Figure 201 represents a second example of a long pestle, with features that separate it widely from that shown in figure 200. It measures seventeen inches in length, lacking one-eighth of an inch, and, instead of being a uniform cylinder, as in the former instance, (figure 200,) is flattened along its whole length, giving it a width nearly double its thickness. Although smoother than the preceding specimen, it shows the marks of the stone-hammer very plainly, except at the ends, which are smoothed but not polished, and perfectly flat and square. There is a slight variation in the width at the two ends, the specimen *gradually* widening from the "handle" to the pestle end. Examples of this kind appear to be very uncommon : of the two hundred and thirty pestles we have, and of those we have seen in other collections, we have not met with a duplicate of this. Schoolcraft* has figured one that is similar in all respects to ours; and this is the only illustration we recall of such an one being found elsewhere. It may be, however, that we have merely failed to meet with them, and that they are not very rare. This flattened pestle, figure 201, weighs but five pounds and a half, and would make a far better "war-club" than the preceding specimen, or any of the heavier, cylindrical examples; but in the hands of an expert Indian even, a powerful blow could not be readily struck with such an instrument, except the object were quiet, while as to throwing them, we do not believe it was done, or, if it was, it was not a customary thing in aboriginal warfare. In case of surprise, these pestles might have been used for defense.

Figure 202 represents a very common style of small pestle, of which we have gathered a large series. They are cylindrical water-worn pebbles, such as are abundant in the bed of the Delaware River, at and above Trenton, N. J., measuring from eight inches to a foot in length, and from two and a half to three inches in diameter. These pestles are not chipped, pecked, or polished into shape, or altered in any way, except that from two-thirds to three-fourths of their length is split off; the splitting ending abruptly at what is apparently an actual cut into the body of the stone.

---

* N. A. Indians, vol. 1, p. 86, pl. 21, fig. 1.

Such a pestle as this shown in figure 202, would be well adapted, as a small war-club, either to be retained in the hand, or thrown, as were the smaller axes or tomahawks; but that it is a pestle seems more probable, inasmuch as the handle is the only portion of the implement showing any indication of polish, which it is not as likely would be the case were the specimen a club. Moreover, the extremity of the globular end is somewhat battered, showing that contact with another stone had been frequent.

Pestles, as a class, vary much in size. The longest we have met with was twenty-five inches in length. The shortest are those little, slender stones used to reduce red clay to paint-powder, in the stone cups which we have described. We have not seen any with flaring bases, such as those figured by Squier and Davis,* of which the description reads, " occasionally they are elaborately worked, but most are rude."

CHAPTER XXIV.

THE POGGAMOGGON AND NET-SINKERS.

With the one exception of arrow-heads, no class of relics is so abundant as the grooved globular or ovoid pebbles, known by many names, but which we have designated by the term " poggamoggon," as such stone implements are called by the present Shoshone Indians.†

Figure 203 gives an accurate representation of an average specimen. Some of them are smaller, but none noticeably larger. In finish they vary much, the extremes being a rough pebble with an irregularly " pecked" groove, and a polished pebble with the groove accurately made and smooth. The absence of battered surfaces at the ends seems to indicate that they were never used as hammers; but, as it has been suggested, they were weights for fishing-lines.

Professor Nilsson, to whose work we have so often referred, says of specimens of this kind:‡ "Those ancient *plummets* which occur most commonly are * * * oval, or ovally rounded, and with a groove round the middle." He figures such, (pl. xi, fig. 217,) and says of it: It has "undoubtedly been a *plummet*—it was brought from Pennsylvania."§ This specimen is not grooved entirely round it, but, according to the figure, is notched rather than grooved. Such specimens from New Jersey we will notice presently. They are always ruder than figure 203. There can be no doubt that the grooved stones, similar to figure 203, are used as *plummets* in Greenland. Professor Nilsson remarks:|| "I was some years ago informed by a person who has long resided in Greenland, how the stones were formed which were used by

---

* Anc. Mon. Miss. Valley; p. 220, fig. 118.

† Exp. up Missouri, vol. 1, p. 425, by Lewis and Clarke.

‡ Nilsson, Stone Age in Scand., p. 25.

§ L. c., p. 25, (foot-note.)

L. c., p. 25.

the natives as plummets. He sketched one. Subsequently, a student presented me with a stone of exactly the same shape as that represented in the sketch just mentioned. This stone was found in the earth in the province of Blekinge, and has evidently been used as a *plummet*."

Mr. John Evans* figures a grooved pebble very large in comparison with our New Jersey specimens, as a " grooved hammer," (?) and says of it and similar ones, " They were originally regarded as stone-hammers, but such as I have examined are made of a softer stone than those usually employed for hammers, *and they are not battered or worn at the ends*. It seems, therefore, probable that they were used as sinkers for nets and lines, for which purpose they are well adapted, the groove being deep enough to protect small cord around it from wear by friction." Our New Jersey specimens generally are hard enough for hammers, but are too small, and, like the English specimens already noticed, are free from battered ends. The main difficulty, we think, in considering them as net-weights or net-plummets, is the absence of any proof that the American Indians ever used a net in fishing.

Loskiel† describes the fishing methods of the Delawares and Iroquois, but says nothing of nets. His words are :

" I am now to describe one of the most favorite diversions of the Indians next to hunting, namely, that of *fishing*. Little boys are even frequently seen wading in shallow brooks, shooting small fishes with their bows and arrows.

" The Indians always carry hooks and small harpoons with them, whenever they are on a hunting party ; but at certain seasons of the year they go out purposely to fish, either alone or in parties. They make use of the neat and light canoes made of birch-bark, * * * and venture with them into spacious rivers."

Loskiel describes a method of shad-fishing similar to that adopted by the early settlers at Trenton, as detailed in the first chapter of this volume. Having mentioned the habit of providing themselves with hooks, and noting, also, that deep-river fishing was customary among the Indians, we see that a suitable " sinker" should also be provided, and we think there can be no doubt that some, at least, of these grooved pebbles were used as such. We say " *some* of these grooved pebbles," since we believe they are separable into two classes; those rough and only grooved by pecking a slight hollow around them, and those ground over their whole surface, and having a wider, semi-polished, and uniformly deep and wide groove. Figure 203 belongs to this latter class. The amount of work that has been expended upon some of these grooved pebbles, as mentioned, and the description of certain weapons now or formerly in use by savage races, induce us to believe that such a stone implement as figure 203 was used much after the manner of a modern slung-shot.

---

* Anc. Stone Imp. of G. B., p. 211, fig. 159.
† Mission to N. A. Indians, p. 95.

Lewis and Clarke* describe a weapon in use among the Shoshone Indians as follows:

"The poggamoggon is an instrument consisting of a handle twenty-two inches long, made of wood, covered with dressed leather, about the size of a whip-handle. At one end is a thong of two inches in length, which is tied to a round stone weighing two pounds, and is held in a cover of leather. At the other end is a loop of the same material which is passed round the wrist so as to secure the hold of the instrument, with which they strike a very severe blow."

In this description we notice that a thong is tied about the stone, and to secure it a shallow groove would be desirable, if not necessary. Such a groove we have in the larger, better-made grooved pebbles we have described, and although our New Jersey specimens do not reach two pounds in weight, they are generally larger than the roughly-finished specimens.

Mr. George C. Musters† has given us a most interesting account of the weapons and hunting implements of the Tehuelche Indians, and in his description of the "bolas" now in use by these savages, refers to ancient bolas, which seem to be identical with the grooved pebbles, or "net-weights," that we have described. Mr. Musters writes: "Ancient bolas (globular stones) are not unfrequently met with. These are highly valued by the Indians, and differ from those in present use *by having grooves cut around them*, and by their larger size and greater weight." There is no reason for believing that the Patagonian bolas were ever in use among the North American Indians; but it is possible that the simplest form of such a weapon, a globular stone with a cord attached —the *Bola perdida* of the Tehuelches—may have originated at some central point, say Brazil, and thence developed into the ordinary two and three balled bolas of Patagonia and the poggamoggon of the northern continent. Nevertheless we see nothing objectionable to the view that these two forms may have arisen separately, the country and game in each case suggesting, in the one the bola, in the other the poggamoggon; and, in the absence of a knowledge of metals, what was more natural than to choose a globular pebble, and to groove it in order to secure the heavy weight to a flexible cord or handle?

As there are simpler forms of "worked" pebbles, which in our opinion were used as "sinkers," as well as the rougher specimens of grooved globular pebbles, we have assumed that specimens such as figure 203 were used as weapons allied to or identical with the poggamoggon. Other uses, however, may have been found for these same globular stones; for instance, we find in Schoolcraft's work an illustration of a war-club with such a small round stone inserted in a notch in the end of the club, giving the completed implement the appearance of an ordinary wrench with a small object held in its jaws.

---

* Exp. up the Missouri, vol. i, page 415. Philadel. 1814.
† At home with the Patagonians, p. 166.

Having divided the grooved globular stones into weapons—the pog-gamoggon (?) and sinkers for fishing-lines—we would now call attention to a more primitive implement, which we have no doubt was used wholly as a sinker. Very probably such a sinker was improvised just before starting out into the river or lake; and again, as the globular form is preferable, not being as likely to be caught by snags or clefts in sunken rocks, it may be that a few flat stones were carried in the canoe, so that if the good sinker were lost, a temporary one could be readily provided.

Figure 204 represents an ordinary specimen of these flat, oval-outlined stones, with a well-defined notch chipped on each side, these notches being always opposite each other. No care appears to have been taken in choosing the pebbles, other than that of not having them too thick; in thickness they vary little from about half an inch.

Figure 205 represents about the maximum size of these flat, side-notched sinkers. It measures a little over 4 inches in length and 2 inches in breadth. The notches are always in the middle of the speci-men, so that the implement is balanced when suspended by a cord pass-ing around them.

The specimens of this class of sinkers vary but little in weight, but curiously enough, and in confirmation of their suggested use, we have noticed that the heavier specimens are found about the Delaware River shore, where the current is strong, and the smaller, lighter ones about the creeks, and where the current is scarcely noticeable. About the up-lands, where all relics are mingled together in the soil, both styles and all sizes and weights of sinkers are, of course, found together, no single form predominating, in a locality like the site of an old village.

We have never met with a sinker like those figured in 204 and 205 with four notches, or with the globular specimens having more than one groove, described by Professor Nilsson as found in Scandinavia.

CHAPTER XXV.

STONE IMPLEMENTS OF UNKNOWN USES.

Our knowledge of the functions of stone implements is, as yet, too im-perfect to enable us to determine in every instance the use to which particular forms were put. A doubt as to their design is still connected with some of the simpler forms, and it is, therefore, not strange that in every large collection there should be a few specimens about which nothing can be positively determined concerning the purpose for which they were made.

Figure 206 represents an excellent example of a highly-polished horn-stone pebble, which has been cut off square at one end and worn to a blunt but highly-polished edge along the curved margin. This would afford a fine specimen of what we have denominated "skinning knives," were the edge sharp. (See chap. xi.) As it is, however, the specimen may have been used as such, the incisions in the skin being previously made with a flint knife.

Since the publication of Mr. Evans's volume, to which we have referred so frequently, it seems more probable that it was used in rubbing down skins in the process of their preparation for clothing. The shape and size of the stone, its high polish, and prevalence among the relics that characterize the sites of villages, seem certainly to indicate that it was a domestic implement.

Figure 207 represents another example of polished pebble, that has been altered little, if any, in shape. A noticeable feature is in its being perforated by five small holes, which are natural, however, being thread-like veins of softer mineral which have been drilled out. One of these perforations occurring near the margin of the stone, the stone itself has been worn off at that point until much thinner than elsewhere, and the hole then enlarged by a very slender stone-drill. A cord was passed through this hole to suspend the implement or ornament.

If an implement, this specimen was used in the same manner as the preceding one. The curved outline is of about the same thickness as figure 206, and appears, like that, to be more highly polished than the other portions of the stone. Either as a "skinning-knife" or a skin-dresser, it is as available as the preceding example.

Professor Nilsson* has figured and described what he terms a "stretching implement," to which class of stone implements both figures 206 and 207 may belong. He says of the illustration which he gives, "The widened part, representing the edge, has been rounded off by *constant wear*, probably from being rubbed against leather or something of that kind. A person who has lived many years as a mechanic in Greenland, thinks he has discovered a great resemblance between this stone implement and the bone implement, provided with a handle, which is there used for stretching skins in order to give them the requisite softness. A somewhat similar stretching implement of iron is still used in those parts of Scania where the winter dress of the peasantry consists of sheep-skin coats." We can readily see that the specimens we have figured, although much smaller, could be used in just such manner as Professor Nilsson describes; and as the deer-skin was the principal material for clothing, these stones may have been used by laborious rubbing with the rounded edge to render the hide flexible ; the edge appearing the same in both Professor Nilsson's and our specimens.

In a previous publication † we have described a New Jersey "stretching implement," which is now believed to have been a true "scraper," and is so classed in chapter XII of this paper. With such scrapers as we find, wherewith to clean the skins, and with these polished porphyry pebbles to stretch and soften them, after their dressing of "brains,"‡ the aborigines could make most comfortable clothing of the hides of our

---

. * Stone Age, p. 77, and pl. ix, fig. 185.   † Amer. Nat., vol. vi, p. 222.
‡ See Catlin's N. A. Indians, vol. i, p. 45.

common deer; and we believe we are not far from right in classing figures 206 and 207 as "stretching implements," using that designation as it is applied by Professor Nilsson.

Figure 208 represents a very carefully-wrought stone implement, of which we can say but little positively. It appears to be a combination of the ordinary grooved oval poggamoggon and the little stone hammer, to be described in the next chapter. As either the one or the other, it is a pretty specimen, but why the characteristics of two such different implements should be combined is indeed puzzling.

The general surface of the stone itself, as well as the groove and deep indentations on each side, are worthy of notice. While not polished to any extent, this stone has a far smoother surface than the majority of either net-weights or hammer-stones. The groove is unusually narrow, and apparently has been *ground* out and not *pecked*, as is the case with net-weights. The hollows or indentations are much deeper than those in any stone hammers in our collection, and, like the grooves, are very smooth, as though drilled with a stone drill, such as figured in chapter xv, figure 155.

There are no indications of battering or roughness at the ends, as in all stone hammers; and, indeed, if such were the intended use, why the very carefully made grooves?

Our specimen, figure 208, bears much resemblance to two of those figured by Professor Nilsson,* *but is a combination of them*, which we think overturns the theory that the use of the two kinds of implements was identical. If figure 208 had no encircling groove, it would be very similar to an oval tool-stone figured by Sir John Lubbock.† This author has not much faith in their having been stone hammers, and adds, "It is very doubtful whether these implements really belong to the stone age."

Whatever may be the use of the specimen we have figured, it is unquestionably a relic of the "stone age" of the North American aborigines, and one that was of value in its day, considering the character and amount of the work on it.

Figure 209 represents a very pretty specimen of those "discoidal stones," about which there has been much conjecture.

We think the following paragraph from Du Pratz's work‡ correctly explains the use of the specimen we have figured:

"The warriors practice a diversion which they call the *game of the pole*, at which only two play at a time. Each pole is about eight feet long, resembling a Roman f, and the game consists in rolling a flat, round stone about three inches in diameter and one inch thick, *with the edges somewhat sloping*, and throwing the pole in such a manner that when the stone rests the pole may be at or near it. Both antagonists throw their pole at the same time, and he whose pole is nearest the stone counts one, and has the right of rolling the stone."

---

* Stone Age, pl. ii, figs. 31 and 33.   † Prehistoric Times, 2d ed., p. 98, fig. 118.
‡ Hist. of Louisiana, 1720, p. 366.

Squier and Davis,* in describing these discoidal stones, make mention of information given them by Rev. J. B. Finley, who states "that among the tribes with which he was acquainted, stones identical with those described were much used in a popular game resembling the modern one of "ten-pins." The form of the stones suggests the manner in which they were held and thrown, or rather rolled. *The concave sides received the thumb and second finger, the forefinger clasping the periphery.*"

This last sentence applies perfectly to the description of our specimen. The concavity on each side, although shallow, is well defined; that of the right side, or the one which the thumb occupies when held in the right hand, being somewhat larger. Of course the stone can be reversed so as to bring the second finger into this larger cavity, but it would naturally be grasped in the manner described by Mr. Finley.

Figure 209, while not polished to any degree, is very smooth, an accurate circle in outline, and has the beveled margin very uniform throughout. The most elevated portion of the beveled edge is not in the middle, so that when standing on edge the stone naturally falls on the *right* or more deeply concave side. When rolled, it generally *tends to the right* and falls with what we have considered the "right" or upper surface down.

Squier and Davis† figure a great variety of this class of relics, and while giving many reasons and quotations tending to show that they were "game stones," add, "they are certainly enigmatic in their purposes."

These disks are not abundant in New Jersey, but in *every* considerable collection of "Indian antiquities" we have visited, we have seen one or more specimens, all exhibiting about the difference shown in the illustrations given by Squier and Davis of those found in the western mounds, except that none were perforated.

Figure 210 is a disk of very compact stone, measuring two and a half inches in diameter, and one inch in thickness. The sides are finely polished, and the edge beveled, having a sharp central ridge, not straight, and somewhat nearer one side than the other. In outline this disk is not a perfect circle, and will only roll a short distance, unless thrown with much force.

This specimen is much ruder in detail than the preceding implement; and while it may be such a stone as Du Pratz describes, being "one inch thick, *with the edges somewhat sloping*," it does not seem sufficiently finished for such a purpose.

This disk, figure 210, bears a marked resemblance to a "stone object" found at the Cape of Good Hope, "probably *an ear-ring*, or rather *button*, for insertion into the lobe of the ear." The African specimen is smaller than that from New Jersey, being an inch and a half in diameter and only three-eighths of an inch thick. Col. Lane Fox‡, in

---

* Anc. Mon. Miss. Valley, p. 223, fig. 121.　　　　　　　† L. c., p. 221.
‡ Journ. Ethnol. Soc. of London ; new series, 1870, vol ii. p. 41 ; pl. 1, fig. 2.

commenting on the Cape of Good Hope specimen, remarks that " such disks were usually supposed to have been used as hammer-stones ; he thought, however, that this was too small to be used for such a purpose, and that the suggestion of Mr. Bowker, that it may have been used for insertion into the lobe of the ear, was a very reasonable one."

While the specimen, figure 210, is somewhat larger and, we suppose, heavier than that above described, we think it very possible that it too was used as a " button " for insertion into the lobe of the ear. It certainly is no larger, and probably no heavier, than many of the extravagant ear-rings which Mr. Catlin saw and painted in his portraits of the Indians of the present century.

Figure 210 is a very solid pebble of limestone, of a delicate bluish gray color, which, when wet, shows beautiful mottlings of pure white ; and, as the stone is thus rendered so very handsome, is it not probable that it was an ornament, and that, when freshly cut and polished, the blue and white contrasted as distinctly as now when immersed in water ? If the present dullness of the tint is the effect of long exposure, to what extent does this fact bear upon the question of age ?

Figure 211 represents an uninteresting-looking pebble, chiefly noticeable in that but little of the natural surface has been left by the grinder and for the astonishing surface-irregularity which it now presents. The pebble is a fine-grained quartz—sand conglomerate, hard and heavy. No doubt the patient fashioner of this specimen had some important object in view in grinding off the natural surface into the many angular surfaces which now exist. Extending around three-fourths of the circumference of the implement is a well-defined but crooked ridge, close to the middle. This ridge, which is the prominent feature of the specimen, was probably intended for some useful purpose ; but what its object was, and even that of the stone itself, is a mystery. As a pebble it would make a very good " sling-stone," but the aborigine certainly did not use the sling. As a " bola " it would give a telling blow to a puma, as described by Mr. Musters ; but although pumas (*Felis concolor*) were common, it is not known that our Indians ever used the bola. It may have been used as a war-club knob, such as Schoolcraft figures, described in the last chapter ; but would a club be any more effective because of elaborate grinding and ridges such as are the surface of this specimen ? We cannot think it was ever intended as a stone-hammer. It was never certainly used as such, having no trace whatever of violent contact with other stones ; however it bears more resemblance to that class of relics than to any other.

We have met with only a few—eight or ten—examples such as figure 211, but all corresponded with this in size, shape, and mostly in material. One or two were hard jasper pebbles, with veins of fine-quartz running through them. All were ground over nearly the whole surface, and most of them were as irregular as the one here illustrated.

Figure 212 represents a form of relic of which we have met with but one example, and unless it be incomplete—an unfinished specimen—we can form no idea of its use.

Squier and Davis have given[*] a series of illustrations of "pendants," to which this specimen bears much resemblance both in size and finish, although it is a little longer than those of the West.

They say, "These pendants are of frequent occurrence in the vicinity of the ancient works, though seldom found, if found at all, in the ancient works themselves. They, for the most part, resemble the plumbs of the architect, and are usually made of rare and beautiful materials." As will be seen at a glance, this specimen readily comes under the head of "pendants," as just described, but the specimens figured by Squier and Davis all have a groove encircling either one end or both, according to the shape of the specimen, whereby a cord was securely attached to pass through the opening in the lobe of the ear, if worn as an "ear-bob," or around the neck to let the "pendant" hang upon the breast. If this specimen, therefore, is simply unfinished, it is a pendant, and not of an "unknown" use; but is it unfinished? A careful examination shows it to be uniformly polished or smoothly ground from one end to the other. There are no rough portions or unfinished places; hence we are compelled to think it had some other use.

The authors we have just quoted give on page 219 of their work figures of two pear-shaped stones, the dimensions of which are not given. They consider it possible that they were used as club-heads or something similar, and quote Carver, who describes "a weapon in use by the tribes beyond the Mississippi River which consisted of a curiously wrought stone, inclosed in leather, as above, (the Chippewayan *poggamoggon*) and fastened like the slung-shot of the present day to a thong a yard and a half long, which was also wound around the wrist. These weapons were used in battle."

A specimen like figure 212 may possibly be a weapon such as above described, but it would appear, for two reasons, that it was not so used. In the first place the size, weight, and careful polishing are not in keeping with such a weapon as the "slung-shot" described by Carver; and, secondly, if a weapon, would it not be oftener met with? It has been suggested that it was a mould, about which clay was spread, to form the bowls of the clay pipes used by the aborigines; but its size is too great for this purpose. We have not seen any clay pipes with a bowl of as great a diameter as this would make. This specimen measures four and a half inches in length, and one inch and three-quarters in its greatest breadth, which is a little above the middle of the specimen. The material is a fine-grained sandstone, and the whole surface being carefully ground and smoothed almost to a polish, the specimens can hardly be considered *merely a pestle*, as it might appear at first glance.

Figure 213 represents one of two specimens found together in a field near Trenton, N. J. We have seen a third, highly polished, of horn-

---

[*] Anc. Mon. Mis. Valley, p. 235, fig. 132.

stone, showing the grooves very distinctly, and with a hole drilled at one side of the end, opposite that which has the grooves or indentations. It is in the museum of Rutgers College, at New Brunswick, N. J. This specimen is an ordinary sandstone pebble, four and seven-eighths inches in length, two inches and a half in width at the grooved end, and sloping from there to the opposite end, which is but an inch in width. There has been a slight rubbing down of the surface generally, which is moderately smooth, and on one side are marks of a stone-hammer at one point; but no depression or cavity has been formed that would attract attention.

The interesting feature of the specimen, figure 213, is a series of deeply-cut grooves, the majority about an inch in length, which extend from or near the middle of the stone to the edge, running in an oblique direction to the left. There are eight, parallel on each side of the stone, and so arranged that, turn either side towards you, the direction of the grooves is the same.

We have seen no description or illustration of a stone implement corresponding exactly with this.

Professor Nilsson* has given us one figure of a *hammer-stone* which bears considerable resemblance to figure 213, and says that it has at its edges " marks of the purpose to which *it was* formerly applied so unmistakably that, when once pointed out, no further doubts can be entertained on the matter." This, we think, settles the question, and that, whatever the resemblance, figure 213 is *not* a *stone-hammer*. Such regular grooves as these cannot be called or considered marks of blows against some hard brittle stone. When we come to consider " hammer " or " tool stones," we will find a vast difference between the marks on this specimen, figure 213, and the relics we have figured as true stone-hammers. Nor can these grooves be considered the natural result of use as a whetstone for sharpening skinning-knives and kindred implements. They are too close, regular, narrow, and short.

When treating of breast-plates, we saw that many of them were notched, and concluded that such notches were records of battles, of persons killed, or scalps taken. Stones such as that here figured are placed in the same class, but with a query. It seems to us that the most probable use of such stones was as records, and we think the fact of having met with one that was perforated strengthens the view that figure 213 is a " record-stone." The other specimen in our collection, however, is much more rude in finish, and has these grooves more scattered about the margin. This rather combats the idea, possibly, of these relics being record-stones, and so coming under the head of ornamental objects.

Figure 214 represents an oval, flattened cobble-stone, about four inches in diameter and two inches thick. The under side has been worn off until it is now a perfectly level plane. The margins are slop-

---

* Nilsson on Stone Age, pl. 1, fig. 11.

ing and somewhat smooth, and in the center of the upper surface of the stone is a depression, perfectly circular at the top, and deepening with regularity to a point at the bottom. The appearance is that of the commencement of a hole by drilling, and is very different from the "finger-pits" which we shall see on stone-hammers, when we come to describe them.

In the specimen here described, as in very many others, there is a decided discoloration of the depression, as though drilled with metal, particles of which had adhered to the sides of the cup or hollow made. It is not a metallic discoloration, however, as proved by examination with a powerful lens.

Just such stones as the one above described are very common throughout the State, and, overlooking the drilled (?) hollow, in the top, are considered simply the "crushers" used with the portable corn-mills. They probably had some other use, as in that case there would be no object in making any mark, however slight, upon the upper surface, which in no way tends to assist in the crushing of the grain, the stone simply being held in the hand and revolved.

We have thought that these stones might be in some way connected with the production of fire. Sir John Lubbock figures[*] a Dacotah fire-drill bow, which consists of two plates or slabs of wood, one at each end of the drill, which is itself revolved by a bow-string being looped around it and the bow then drawn rapidly to and fro. That is developed by the rapid revolutions of the drill, and communicated to fragments of rotten wood applied to the lower end of the drill. Now, as we find these stone slabs most abundant on the sites of old Indian villages, they are probably a domestic implement, and we have thought they were used as the lower plate in which the fire-drill revolved ; fibers of dead wood being heaped about the drill, where it enters the little depression on the top of the plate, would be ignited very readily.

Sir John Lubbock does not say whether the slabs, seen in his illustration of a fire-drill, are wood or stone.

We are under the impression, however, that fire was produced among our New Jersey Indians by friction in simply violently rubbing one stick upon another, and *if solely* obtained in that manner, we can give no explanation of the presence of these large stones, which by trial we find well adapted for the purpose suggested, in connection with the bow-drill.

Figure 215 represents a peculiarly-chipped piece of yellowish-brown jasper, which, when found, was exactly twice its present length, and was the more valuable because the fragment which was broken off extended nearly at right-angles to the portion here illustrated. In its present condition this specimen measures three and a half inches in length, is an inch and a half wide, and half an inch thick. The under side is comparatively smooth—about as the majority of jasper spear and arrow points ; the

*Prehistoric Times, 2d ed., p. 514, fig. 224.

upper side is more uneven, having zigzag ridges made by the deep chip-pings which produce the large serrations so noticeable upon the outer side of the implement. Before being broken, the character of the chip-ping and general appearance of the fragment were, as they even now are, totally different from anything we have seen in chipped jasper, either from New Jersey or other localities. The other "half" of the specimen still left the implement incomplete, which appeared to have been much the size and shape of a modern horseshoe. Before it was broken, this specimen bore much resemblance to one of a number of flint implements from Honduras, described by Dr. Daniel Wilson,* with an illustration ; and also figured and described by E. T. Stevens.† One of these Honduras specimens is "a crescent with projecting points." It is said to measure seventeen inches in greatest length. This New Jersey fragment is a portion of a crescent, *without* projecting points, which was about ten inches in greatest length. Whatever may have been the object of this Honduras crescent, in all probability the same object was had in view in our New Jersey specimen, and we know of no more inter-esting instance of similarity between specimens of distant localities than occurs in this case, unsatisfactory though it may be, in consequence of our specimen being but a small fragment of the original implement.

Figure 216 represents a very curious and interesting form of stone im-plement, of a pattern of which we have seen but this one example, which is in the possession of Joseph Newbold, esq., of Burlington County, New Jersey. The specimen is a polished horn-stone pebble, perfectly flat upon one side, and rounded, edged, grooved, and conically headed upon the other. It measures seven and a half inches in length and two and three-eighth inches in greatest width, this point being about one inch and three-quarters from the end, which is brought to a sharp cut-ting-edge. Four and a quarter inches from this cutting-edge in front, the implement narrows very decidedly, and is also here grooved, the groove being something over an inch in width. The groove is followed by a conical head an inch and seven-eighths in length, the base being of equal width with the opposite margin of the groove and "waist" of the implement. The cutting-edge of this specimen is so carefully worked and is still so well preserved that it cannot be overlooked in considering the probable use of such an implement. If we look only to the edge, we naturally conclude that it was a skinning-knife, of a some-what peculiar pattern, being flat upon one side ; but when we take into consideration the length of the blade and the wide and well-wrought groove and conical head, we are forced to believe that it was not made for any but an important purpose ; and as that was not, *could not have been*, with reference to the skinning of animals, what was its use?

As stated, we have seen but this one specimen, and find, on inquiry, no one possessing such an implement in his cabinet, or admitting that he had ever seen its like. The published works to which we have

---

* Prehistoric Man, 2d ed., p. 139, fig. 7.   † Flint Chips, p. 289, pl. i.

STONE AGE IN NEW JERSEY.

had access contain no illustration or description of just such a specimen as figure 216.*

It will be found, on comparison with the hoe which we represent in figure 174, that it bears some resemblance to it; but there is no indication whatever of figure 216 ever having been used for agricultural purposes; there are no scratches or striæ, as would be the case had it been so used. It is smoothly polished over its whole surface, but the smooth surface is that of the hand-ax and skinning-knife, and not the *scoured* smoothness of a well-worn hoe.

Having a cutting-edge at one end, and that a very good one, it would seem proper to place this specimen in chapter xiv, with the chisels and gouges, a fitting place on some accounts, but the chisel was not available as a tool without a hammer, and the conical head of this specimen is as smooth, as highly polished, and as free as any portion of the implement from every trace of violent contact with other stones. If a chisel, it has never been used, and is more elaborately finished than any other specimen, with perhaps one exception, that we have met with. The whole amount of the work of fashioning chisels and gouges as a class is expended upon the edge. The gouge, figure 139, for instance, is beautifully wrought at the edge, which is accurately curved; but elsewhere this specimen is quite rough as compared with the edge.

It has been suggested by a successful collector and student of Indian antiquities, that this implement might have been used in detaching bark from trees, either for canoe purposes or for coverings for their huts; that by placing the flat side down or upon the body of the tree, and pushing the implement forward, the bark would be detached from the trunk of the tree without danger of cutting it, as the edge of the implement pressed upon the wood, and the curved back of the blade lifted the bark up as the blade moved forward. This certainly is an ingenious speculation on the part of Mr. Newbold; but we cannot see why the groove and tapering head of the implement should have been added, if such were its use, and certainly they are too well made and carefully finished to be placed there as ornaments merely. It may be, however, that the narrowed part was so made that a cord could be placed about it to facilitate its carriage, as it is easier to make a groove around such an object than it is to drill a hole. If so, the specimen may be a *"bark-detacher."*

CHAPTER XXVI.

FLAKING-HAMMERS AND POLISHING-TOOLS.

Every considerable collection of Indian antiquities we have seen from New Jersey, has included certain globular, oval, cylindrical, and

---

* Figures 216a and 216b represent a fine specimen of a "tally-stick," found near Freehold, N. J. The series of deeply-cut notches are indicative of its use as a record or tally. We have seen no other specimen of this pattern from New Jersey. It was received from Rev. S. Lockwood too late for further description.

long, flat stones, each possessing certain characteristic marks, which decide that it is, in archæological parlance, either a stone-hammer or a polishing-tool—a tool to block out or a tool for finishing an implement.

Figure 217 represents a good average specimen of a stone or flaking hammer such as found in New Jersey. It is a triangular sandstone pebble, the sides measuring about three inches each. The thickness of the specimen is a little less than two inches. On each side, very nearly in the center of the specimen, is a shallow, circular pit or depression, for the insertion of the ends of the thumb and second finger, the forefinger being curved over the margin of the stone-hammer. Held thus, we find it a useful tool, that does not weary the hand in holding, and is admirably adapted for the purposes intended by the original owner, that of chipping stones into desired shapes for arrow and spear points, and "pecking" the unshapely water-worn cobble-stones into axes.

If this specimen, figure 217, is held in the manner above described, it will be noticed that the outermost angle of the stone as then held has a battered appearance, which feature is proof positive of the correctness of the designation of the specimen as a stone-hammer. In the case of figure 173, two of the angles have been considerably battered, one much more than the other, showing that when one projecting point was too much worn the stone was shifted so that a new angle was the outermost. In this specimen, one angle has been completely used up, another is somewhat worn or battered off, the third is still intact. We have seldom met with an example of stone-hammer that told the story of its usefulness more plainly than this does.

Figure 218 represents a smaller circular stone or flaking hammer, of a size and shape like the majority of those which we find, the circular form being somewhat more abundant than the triangular. Figure 218, like the preceding, has the characteristic finger-pits, which in this case are considerably smaller in both measurements of diameter and depth. These "finger-pits" are rudely "pecked" out, and are not smooth, truly circular, or uniform as in those evidently drilled depressions noticed in figures 209 and 215.

Figure 218 is "completely battered up" over the whole extent of the margin of the specimen, there being only a circular space about each finger-pit of the natural surface of the water-worn pebble that has been used in fashioning this hammer. These stone-hammers were continually turned in the hand when being used, that they might retain their circular form. After being worn too small for "pecking" stone axes, they were probably utilized as net-weights or war-club knobs.

Figure 219 represents a third form of stone or flaking hammer which has some interesting features. It is from a mineral which we do not know, of blackish-brown color, and very smooth and polished upon the natural surface. It has much the appearance of, but is not, a hornblende pebble.

This implement, instead of having the finger-pits of figures 217 and 218, has the natural, smooth surface of the pebble retained, and, curiously enough, a small, smooth spot also is retained on the margin of the specimen. If we take up this, as we would those having "finger-pits," and place the end of the forefinger on the smooth surface upon the margin, we find that the point directly opposite the forefinger's end is that which has been worn off and battered by contact with other and harder minerals. The margin itself has been purposely chipped to bring the pebble into proper shape, and the point above mentioned is the only one that shows the specimen to have been used, and that it was designed solely as a stone-hammer. As in figure 217, the battered surface at that one point opposite the *natural* resting-point for the forefinger makes it a matter of certainty how this implement was utilized.

Figure 220 represents a pretty little stone-hammer, made from a small cylindrical pebble. The sides still retain their natural surface, but the ends are well battered, showing that the implement has done good serv_ice. Such a specimen is the most simple form of tool that we have in our collection. It is merely a pebble from the bed of a brook, and per_haps the battering it has received was caused by repairing a weapon of jasper which had become dulled on its edges or had lost the point. We think it probable that every aborigine was more or less competent to work in flint; otherwise, on extended journeys or during a day's hunting, many implements would be useless from some slight accident which would have to be repaired by the professional tool or arrow maker. We have often visited localities where jasper was extensively worked, and have seldom met with any but the more finished stone or flaking hammers.

Professor Nilsson* has described a series of stone-hammers from Scandinavia, *with one from the Delaware River*, which are in most respects similar to our New Jersey specimens. He says of them, "there are antiquaries who would deny that the stone implements here represented and described (as hammer-stones) were used in the manner just mentioned, but I have never heard any one able even to guess for what other purpose they were used. As grindstones for iron they do not answer; and the marks of blows found on them were, as must be evident to every one not totally ignorant of the subject, occasioned by blows on some hard brittle *stone;* not against any kind of metal whatsoever. Similar chipping-stones are, besides, found from the pole to the equator, among all nations who use stone implements. The only objection to my view is, that similar stones have been found among iron articles. I have hinted that possibly these were amulets. That they were grindstones for iron arms is, as above stated, utterly impossible. It rests with the doubter, therefore, to specify for what purpose they were used, according to his opinion. On all these stones * * * we find at the edges marks of the purpose to which they were formerly applied so unmistakable, that when once pointed out no further doubts can be entertained on the matter." The only real difference we notice between those of New Jersey and Scandinavia, is the absence of *per-*

* Stone Age, 3d ed., p. 10, pl. i, figs. 1–11.

forated specimens. We have seen that certain stones, bearing marks of human workmanship, have been, in part, the tools with which were fashioned the vast majority of the relics which we find.

A stone-hammer to block out and rudely shape another stone was not all that was required by the stone-implement maker. The finished implements generally have lost the majority of the stone-hammer marks, and such wearing-off was evidently not done by the mere use of the implement. It was designed, and not accidental. This "rubbing-down" was, at first, accomplished by simply taking the weapon and *any* other pebble of suitable size and rubbing the one upon the other; but in time there was an advance over this primitive method. Stones of a particular shape, grain, degree of hardness, &c., were chosen as the best adapted for the purpose of smoothing weapons, and instead of being utilized once and thrown aside they were retained for future use, themselves soon becoming altered in shape and possessed of one or more of those long, slender, polished surfaces, common to them all, and whereby they are characterized as a distinct class. These relics we have designated "polishing-tools."

Figure 221 represents a good average polishing-tool, or, as designated by Nilsson, "whetstone." This specimen is an oblong, flattened cobble-stone, such as are found by thousands in the bed of the Delaware River. The upper surface has been considerably used, and is now much smoother than the natural or unused surface of the implement. At one side about half of the edge has been worn off, leaving the ends intact. This wearing away has extended deeply into the body of the stone, and the polishing space thus produced, with the oval ends of the stone, give the specimen a more tool-like appearance than is common to whetstones generally. This specimen, figure 221, measures nine inches in length, and about two and one-half in width, and is about the maximum size of polishing-tools as they occur in New Jersey, excepting, of course, portions of immovable bowlders, which being handy and of proper material, were used by stone-implement makers when not inconveniently distant from the workshop. The immense bowlder in Center street, Trenton, N. J., in which is the mortar described in chapter xxiv, figure 200, had a surface over a foot in length, and seven inches wide. The red man evidently was accustomed to go to this to renew the fine edge which characterized a well-made porphyry hand-ax or skinning-knife, or to give new polish to a cherished breast-plate.

Figure 222 represents a second example of polishing-tool, being a stone of much finer grain than that of the preceding example, and having a number of very smooth, level surfaces, it is still admirably adapted for polishing porphyry and horn-stone implements. About seven inches long and one inch and a half wide, it is of just the size for a whetstone, and yet is easily carried about. Considering the amount of wear it has had, and its virtues as a sharpening-tool, and even now for *metallic* implements, we doubt not but it was a cherished specimen. At various points on the surface of the specimen there are narrow, deep lines, which, we doubt not, are the scratches of porphyry skinning-knives, whose dulled edges were being restored. The principal sharpening-surface is on the upper edge of the specimen, which is here about three-fourths of an inch wide, and extends over about one-half of the length, leaving one-fourth at each end, just as in the preceding specimen, which has not been used, and presents the rough, pitted, natural surface of the stone.

Polishing and sharpening stone with such a tool as this is facilitated very much by the addition of water and very fine sand, and both were probably used by the aborigines, as we know them to have been used in drilling the beautiful banner-stones.

Figure 223 represents a very common form of polishing-tool, and one perhaps more properly named than the two preceding specimens, which might be classed by themselves as whetstones. It is a small quadrangular pebble of horn-stone, which has been " pecked " over the whole surface to bring it into its present shape. The middle of the specimen is widest and thickest, and from thence it slopes toward each side and end. One end, as will be noticed in the illustration, is curved instead of square, and polished instead of " pecked." This polished surface is the *polishing point*, being that which was rubbed in the grooves of axes and other similar points to give them a smooth surface. This rubbing has produced a sort of an edge at one corner, but not sharp at all, like a skinning-knife. When once a rounded corner has been produced on a polishing-tool, as in this specimen, which is of hard mineral, it is comparatively easy, with the addition of sand and water, to deepen, smooth, and accurately curve a groove such as we find on the ordinary cobble-stone ax, some of which, as we have seen, have beautifully-polished grooves, which, of course, are rendered smoother and perhaps deeper by the wear of the withes or sinews used in strapping the handle.

CONCLUSION.

Having given such facts as appeared to be pertinent to the subject in describing the several classes of implements of which we have here treated, there is little remaining to be said. Until future discoveries throw more light upon the particular uses of each kind of implement and weapon, but little more will be learned from these specimens beyond the facts given of the unquestionable identity of stone implements throughout the world, and their indication of man's original barbaric condition.

No question in the whole range of anthropological science has received more attention than how America was originally peopled, and everything bearing upon it, however remotely, is of value to those who seek to answer it. The stone implements we have been describing have something to do with this question. Maintaining, of course, the development of all mankind from a palaeolithic to a neolithic condition, and believing that the " rude implements " which we have described in

chapter ii to be strictly palaeolithic in their character and age, in order
to prove that the aborigines came from another continent, it must be
shown that such a paleolithic people were possessed of canoes which
would stand the hap-hazard rudderless journeys that Sir Charles Lyell
has described as one great means whereby distant islands and continents
have been populated.*

Sir Charles Lyell remarks :† " Were the whole of mankind now cut off,
with the exception of one family, inhabiting the old or new continent,
or Australia, or even some coral isle of the Pacific, we might expect
their descendants, though they should never become more enlightened
than the Australians, the South Sea islanders, or the Esquimaux, to spread
in the course of ages over the whole earth, diffused partly by the tendency of population to increase, in a limited district, beyond the means
of subsistence, and partly by the accidental drifting of canoes by tides
and currents to distant shores;" but it is impossible to determine the
range of capabilities of paleolithic people, even in the matter of migrations; and estimating a people's capabilities by a study of their "rude
implements," we are of the opinion that an overland journey from the
southern continent or Central America was more probable than a
canoe voyage from any of the islands of the Atlantic or Pacific. If we
heed the traditions of the aborigines, that they came from another country, then they sailed over some portion of the Pacific and not the Atlantic, all the various tribes having traditions of coming from the west; but
it would be well to remember that these traditions refer also to some
preceding or pre-occupying people whom the incoming race conquered.
If the Delaware Indians, who two centuries ago were in peaceful possession of New Jersey, really came from the west, and on arriving en-
countered *another* people and drove them off, all of which their traditions claim, the question arises, who were their predecessors ? Were
they a more primitive people than the red Indian, and the fashioners
of the old, rude implements ? Were they the paleolithic folk of the Delaware Valley, and the red Indians the neolithic people ?

While we cannot but accept the suggestions of Professor Huxley, as
expressed in our introductory chapter, in preference to the exotic origin
of our red Indians asserted by Sir Charles Lyell, we are nevertheless
compelled to return to the point from which we started, and admit that
the origin of the aborigines is still enveloped in what *has* proved an
impenetrable mist; but now that so much attention is being paid
throughout the world to anthropological science, it is almost safe to
predict that the origin of the red Indian and his prehistoric history will
yet be correctly outlined.

Sir John Lubbock has given excellent reasons for his belief in the
indigenous origin of the Mexican civilization. He remarks: "Take the
case of the Mexicans. Even if we suppose that they were descended

---

* See February and June numbers of American Naturalist for additional remarks on
this subject, based upon further discoveries of aboriginal relics.

† Principles of Geology, 11th ed., vol. ii, p. 474, Amer. ed.

from a primitively-civilized race and had gradually and completely lost both the use and tradition of letters—to my mind a most improbable hypothesis—still we must look on their system of picture-writing as being of American origin. Even if a system of writing by letters could ever be altogether lost, which I doubt, it certainly could not be abandoned for that of picture-writing, which is inferior in every point of view. If the Mexicans had owed their civilization not to their own gradual improvement but to the influence of some European visitors, driven by stress of weather or the pursuit of adventure on to their coasts, we should have found in their system of writing and in other respects unmistakable proofs of such an influence. Although, therefore, we have no historical proof that the civilization of America was indigenous, we have in its very character evidence more satisfactory perhaps than any historical statements would be."

Dr. Daniel Wilson, who endeavors to prove the Asiatic origin of the aboriginal American, says of him, he "is among the ancients of the earth,"[*] and that, " whencesoever he derived his origin, he presents to us just such a type of unprogressive life as the nomads of the Asiatic steppes. The red Indian of the Northwest exhibits no change from his precursors of the fifteenth century; and for aught that appears in him of a capacity for development, the forests of the American continent may have sheltered hunting and warring tribes of Indians, just as they have sheltered and pastured its wild herds of buffaloes, for countless centuries since the continent rose from its ocean bed. That he is no recent intruder is indisputably proved alike by physical and intellectual evidence.[†]" Further on the same writer observes: " Man entered on the occupation of the New World in centuries which there, as in older historic regions, stretch backward as we strive to explore them. His early history is lost, for it is not yet four centuries since the red man and this western world were made known to us; and he still exists as he did then, a being apart from all that specially distinguishes either the cultivated or uncultured man of Europe."[‡] Does not this admission of the great antiquity of the American aborigines carry with it, of itself, a proof of the autochthonic origin of the Indian? And the similarity of races—is it not but a repetition of what we have seen in the stone implements themselves, that like surroundings will produce similar weapons and tools?

Certainly one would not endeavor to trace a relationship between the ancient people who fashioned and used the rude and elaborate stone implements of Great Britain and the red Indians who chipped and polished the specimens here figured, yet, excepting the minerals of which they are made, how similar are they to the English specimens!

What though the Mongol does resemble the American, does this in itself prove relationship? And, also, it may be asked, which of the American aborigines, as they now are, does the Asiatic Mongol most resemble; or has each American tribe a representative in the other

---

[*] Prehistoric Man, 2d ed., p. 11.   [†] L. c., p. 10.   [‡] L. c., p. 13.

continent? Dr. Wilson asserts that " the theory of an aboriginal unity pervading our indigenous American race from the Arctic circle to Tierra del Fuego has been shown to be baseless ;"* but how can it be proved that the Indians appearing most nearly allied to Asiatic races are the oldest or *original* aborigines? We doubt that all American races are related, and if so different, as Dr. Wilson assumes, who can demonstrate now which type or pattern was the central from which came the others that climate, food, and surroundings generally, finally produced?

Whatever the origin of the American aborigine, however, there can be no question as to his *condition* from the date of his first appearance on American soil to the time of the arrival of the European settler, a period of immense duration, during which the puzzling red man passed from the paleolithic to a neolithic condition; and if we may correctly estimate the advance in culture which a race has made, by the traces of their arts that are still left to tell the story of their former presence, then in New Jersey the Indian was once a paleolithic man, and, from whatever source he came, here advanced without supernatural revelation, or the missionary efforts of a superior people, to a condition which is best known as " neolithic," or that stage of culture when stone was utilized to the best advantage, every quality of the mineral being recognized and the weapons fashioned accordingly.

The theory of the gradual progress of mankind, which needs no further discoveries to prove it true, is demonstrated, as in Europe, in the condition and general position of the stone implements found in New Jersey, although the older Stone age of the American race or races does not date back as far into prehistoric ages as is probable in other continents. It is true of New Jersey, as of Europe, that " all our recent investigations * * * into the state of the arts in the earlier Stone age, lead clearly to the opinion that at a period many thousands of years anterior to historical times, man was in a state of great barbarism and ignorance, exceeding that of the most savage tribes of modern times. He was evidently ignorant of all metals, and of the arts of polishing stone implements and of making pottery."† And finally, if the pride of man is to be considered in the demonstration of the truth in nature, is it not more pleasant to believe that we are an improvement over, rather than a degeneration from, our remote ancestry; and should we not be thankful to " Time, which antiquates antiquities, and hath an art to make dust of all things," that he " hath yet spared these minor monuments" to us to prove the advance which we have made over a distinct people of the globe, a fact which is now shown to be quite in accordance with " the convictions of the great body of the learned," and with the facts of history and of prehistoric times?

---

*L. c., p. 513.   † Lyell, l. c., vol. ii, p. 485.

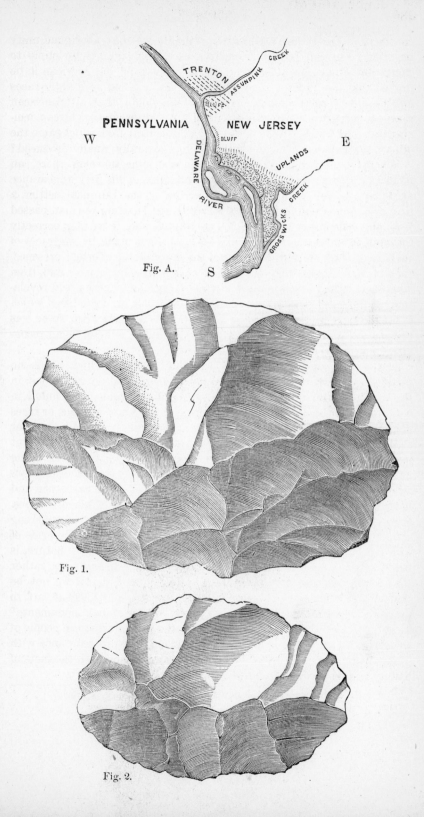

Fig. A.

Fig. 1.

Fig. 2.

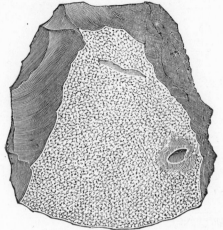

Fig. 3.

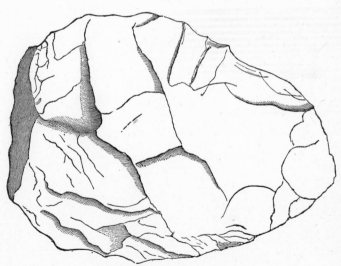

Fig. 4.—Natural size.

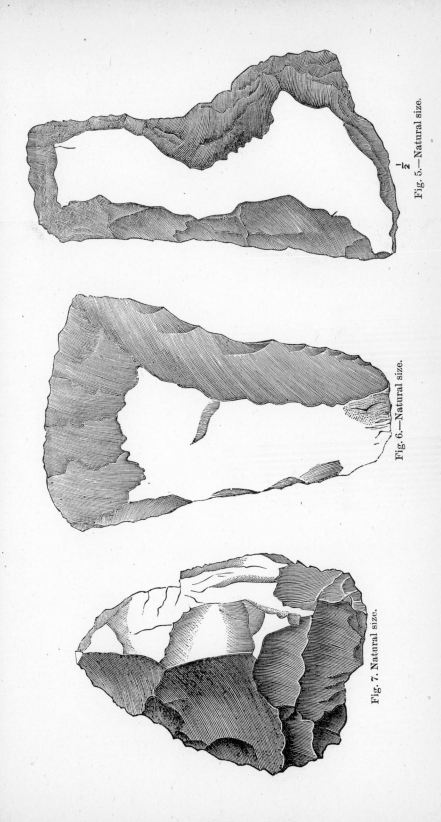

Fig. 5.—Natural size.

$\frac{1}{2}$

Fig. 6.—Natural size.

Fig. 7. Natural size.

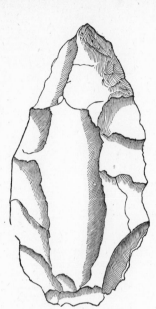

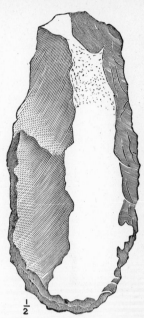

Fig. 8.—½ nat. size.

Fig. 9.

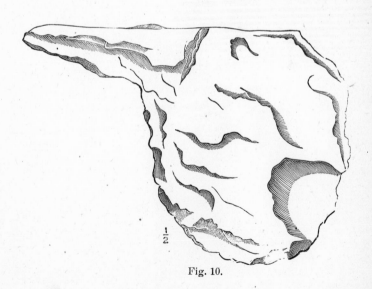

½

Fig. 10.

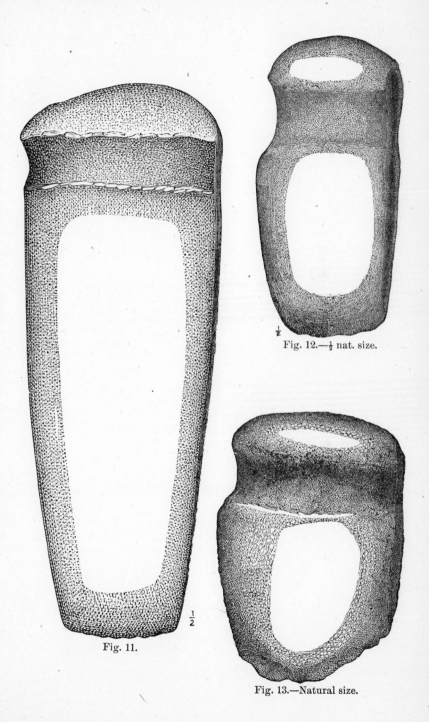

Fig. 11.

$\frac{1}{2}$

Fig. 12.—$\frac{1}{2}$ nat. size.

Fig. 13.—Natural size.

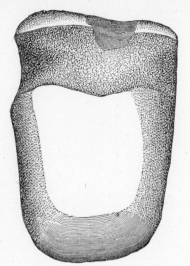

Fig. 14.

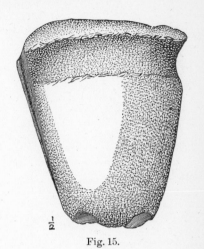

$\frac{1}{2}$

Fig. 15.

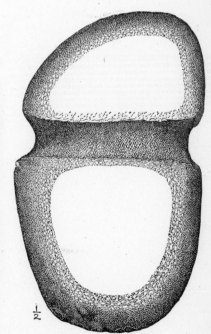

$\frac{1}{2}$

Fig. 16.

$\frac{1}{2}$ nat. size (side view).

$\frac{1}{2}$ nat. size.
(end view).

$\frac{1}{2}$

Fig. 17.—$\frac{1}{2}$ nat. size

Fig. 18.

Fig. 19.—½ natural size.

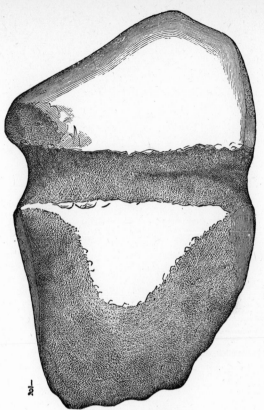

$\frac{1}{2}$

Fig. 20.—$\frac{1}{2}$ natural size.

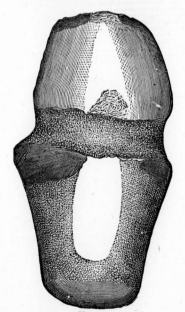

Fig. 21.

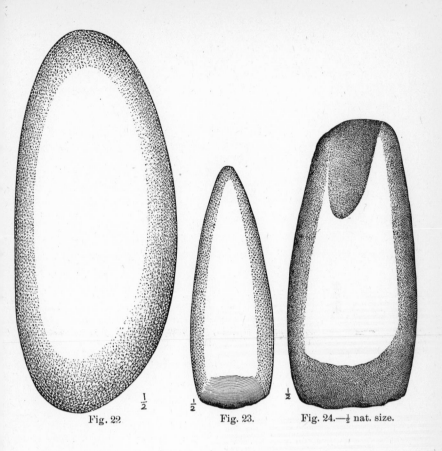

$\frac{1}{2}$

Fig. 22

$\frac{1}{2}$ Fig. 23.

$\frac{1}{2}$

Fig. 24.—$\frac{1}{2}$ nat. size.

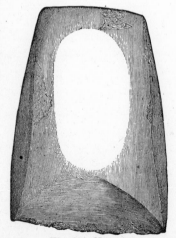

Fig. 25.— Nat. size.

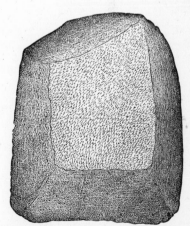

Fig. 26.—Natural size

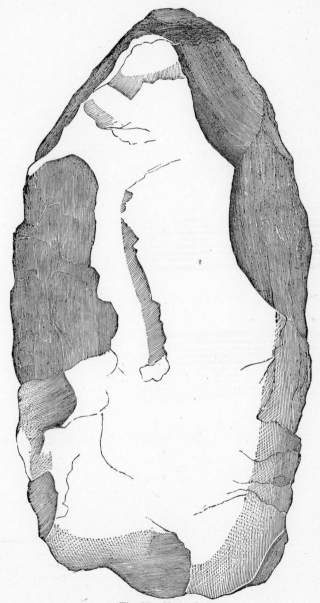

Fig. 27—Natural size.

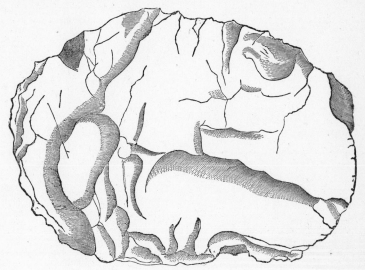

Fig. 28.—Natural size.

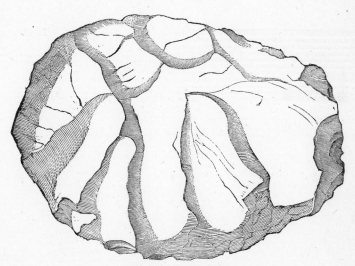

Fig. 29.—Natural size.

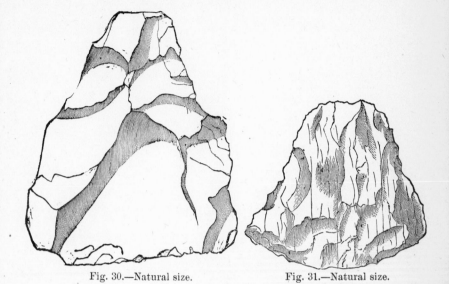

Fig. 30.—Natural size.   Fig. 31.—Natural size.

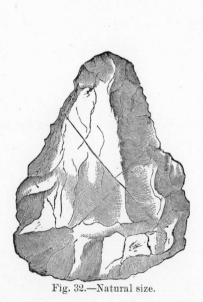

Fig. 32.—Natural size.

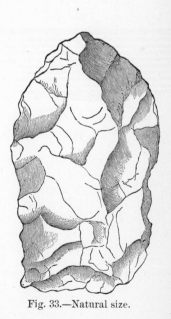

Fig. 33.—Natural size.

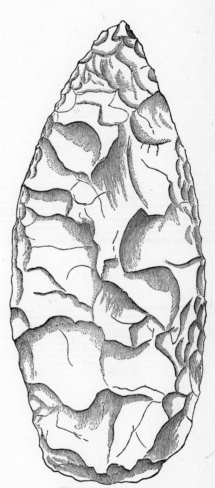

Fig. 34.—¼ natural size.

Fig. 36.—Natural size.

Fig. 37.

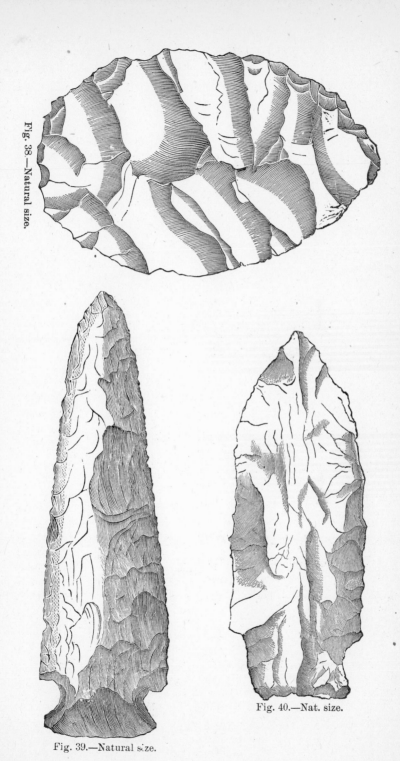

Fig. 38.—Natural size.

Fig. 39.—Natural size.

Fig. 40.—Nat. size.

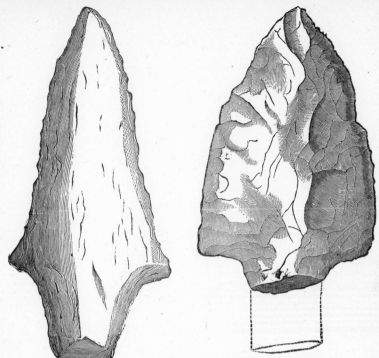

Fig. 41.

Fig. 42.—Natural size.

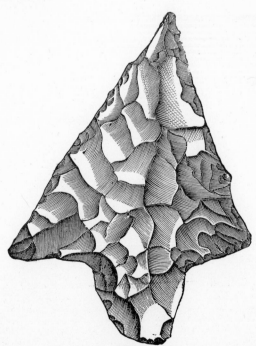

Fig. 43.

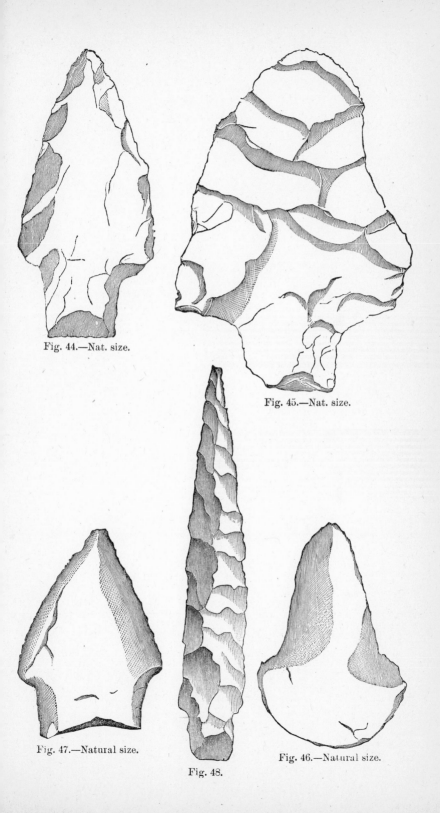

Fig. 44.—Nat. size.

Fig. 45.—Nat. size.

Fig. 47.—Natural size.

Fig. 48.

Fig. 46.—Natural size.

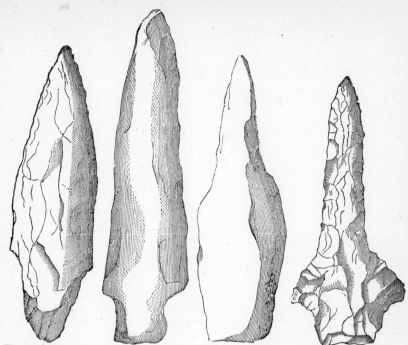

Fig. 49.—Nat. size.   Fig. 50.—Nat. size.   Fig. 51 —Nat. size.   Fig. 52.—Nat. size.

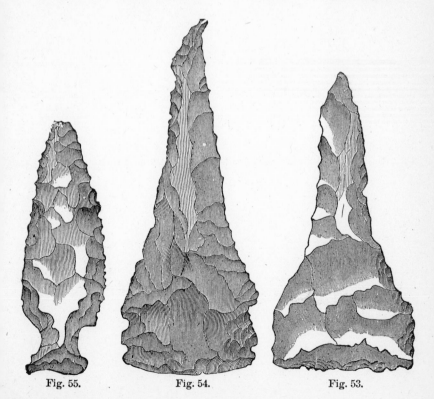

Fig. 55.   Fig. 54.   Fig. 53.

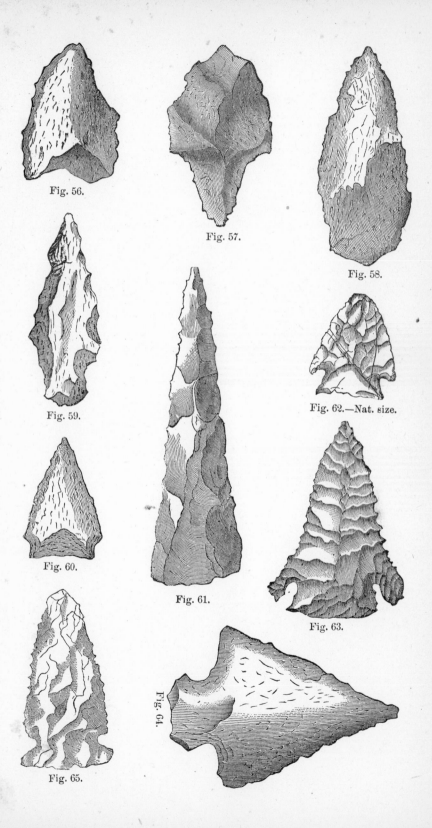

Fig. 56.

Fig. 57.

Fig. 58.

Fig. 59.

Fig. 62.—Nat. size.

Fig. 60.

Fig. 61.

Fig. 63.

Fig. 64.

Fig. 65.

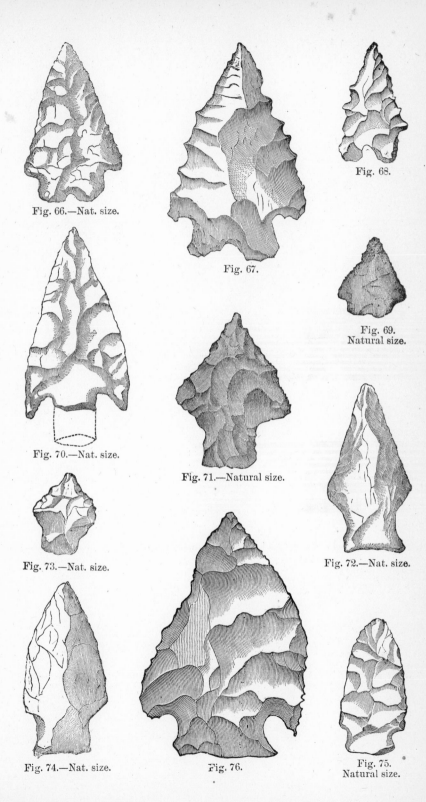

Fig. 66.—Nat. size.

Fig. 67.

Fig. 68.

Fig. 69.
Natural size.

Fig. 70.—Nat. size.

Fig. 71.—Natural size.

Fig. 73.—Nat. size.

Fig. 72.—Nat. size.

Fig. 74.—Nat. size.

Fig. 76.

Fig. 75.
Natural size.

Fig. 77.

Fig. 80.—Nat. size.

Fig. 84.—Nat. size.

Fig. 85.—Nat. size.

Fig. 78.

Fig. 81.—Nat. size.

Fig. 86.—Nat. size.

Fig. 87.

Fig. 79.—Nat. size.

Fig. 82.—Nat. size.

Fig. 83. Nat.—size.

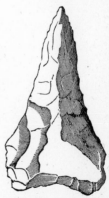

Fig. 88.—Nat. size.

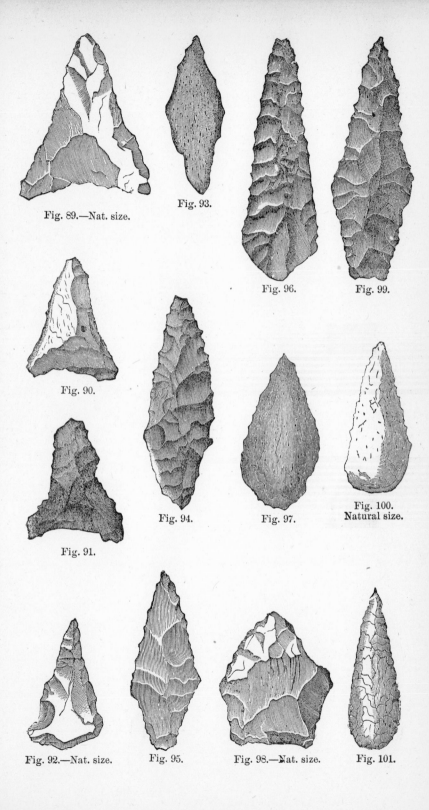

Fig. 89.—Nat. size.

Fig. 93.

Fig. 96.

Fig. 99.

Fig. 90.

Fig. 91.

Fig. 94.

Fig. 97.

Fig. 100.
Natural size.

Fig. 92.—Nat. size.

Fig. 95.

Fig. 98.—Nat. size.

Fig. 101.

Fig. 102.

Fig. 103.

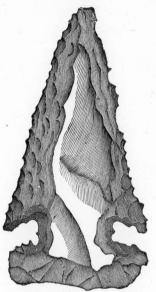

Fig. 104.

Fig. 105.

Fig. 106.

Fig. 107.

Fig. 108.—Nat. size.   Fig. 112.   Fig. 109.

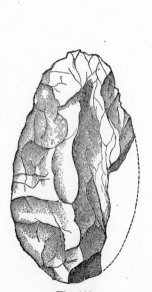

Fig. 110.   Fig. 111.   Fig. 112.

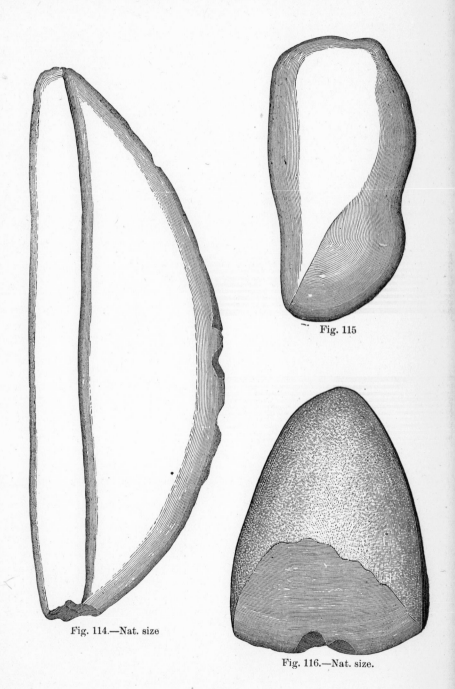

Fig. 114.—Nat. size

Fig. 115

Fig. 116.—Nat. size.

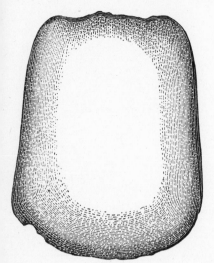

Fig. 117.

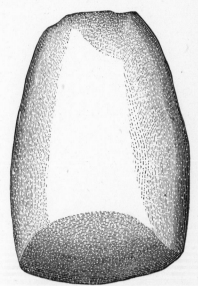

Fig. 118.—Nat. size.

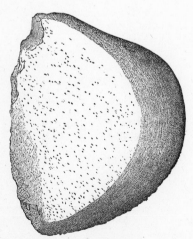

Fig. 119.—Nat. size.

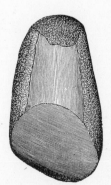

Fig. 120.

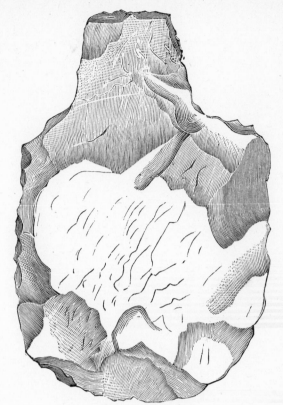

Fig. 121.—Nat. size.

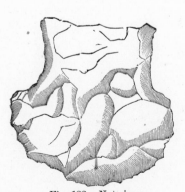

Fig. 122.—Nat size.

Fig. 123.—Nat. size.

Fig. 124.—Nat. size.

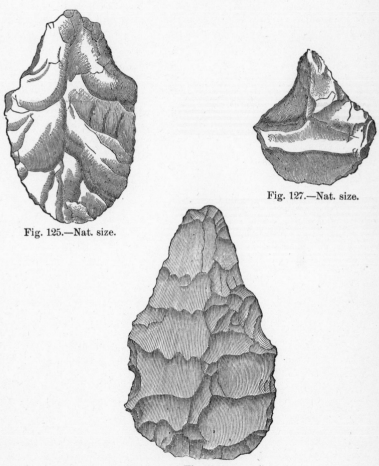

Fig. 125.—Nat. size.

Fig. 127.—Nat. size.

Fig. 126.

Fig. 128.—Nat. size.

Fig. 129.—Nat. size.

Fig. 130.

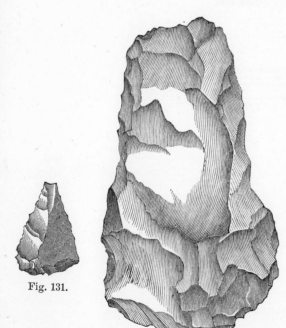

Fig. 131.

Fig. 133.

Fig. 132.

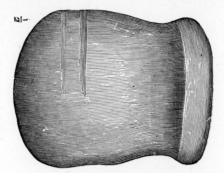

Fig. 136.—½ nat. size.

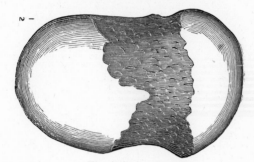

Fig. 135.—½ nat. size.

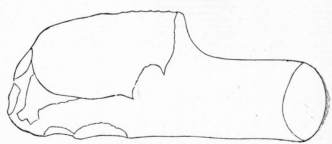

Fig. 134.—⅛ nat. size.

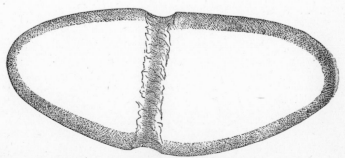

Fig. 133 a.—½ nat. size.

Fig. 137 wanting.

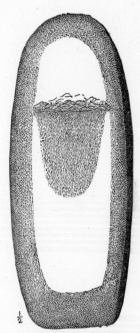

Fig. 138.—½ nat. size.

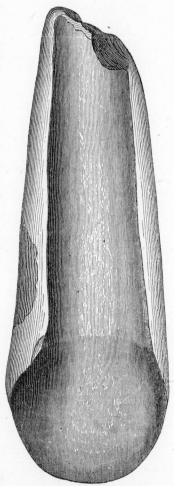

Fig. 139.

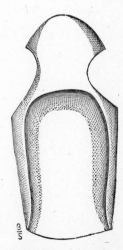

Fig. 140.—⅗ nat. size.

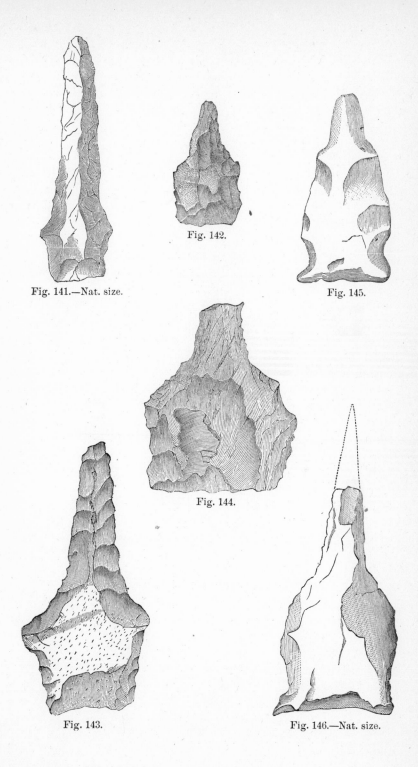

Fig. 141.—Nat. size.

Fig. 142.

Fig. 145.

Fig. 144.

Fig. 143.

Fig. 146.—Nat. size.

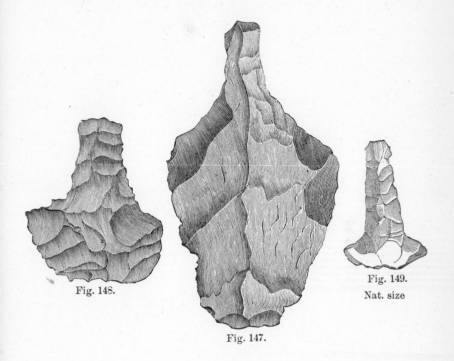

Fig. 148.

Fig. 147.

Fig. 149.
Nat. size

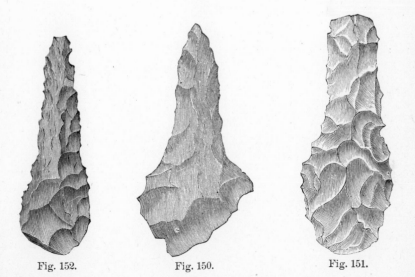

Fig. 152.

Fig. 150.

Fig. 151.

Fig. 153.—Nat. size.

Fig. 154.
Nat. sizo.

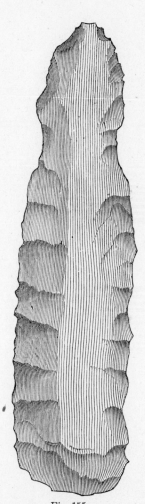

Fig. 155.

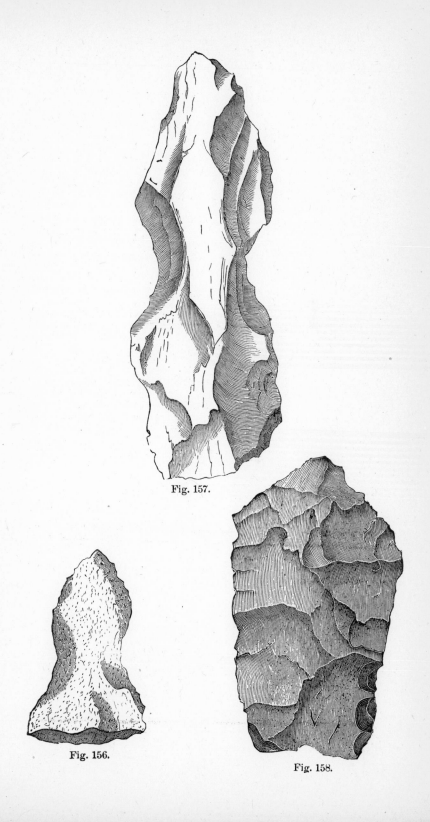

Fig. 157.

Fig. 156.

Fig. 158.

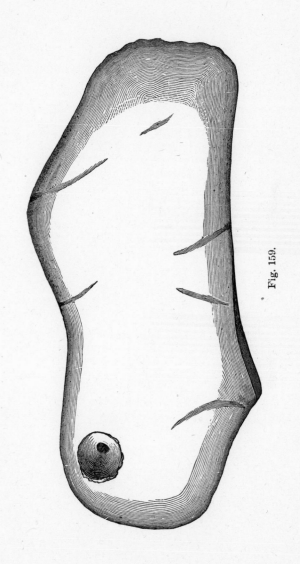

Fig. 159.

Fig. 161.

Fig. 162.

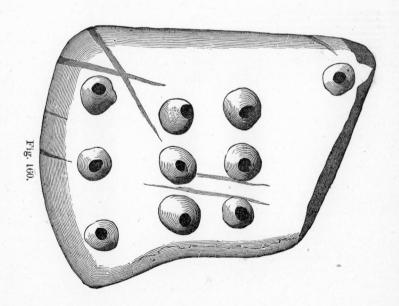

Fig. 160.

Fig. 165.

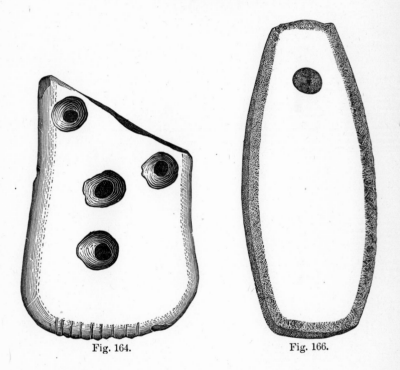

Fig. 164.

Fig. 166.

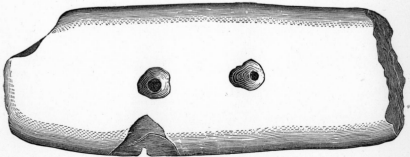

Fig. 163.

Fig. 167.

Fig. 168.

Fig. 170.

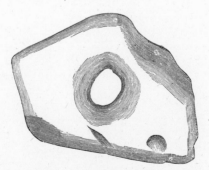

Fig. 169.

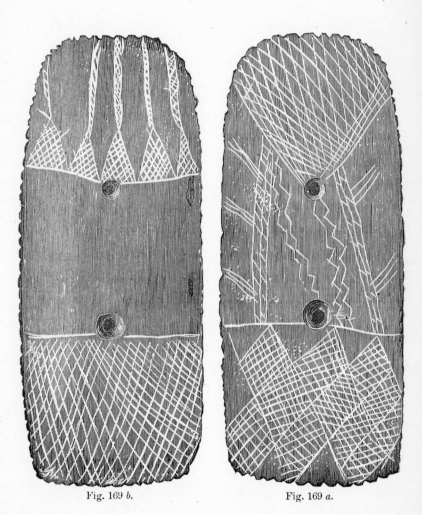

Fig. 169 b.   Fig. 169 a.

Fig. 171, wanting.

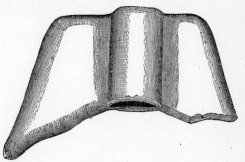

Fig. 173.—Nat. size.

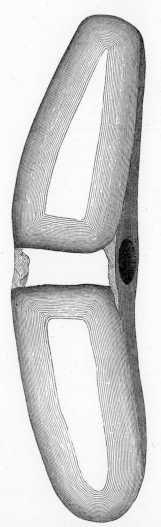

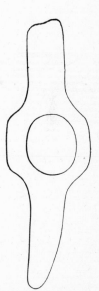

Fig. 173 a.—Section.

Fig. 172.

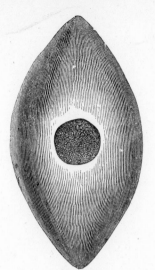

Fig. 174.

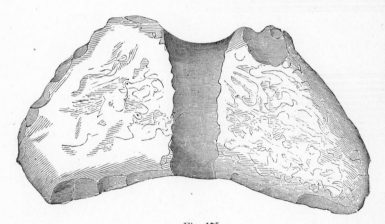

Fig. 175.

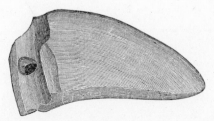

Fig. 176.

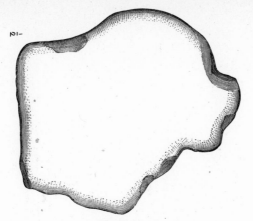

Fig. 177.

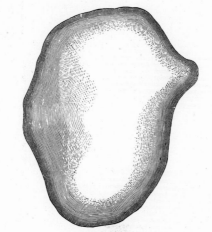

Fig. 177 a.

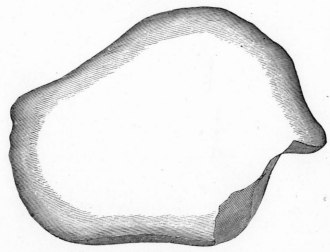

Fig. 178.

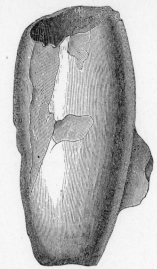

Fig. 179.

Fig. 180.

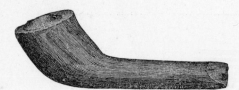

Fig. 181.

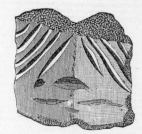

Fig. 183.

Fig. 182.

Fig. 185.—Nat. size.

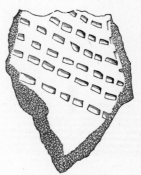

Fig. 186.—Nat. size.

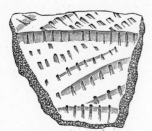

Fig. 184.—Nat. size.

Fig. 189

Fig. 188.

Fig. 187.—Nat. size

Fig. 190.

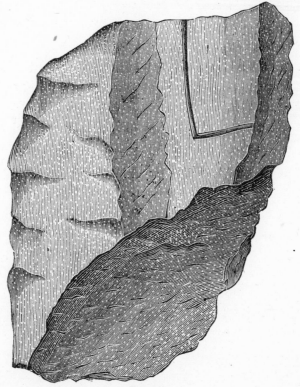

Fig. 191.

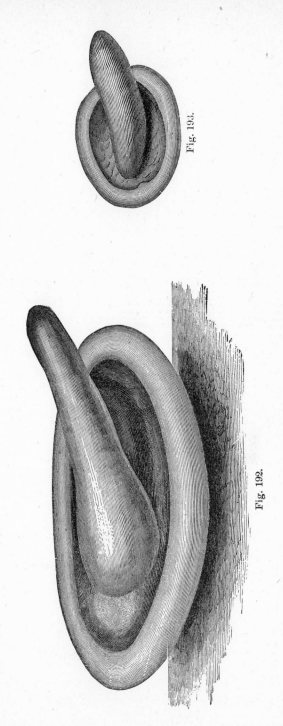

Fig. 193.

Fig. 192.

$\frac{1}{2}$

Fig. 194.

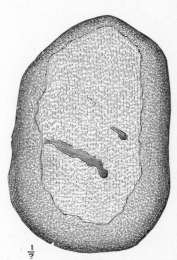

$\frac{1}{2}$

Fig. 198.

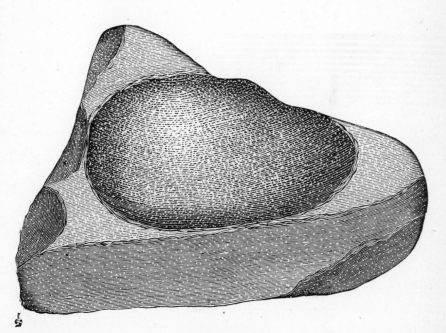

$\frac{1}{5}$

Fig. 197.

Fig. 196, wanting.
Fig. 196a, wanting.

Fig. 195.—Nat. size.

Fig. 199

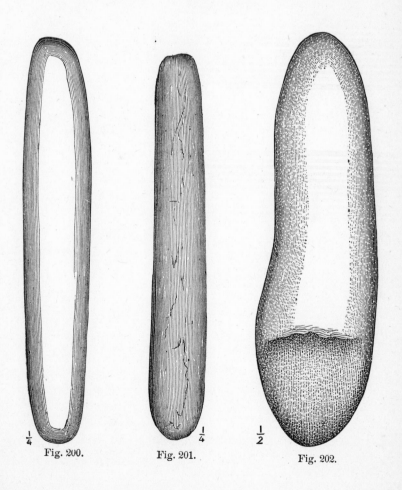

¼

Fig. 200.

¼

Fig. 201.

½

Fig. 202.

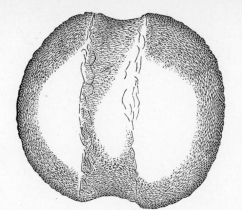

Fig. 203.

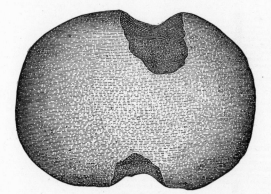

Fig. 204.

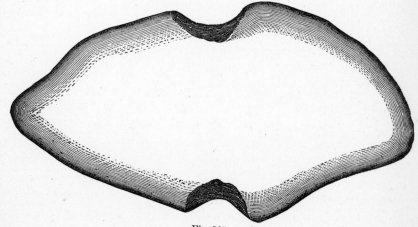

Fig. 205.

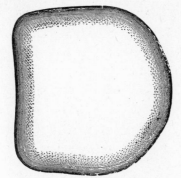

Fig. 206.

Fig. 207.

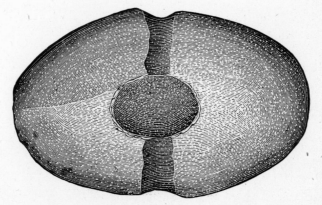

Fig. 208.

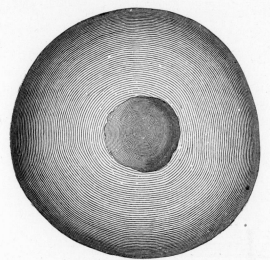

Fig. 209.

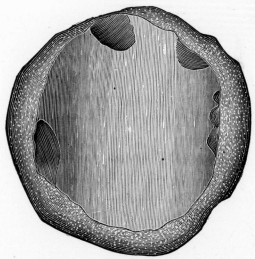

Fig. 210.

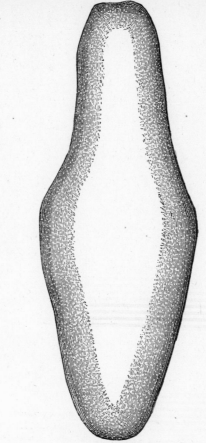

Fig. 211.

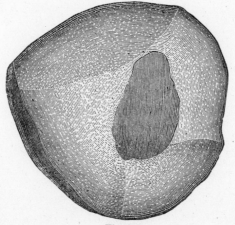

Fig. 212.

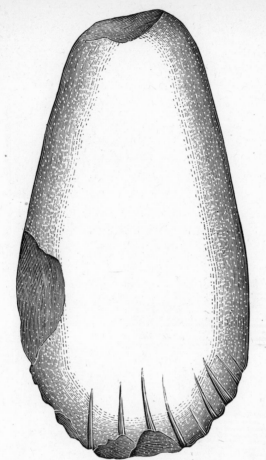

Fig. 213.

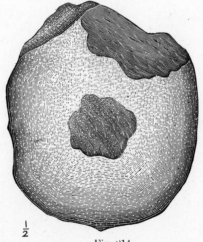

$\frac{1}{2}$

Fig. 214.

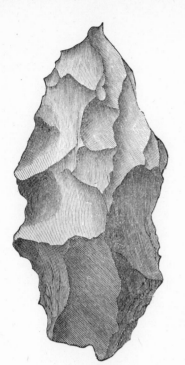

Fig. 215.

$\frac{1}{2}$

Fig. 216.—$\frac{1}{2}$ nat. size.

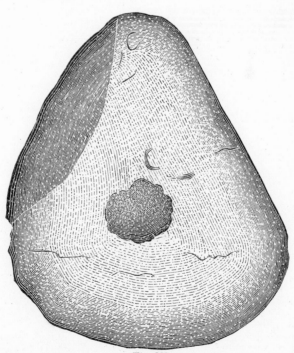

Fig. 217.

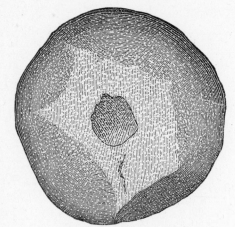

Fig. 218.

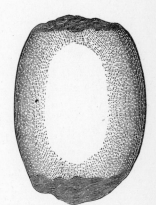

Fig. 220.

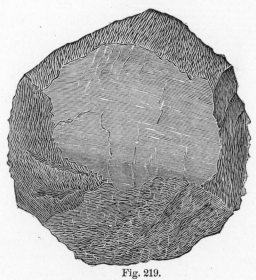

Fig. 219.

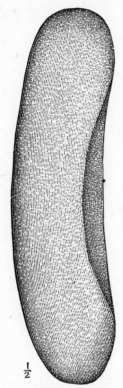

$\frac{1}{2}$

Fig. 221.—$\frac{1}{2}$ nat. size.

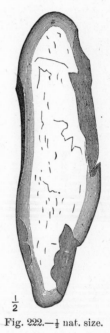

$\frac{1}{2}$

Fig. 222.—$\frac{1}{2}$ nat. size.

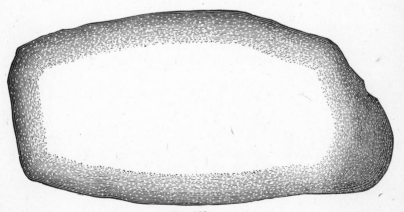

Fig. 223.

CONTENTS.

GENERAL APPENDIX.

CONTENTS.

LIST OF ILLUSTRATIONS

S. Mis. 115——25

INDEX.

391

Page.